SCIENTIFIC PRINCIPLES

OF COACHING

PRENTICE-HALL
PHYSICAL EDUCATION SERIES

Elmer D. Mitchell, *Editor*

John W. Bunn

BASKETBALL COACH
COLORADO STATE COLLEGE

SCIENTIFIC
PRINCIPLES
of
COACHING

Englewood Cliffs, N. J.
PRENTICE-HALL, Inc.

Fifth printing........January, 1964
(with Revisions)

Printed in the United States of America
Library of Congress Catalog Card No.: 54-9321

79616—C

Dedicated to a more objective and scientific approach to the teaching of techniques and skills in sports.

Preface

Being an engineer by training, I have recognized for years the analogy between the action of machines and mechanical devices and the movements of human beings in athletic activities. I have employed successfully the principles of mechanics and the laws of physics in analyzing the motor movements of man and in teaching fundamental techniques in baseball, golf, swimming, football, tennis, basketball and track.

Yet I have been disturbed by the tendency in others to accept blindly the methods employed by the star athlete and to assume that these methods are correct merely because the man is a top performer. By the same token, the methods taught by the successful coach are often considered to be the last word because that particular coach has a winning team. Few seem to question or inquire into the methods or to consider the possibility that the star athlete or the championship team may be successful *in spite of* the methods employed.

A few physical educators have explored the science of mechanics and physics and have examined the application of the principles involved therein to the motor movements of human beings. However, no book has been written that may be used as a guide for teaching these principles in physical education or as an understandable reference for coaches and athletes. There has long been a need for such a book—a book that would relate carefully the laws of physics to all phases of sport techniques. At the same time, to be generally useful, the book should be written so that those readers without a ready knowledge of physics will have no difficulty in understanding its content or in making the desired applications. A scientific approach to teaching the techniques of sport gives the only sound and sensible basis for such teaching. And furthermore, such an approach makes the techniques meaningful to both the coach and the player.

I have written this book to fill these needs. It represents an attempt to apply some of the principles of physics to the various skills in athletic activities. It further attempts to test the validity of these skills by means of those same principles. It dares to verify or deny the various theories and philosophies propounded by coaches and teachers of sports. Finally, it proposes to establish a sound basis for teaching techniques in athletics by stating principles and guides based upon scientific laws.

The book is divided into two parts. Part I states and demonstrates certain laws of physics, relates them to athletic activities, and develops principles from these laws that explain fundamental movements that are necessary in the successful execution of various techniques. The illustrations used apply the principles and laws involved directly to athletic activities.

Each chapter closes with a list of questions that may be used for group discussion. There is also a generous supply of problems that are intended to demonstrate the principles concerned and to provide a means for readers to gain a sound understanding of the materials presented. The problems will also enable readers to see the results of the application of the principles presented.

Part II consists of a careful analysis of many athletic activities. The laws of physics and the principles developed in Part I are applied directly. They are used to explain *why* techniques should follow a specific pattern. The purpose of this part is to provide a definite and scientific basis for teaching techniques in order to obtain (after mastery by the performer) the most efficient and effective results.

Coaches and players in all sports should find the book invaluable to them as a guide to more effective performance in their coaching and participation. The book can be helpful as a means of establishing or confirming and explaining techniques that the coach and player are employing. I hope that this book will provide a means for the development of a course on the mechanical analysis of motor movement for all curricula in institutions offering majors in physical education.

I am deeply indebted to Dr. C. H. McCloy for the stimulus that he has given me in this field and for many of the basic principles presented. Several unpublished theses that have been of value to me are referred to and listed for the information of the reader.

The book deals only with the mechanics of sports activities. The value of strategy, emotion, psychology, personal relations, neuro-muscular coordination, reaction time, fatigue, training and conditioning, group harmony, and team play are also recognized as factors that influence performance. No desire to de-emphasize these factors is intended. They should receive equal attention and study. Without the effective use and coordination of all these factors, application of the correct mechanical principles will probably not produce the best performance. On the other hand, the best combination of these factors in a particular situation coupled with the use of sound principles of mechanics will produce results previously undreamed.

Competition in all fields of sport has developed to such a high degree that no coach or player can afford to neglect the application of scientific principles that can give him an advantage over, or at least keep him apace with, his opponent. I wish you—the coach, teacher, student, or participator—the same success I have enjoyed in my coaching methods, through the implementation of the material presented here.

J. W. B.

Contents

xi

Part I

Principles of Physics in Sports

1.

Principles of Mechanics

The basic purpose of this book is to relate the laws of physics, particularly those governing that phase of physics called mechanics, to the fundamental techniques employed in the various sports activities. It is assumed in all cases that the end product of all these discussions is that perfection in performance will provide the optimum results: that is, more touchdowns, faster time, greater distances, higher scores, stronger defense, and so forth. In order to show such an analogy, it is first necessary to analyze fundamental sports techniques in terms of the mechanics of physics. When this has been done, the reader will be able readily to recognize the relationship. More particularly, he will be able to evaluate the validity of the fundamentals that he is teaching or applying. By such a critical and scientific approach to his methods, he should be able to make adjustments where necessary and to devise procedures which will improve performance measurably.

By adopting the above procedure in the selection and development of fundamental skills, one can have confidence in the soundness of his conclusions. He can be assured, assuming that other characteristics (perfection in mastery of the skills, strategy, mental poise, personal relations) are favorable, of the optimum in performance. It is surprising what tremendous interest and confidence can be developed in players by following the above procedure in the presentation of fundamentals. Proof based on the evidence of our immutable laws of physics is both convincing and motivating.

Certain basic principles are inherent in the fundamentals of all sports. A principle may be applied for the attainment of different, even opposite, results but it is, nevertheless, present. For example, the runner or the swimmer at the start of a race desires to assume a position from which he can move most quickly; the football lineman or the wrestler, on the other hand, under certain conditions of competition, attempt to assume positions from which they cannot be moved. In each of these examples, the principle of equilibrium is involved but the principle is employed for a different result in each case.

First, those principles which in general are present in the fundamentals of most sports will be stated and developed. Then, those principles which apply to particular sports or are peculiar to special techniques will be discussed.

Equilibrium

Equilibrium is probably the most significant of all the physical principles, in mechanics, that are involved in sports techniques. Reference has already been made to this factor. In sports parlance, it is called balance, position, and stance. Depending upon the result desired, various aspects of equilibrium are maintained. Equilibrium is a state of rest of a body. If a high degree of immobility is desired, then a position which will provide great stability for a particular sport will be created. Reference has been made to the football lineman and to the wrestler. If a delicate degree of stability is needed, a position which will permit upsetting equilibrium easily will be advocated. The starting position for the swimmer and track athlete have been mentioned.

Still another aspect of equilibrium is in the positions taken by the tennis player, the boxer, the handball player, the baseball fielder, the basketball offensive and defensive player. In each case, the degree of stability is dependent upon the objective which is desired. In the case of the boxer and in those of tennis, handball, basketball, and baseball players, they must be ready to start and stop instantaneously, to move in any direction quickly in accordance with their strategy and that of their opponents. Their objectives, therefore, are quite different from those of the swimmer, trackman, football lineman, and wrestler as previously discussed. The position which each would assume in terms of equilibrium would, therefore, be considerably different. Likewise, the position or stance of each would be altered in accordance with the demands of the sport. But, always, the principles which govern equilibrium must not be violated.

The *center of gravity* of the body (that point at which the effective weight of the body is centered) is involved in all considerations of equilibriums. The position of the center of gravity of the body is a major factor in determining the soundness of the stance which is advocated in any technique in any sport in order to accomplish the desired objective most effectively. This factor must, therefore, receive most careful attention. This principle is developed and demonstrated in Chapter 2.

Motion

Motion is the prime element in most sports. It is, therefore, essential to know the laws which govern or describe motion if the coach or athlete is to obtain the most efficient and effective results from the motion which may be developed. In order to know how to move most effectively one must know the why of the movement.

In the first place, for all practical purposes in athletics, movement consists of destroying or upsetting the equilibrium of a body. It involves a change of position of a body. From these statements, it is evident that there is a close relationship between equilibrium and motion. Therefore, the principles governing them and their inter-relations must be understood. For example, as one of the factors in attaining a high rate of speed, a runner should assume a position that will throw his body out of equilibrium but which at the same time will prevent him from falling on his face.

Linear motion. Motion is of two types: linear or rotary. There may be a combination of both. *Linear motion* as the word implies, consists of motion, in a straight line, from one point directly to another. If, as in the case of the track athlete, it is desired to move from the start to the finish line in the shortest space of time, there should be no deviation from the direct line which connects the starting point with the finish. Any deviation would tend to divert from the ultimate goal and thus require longer time to cover the distance. All this implies that there should not only be no change in direction of movement from the start to the finish but also that the movements of all members of the body should be co-ordinated to prevent sideward movement or sway.

Rotary motion consists of movement of a body about a center of rotation. Here the relationship of linear speed to the radius of the circle of rotation and the integration of rotary motion with linear motion to gain the optimum results are of prime importance. To use the example of the runner again, the motion of the legs is rotary with the hip joint as the center of rotation. In order that the rotary movement of the leg may work effectively with the linear movement of the body toward the finish line, it is necessary that the leg move forward to stride position as quickly as possible. To facilitate this action, the leg is bent at the knee with the heel practically touching the glutii muscles (the buttock). This action shortens the radius of rotation of the leg and permits faster recovery to the stride position. Thus the use of one of the principles of rotary motion is applied to increase the speed of movement in a linear direction (see Chapter 3).

Falling body. The characteristics of motion incident to a *falling body* have tremendous impact on athletic activities. The distance reached by the broad jumper, the height attained by the high jumper, the difference between safe and out by the base runner who leaps in his last stride to first base, the distance of the shot put, the distance traveled by a thrown baseball, the distance of the football kick, and the time of the track runner previously referred to are all effected by the laws governing a falling body.

It is an interesting and vitally significant fact that bodies (for all practical purposes in athletics) falling from the same height regardless of whether or not their direction downward is the same (providing no impetus is given to the downward direction) will reach the same level at the same time. Runners desire to avoid the effects of a falling body by not permitting the center of gravity to rise while the others mentioned above desire to profit by the laws governing a falling body by attaining optimum heights.

Closely allied with the motion of a falling body is the path traced by a projectile. If maximum horizontal distance is the goal, as in the shot put or broad jump, the shot or the body should remain in the air as long as possible without sacrificing distance. On the other hand, if time is a factor, as in running a race or to a base, the body should be kept in the air for as short a time as possible. These factors determine the height to which a body shall be projected into the air. In this connection the angle of take-off is involved. The angle at which a ball should be thrown, hit, or kicked, the angle of take-off in the broad jump, the angle at which the javelin and discus should be thrown and the angle of the put of the shot are all controlled by the principles governing the flight of a projectile.

Velocity and acceleration. Finally, motion depends upon *speed and direction.* These facts have been more or less implicit in the foregoing comments. Suffice it to say, at this point, that speed of movement is indicated by the term velocity. *Velocity* is the rate of change of position in a given direction. *Acceleration* is the rate of change in velocity, may or may not be uniform, and may be positive or negative. These factors become of tremendous importance in the consideration of the techniques of the golf swing, batting, throwing the baseball, taking a lead off a base in baseball, running a race, and so forth.

Direction of motion, as applied to athletic activities, has significance in the integration of the movements of various parts of the body in the execution of techniques and in the economy of effort. Direction, of course, is either vertical or horizontal or at an angle with the vertical or horizontal. To understand the real effect of direction of motion in the outcome of an effort, an understanding of vectors (which involves trigonometric functions) is necessary. For the purpose of review and for the convenience of the reader, the simple functions needed for application in the text material and the trigonometric tables will be found in Appendix B, page 265.

Force

Force is the third concept in mechanics which has wide application in athletics. Force is the effect which one body exerts on another. Force and motion are closely associated. It is only through force that motion is created. There may be force without motion, but not motion without force. For example, a wrestler on the defense is holding his position against his opponent. To do this, he is straining with great effort to offset the equally strong attack of this opponent. Tremendous force is being exerted by each, yet there may be little or no apparent motion. Contrast this with the mighty swing of the bat by a Babe Ruth that results in the speedy flight of the ball over the fence. In each case, there is great force. In one no movement results. In the other, the speed of movement reaches a velocity of well over 100 feet per second. Since motion is derived from force, many of the comments which were made with respect to motion can be made with equal emphasis in connection with force.

Force is a function of the mass of a body multiplied by the rate of change in its velocity.   Since force is such an important factor in the outcome of many athletic contests, it would appear that the individual who could generate the greatest amount of force, that is, the individual who was the biggest and the fastest, would be the successful competitor. However, it is one thing to be able to develop a large amount of force and quite another to effectively utilize this quantity of force.

The factors of (1) the direction of force, (2) point of application of the available force, (3) the proper sequence in the application of generated forces, (4) the resultant effect of the forces applied, and (5) the time of application of the force are much more important than the mere presence of "brute" force.   Therefore, those factors which are related to force and which refine it or make it effective, must receive the attention of the coach and the competitor if they are to derive the best results in competition.   The proper *harnessing* of force becomes the problem.   It is not always the biggest, strongest and fastest who puts the shot the farthest, hits the golf ball the longest distance, drives the baseball over the fence, becomes the most outstanding tackle, the world's heavy weight boxing champion, or the champion weight lifter.

Newton's Laws

The factors which explain force and which are related to it will be developed and elaborated in subsequent chapters.   At this point it will suffice to examine merely the fundamentals of those principles which control force.   Since the whole science of force is based on three fundamental laws known as Newton's laws of motion, they should be of primary consideration in this discussion.   The Newtonian laws of motion may be simply stated as follows:

1. *Every body continues in its state of rest or of uniform motion in a straight line except insofar as it is compelled by forces to change that state.*

The proper technique in broken field running in football, in running around a curved track, and in dodging technique in basketball or lacrosse are dependent upon the successful application of this law.

2. Newton's second law may be stated as: *the acceleration of a body is proportional to the force causing it.*

This in effect says that a greater force is required to reach a certain speed in a given time if one starts from a stationary position than if one is already in motion. Applied to sports, a base runner can reach top speed sooner and thus have a better chance of reaching a base safely if he is in motion prior to his dash. For example, imagine that there is a runner on third base. A fly is hit to the outfield. The runner will have a better chance of scoring (if rules permitted) after the catch if he starts from the left field side of third base so that he touches third base as the catch is made while traveling at near his top speed than if he is stationary on the base when the ball is caught.

3. *For every action there is always an equal and contrary reaction.*

A runner pushes back against the ground with a force equal to that which propels him forward. If the track is solid he can move forward faster than if he were running in loose sand. The shot putter should keep his foot rigidly in contact with the surface in the ring as he makes his put in order to be able to exert a maximum force in the direction of the put. The batter should grip the bat firmly at the moment of contact with the ball for the same reason.

Related to these laws and in application of them are the principles relating to levers both within the body and outside, friction, the parallelogram of forces, centrifugal force, centripetal force, the force of gravity, moments of force, impact and elasticity. All have their importance in teaching the proper fundamentals in sports.

Other Principles

The foregoing (equilibrium, motion, and force) constitute the basic principles of mechanics which relate particularly to the fundamentals of sports. The laws covering work, energy, efficiency, power, also have a very important and direct application to athletics. However, measuring the work done and energy expended by the athlete is so difficult that little practical application can be made for the purpose of this text. Most studies in this field must be made in the laboratory where controlled conditions can be set up. As a consequence, in the general run of athletic activities, these factors are not easily accessible to measurement. A few rough references will be made and some situations developed but no extensive application can be made.

Some principles of hydrostatics are related to the techniques of swimming. The factors of wave making, skin friction, tail suction, eddies, slip, and cavitation are important to propulsion in swimming. Since they are peculiar to swimming, they are discussed in Chapter 11 where the techniques of swimming are analyzed.

Some of the principles of aerodynamics are applicable to the discus throw and the flight of the football. Since they are limited to so few activities, reference is made to them in the chapters which discuss these activities.

Limitations

Finally, in a study of this kind which relates the laws of mechanics to athletic activities, the reader must be cautioned against making absolute predictions and drawing absolute conclusions. In dealing with material objects, accurate predictions can be made because all of the conditions effecting the results can be controlled and measured. Whereas in dealing with the human body, because of the variations in the anatomy and physiology, all of the conditions are not known and cannot always be controlled or measured. For example, skeletal differences in individuals cause a difference in the leverages in the body. The mesomorphic body type has better leverage than the ectomorphic. Likewise, the exact point of attachment of muscles is difficult to determine. The angle (it is seldom at right angles) at which the force is exerted by a muscle is also difficult to determine with accuracy. The length of the weight arm and power arm cannot be determined with accuracy. Neither is the strength of muscle of each individual known.

Earlier, it was stated that force was a function of weight and acceleration. Yet in the case of a muscle the available force is inversely proportional to the velocity of movement. Thus, when a muscle contracts at its maximum speed, no effective force for the accomplishment of external work will be available. This would seem to deny the definition of force, yet it appears to be true, since all the factors (for example, the amount of heat generated) are not known.

It has been discovered that in jumping vertically, the center of gravity can be raised higher by a slight crouch for a weaker muscle than by a deep crouch. Raising the body represents work done. Work is equal to the force exerted multiplied by the distance through which the force acts. Since the force in this case acts through a greater distance with the deep crouch, this principle would seem to be denied.   Again, all the factors are not known to explain this apparent discrepancy.

A muscle under stretch is stronger.   The biceps can be put under greatest stretch when the forearm is fully extended so that the angle of pull on the forearm is practically zero.   The force exerted on a lever is always measured at right angles to the lever.   To resolve the force in a right angle direction in this case, the force is multiplied by the sine of the angle.   Since the angle is approximately zero, the sine is approximately zero which makes the force approximately zero.   Yet this is contrary to fact.

These limitations are not stated to discount the laws of mechanics when applied to the performance of a human being but, rather, to indicate that in a few instances, the reader must move with caution because all the facts are not known.   In most instances, there are no apparent discrepancies.

With these explanations, the following chapters are devoted to reviewing the mechanical principles which have been enumerated and establishing their validity in connection with athletic performance. These laws and principles are represented by formula stated in algebraic equations.   It is the job of the teacher or coach to test all techniques by applying these formulae in order to discover the most efficient methods.   This is the only sound basis for developing the correct mechanical methods for all sports techniques.

QUESTIONS AND TOPICS FOR DISCUSSION AND REVIEW

1. What is the basic purpose of the text?
2. The methods of the top performer represent the pattern which others should emulate if they would be stars. Discuss this statement.
3. The correct application of mechanical principles alone will not produce the best performance. Discuss.
4. What three divisions of mechanics are most common to the field of sports?
5. What is meant by equilibrium?
6. What is meant by the center of gravity of the body?
7. How is the center of gravity related to equilibrium?
8. Define motion as it is related to sports.
9. What is the relationship between equilibrium and motion?
10. What are the two types of motion common to sports? Describe each.
11. What is the significance of the law of a falling body to sports?
12. In some cases in sports, why is it desirable to emphasize height from the ground, whereas in other cases this is de-emphasized?
13. Define velocity and acceleration.

14. Define force.

15. What is the relationship between force and motion?

16. Force is a function of what two factors?

17. Which is more important for the best results in sports—a great amount of force or the correct application of force? Why?

18. State Newton's three laws of motion. Explain each.

19. Name five other phases of mechanics which are related to performance in sports.

20. What are some of the limitations upon the application of mechanical principles to the fundamentals of sports? Explain.

2.

Balance or Equilibrium

A body which is in balance or equilibrium is at a state of rest. The body may be in any one of innumerable positions and yet be in equilibrium in each one. Equilibrium may have various stages of stability. The degree of stability depends upon five factors:

1. *Stability is directly proportional to the area of the base on which the body rests.*

A person standing on tip toes with feet together is in equilibrium but of unstable degree because he can be thrown off balance by a very slight push. The same person standing erect with feet spread about 12 inches is in a more stable position than when he is standing on tip toes. He has a greater base. If this person takes a position with both hands and feet on the ground in a four point football stance he has established an even wider base. It is more difficult to push him off balance in this last position than it is in the first two. Now, if he will take the wrestler's defensive "down" position, in which the arms are spread the width of the shoulders and both the knees and feet are in contact with the mat, he will have established a base of even greater area, will be in an even more stable position, and it will be more difficult to dislodge him. Of course, it is evident that if the person lies flat on the floor with the arms and feet spread, he will have established an even larger base and more stable position. However, in the last position (from an athletic point of view), he is in no position to perform. Figure 1 shows an athlete in different degrees of stability. In each case, notice the size of the base and the position of the center of gravity.

2. *Stability in a given direction is directly proportional to the horizontal distance of the center of gravity from that edge of the base toward the given direction of movement.*

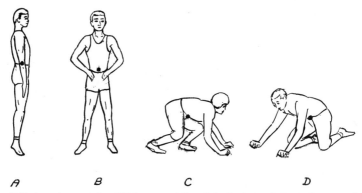

A   *B*   *C*   *D*

Fig. 1. Various degrees of equilibrium or stability of the body in relation to the area of the base of the body. Stability increases from A to D as the area of the base increases Note also that stability increases as the center of gravity approaches the base.

This is true for any given height of the center of gravity above the base. For example, if a runner who is on his mark for the start leans forward so that his center of gravity is directly above his hands, his tendency to fall forward is greater than if his center of gravity were over his feet. Contrariwise, if a basketball player, who is running forward rapidly, stops in a stride-stop so that his center of gravity is over his rear foot instead of his forward foot, he is less likely to fall forward. His center of gravity, when over the rear foot, is farther from that edge of the base next to the direction of movement than if his weight were over his front foot.

3. *Stability is directly proportional to the weight of the body.*

If the same positions as described above and illustrated in Figure 1 were assumed by two individuals of different weights, it would be found that it is more difficult to move or upset the equilibrium of the heavier person.

4. *Stability is indirectly proportional to the distance of the center of gravity of the body above the base.*

The center of gravity of a body is a point from which the body can be suspended in perfect balance. It might be considered as the center of weight of the body.   As the various members of the body change position, this point (the center of gravity) may change.   When the body is in certain positions, the center of gravity may fall at a point outside the body.   Its position varies according to the build and consequent distribution of the weight of the body.

Roughly speaking, the center of gravity will be found at about the height of the hips (the crest of the ilium) midway between the front and back of an individual standing erect or lying in a prone or supine position with the arms at the sides.   If the arms are lifted, the position of the center of gravity would change.   Likewise, if a leg or legs are lifted, the center of gravity would be moved.   This point can be illustrated by placing a person in a supine position (on his back) on a board across a saw horse (teeter-totter) so that it is in balance.   Now, if the person raises his arms, the balance will be destroyed because the center of gravity has been moved.   This will be demonstrated by the fact that the board will tip.   The same will prove true if the legs are brought up to the abdomen.   In each case, if the person changes position on the teeter-totter until balance is re-established, the new position of the center of gravity can be determined approximately.

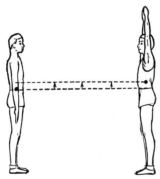

Fig. 2. The center of gravity changes position with any change in position of members of the body.

The above example deals with a body in a horizontal position.   The change of the position of the center of gravity in a vertical direction is analogous when the change of position of members of the body is in a vertical direction.   Figure 2 shows diagrammatically how the position of the center of gravity in the body may change when the position of members of the body change their elevation.   The center of gravity may move up and down through a range of as much as five inches. In Figure 1, which demonstrated the change in stability with the change in base, it will be observed that in each case where greater stability was produced, the center of gravity approached closer to the base.

5. *For equilibrium to exist, the center of gravity of a body must fall within its base.*

This means that if a line is projected vertically from the center of gravity, it will intersect the base upon which the body rests. In order to maintain a handstand, the performer must be able to keep the vertical

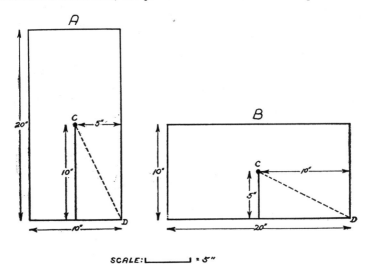

Fig. 3. This homogeneous wooden block illustrates the principles of equilibrium.   It takes less effort to upset Block A than it does to upset Block B.   C is the position of the center of gravity; D is the edge on which the block is tipped.

line from his center of gravity between his hands which in this case form the boundaries of his base.

These principles can be clearly illustrated by means of two wooden blocks (Figure 3).   Assume that each block weighs 10 pounds and that the size of each is 20 by 10 by 10 inches.   Block *A* stands on its 10 by 10-inch base, while block *B* rests on a 20 by 10-inch base.   Both blocks are homogeneous, so that the center of gravity is at the center of each.   The center of gravity of block *A* is 10 inches above its base, while that of *B* is 5 inches above its base.   Both blocks are at rest and in equilibrium.

To upset the blocks or to destroy their equilibrium, it is necessary to move the blocks so that their centers of gravity fall outside their bases. To do this, it will be necessary to tip the blocks. The edge at D is chosen as the axis of rotation for tilting the blocks. The center of gravity, as the blocks are tipped, rotates about the point D with a radius of rotation equal to CD. The length of CD is found to be approximately 11.18 inches.

When CD reaches a vertical position, the center of gravity in each block will be 11.18 inches above the foundation on which the blocks are resting. Any further tipping would cause the center of gravity of the block to fall outside its base and thus destroy the equilibrium of the previous set up. Since the center of gravity in block A was 10 inches above its base at the start, it has been raised 1.18 in. The center of gravity of block B was 5 inches above its base, so it has been raised 6.18 inches. Thus, it can be seen that the center of gravity of block B was raised 5 inches higher than the center of gravity of block A before it would fall outside its base. Since both blocks weigh the same (10 pounds), 5 times 10 or 50-inch-pounds, more effort must be exerted on block B to upset its equilibrium. The stability of block B is greater than the stability of block A. B could not be tipped as easily. Its base was greater, its center of gravity was closer to its base. The weights were made constant to simplify the problem.

If the weight of block A were twice as much as the weight of block B, 20 pounds and 10 pounds respectively, block B would still be in a more stable state of equilibrium. It would require 38.20 inch-pounds more to upset its equilibrium. By causing these extremes in weight, it can be readily seen that position, area of base, and distance of center of gravity are much more important than weight. This is a fortunate circumstance because in athletics it provides the lighter person a means of compensating in certain activities for his lack of weight.

If this illustration is applied to athletic situations, some valuable conclusions can be drawn. If it is desired to start running as quickly as possible, it will require less effort to upset one's equilibrium from position A than from position B. There are other factors involved such as the force exerted in pushing off but certainly the fact of throwing the center of gravity outside the base is a prime requisite to starting in motion.

On the other hand, if it is desired to resist displacement by an outside force such as a charge in a football game or an opponent in a

wrestling match, the position of B would be more advantageous because it requires more effort to upset the equilibrium of the body. By
the same token, if a body is moving rapidly and desires to stop instantaneously, he could accomplish his purpose more effectively by
assuming position B. Thus, a basketball player can stop more quickly
by crouching low as he plants his feet on the floor. The low crouch
creates a wide base, drops the center of gravity close to the floor and
tends to keep it within its base and thus establishes a more stable state
of equilibrium than a higher position. This illustration demonstrates
the above example in reverse.

Only a few applications of equilibrium have been made here. The
reader can from this introduction carry the application to other sports
and techniques. There is practically no sport where equilibrium is
not a factor to consider. The problem is to apply the principles involved to accomplish the desired results. In this connection, a famous
football coach, a disciple of the "T" formation, applies the principles of
equilibrium in an unique fashion in developing the stance for his linemen. Usually a lineman is taught to assume a very stable position,
one from which he cannot be dislodged easily and yet one from which
he can move readily in several directions. This coach, however, de-
parts from these established theories. He does this because of his
objective and organization of play. His offensive system requires that
his linemen move straight ahead and as quickly as possible. As a
consequence, he teaches a high stance, with the center of gravity
nearer the hands, the front edge of the base, the same as that of the
starting position of a sprinter. He realizes that this position has less
stability, deception, and versatility of movement, but it aids his linemen to better accomplish the goal set for them. His application of
the principles of equilibrium are certainly sound in gaining his goal.

Summary and Principles

In summary, the following are important applications to athletic
activities:

1. To start quickly in one direction, keep the center of gravity as
high as possible and as near as possible to the edge of the base in the
direction of movement.

2. For greatest immobility or stability, increase the area of the base and lower the center of gravity as much as is consistent with the activity involved.

3. To stop quickly when in rapid motion, spread the base and drop the center of gravity as low as possible consistent with subsequent movements.

4. A body is in equilibrium when its center of gravity falls within its base. It loses equilibrium when the center of gravity falls outside of the base.

In a head stand, the hands should be kept well back of the head. This gives a greater base area within which to keep the center of gravity.

5. In all arm support activities, the center of gravity of the body should be as nearly as possible over the point of support (the hands). In vaulting exercises, move the center of gravity in the direction of the vault. Horse, buck, and bar activities are facilitated by adherence to this principle. On the flying rings, the hands should be kept at the trochanter to maintain good balance.

Activities on the horse necessitate that the center of gravity be kept over the hands. To do this, the shoulders are thrown in one direction and the hips in the opposite direction.

6. Movements of the body when suspended in the air or when hanging by arms or legs follow a definite pattern which tends to maintain body balance.

(a) When the body is free in the air, if the head and feet move up, the hips move down and vice versa.

(b) When either hands or feet are supported, if one moves up, then the hips move down and vice versa.

This principle is illustrated in the high jump. At the take-off, the head and feet are up as high as possible. Then, they straighten out as the greatest height is reached so that the hips are raised to clear the bar.

The jackknife dive is another example as is the upstart on the bar. To a certain extent the principle is demonstrated in the hurdles and broad jump.

The pole vaulter uses this principle. The feet are up as they go over the bar. Then, the feet drop to pull up the middle so it will clear.

7. If a performer is in the air free of support, the height to which the center of gravity can be raised above the floor cannot be effected by body movements but the position of the center of gravity within the

body can be changed and the body may be lowered or raised above the
floor by the movement or change in position of a member of the body.

In the Sargent jump, bringing the hands down sharply just before
the greatest height is reached raises the head several inches higher.
The height jumped to tip a basketball may be increased by forcibly
lowering the hand not used to tip just before the maximum height is
reached. The exact increase will be equal to the distance the center of
gravity is displaced in a vertical direction.

QUESTIONS AND TOPICS FOR DISCUSSION AND REVIEW

1. Name the five factors which determine the degree of stability.
2. Is a moving body in equilibrium? Discuss.
3. How is the center of gravity related to equilibrium?
4. Are there various stages of equilibrium?
5. What is the significance of equilibrium in sports? Demonstrate.
6. What is necessary in order for a body to lose its equilibrium?
7. Which is the least important factor in establishing stable equilibrium?
8. What is the difference between the stability of the wrestler in a defensive position on the mat and a sprinter in the "get-set" position?
9. When is a body in equilibrium?
10. What should be done to produce the greatest immobility or stability?
11. What should be done to stop quickly?
12. How does one start quickly?
13. What is the position of the center of gravity in all arm support activities? Give an example.
14. What are the principles of the ends and the middle? Give examples in sports.

PROBLEMS

(Answers to problems are given in Appendix D, page 293.)

1. Two runners each weigh 150 pounds. The center of gravity of each is
the same distance from the ground. The center of gravity of one is 6 inches
back of the edge of the base toward the direction in which he will run. The
center of gravity of the other is directly over this edge. Which will require
more effort to upset his equilibrium?

2. Demonstrate the solution to question (1) mathematically and by use of
diagrams.

3. Two linemen are in position on the line. One weighs 200 pounds, the
other 150 pounds. What must be the position of each in order that they
have the same stability in a given direction? Demonstrate your solution
mathematically and by diagrams.

4. An individual weighs 180 pounds. He is 6 feet tall. Assume that his
weight is uniformly distributed throughout his length. At what height will
his center of gravity be located?

5. In problem 4, assume that the individual raises his arms above his head so that the height through which his weight is distributed is 7 feet. Assume that the weight is again equally distributed throughout his length, how much did the center of gravity move? Did it move up or down?

6. A player jumps into the air with both arms extended vertically overhead. Just before the maximum height is reached, one arm is forcibly lowered so that the center of gravity is lowered $1\frac{1}{2}$ inches in the body. Do the finger tips of the other hand go higher or lower as a result? How much?

7. A football lineman takes a position with his center of gravity over the center of his base. In one case his base is 12 by 12 inches. In another his base is 18 by 24 inches. If his center of gravity is the same distance above the base in each position, is one position more stable than the other? If so, which one? If one is more stable, how much more effort is required to upset the equilibrium of this position?

8. If the center of gravity of one body is 3 feet above its base and the center of gravity of another body is 4 feet above its base, how much more stable is one than the other? Assume that all other factors are the same.

3.

Motion[*]

Motion is the prime element in most sports. They either involve motion or resistance against efforts to move. Motion consists of the movement of the body as a whole, the movement of some member of the body, or the movement of some object or implement by the body. This motion is a function of direction and speed. It may be in a horizontal direction, a vertical direction, at an angle with the horizontal or vertical, or it may consist of circular motion about some point as a center of rotation. Speed is indicated by the terms velocity and acceleration. Velocity is the rate of change of position in a given direction. Acceleration is the rate of change in velocity, may or may not be uniform and may be positive or negative.

Velocity

Formulae have been derived to demonstrate the above statements. Some of these will be repeated here so that the reader will be able to understand the significance of the principles of motion when applied to athletic situations. If all the characteristics of a movement are known, the results of the motion can be determined. For example, if a runner is moving in a horizontal direction at an average rate of

---

* The formulae presented in this and succeeding chapters have been taken from texts on physics. It serves the purpose here merely to state the formulae without developing them.

speed of 30 ft/sec, he will run a hundred yards in 10 seconds. The rate of speed is called velocity and is represented by V. The distance traveled is represented by D and the time required to cover the distance at the velocity indicated is represented by t. Thus:

$$D = Vt \qquad (1)$$

Substituting: 300 ft $= 30 \times 10 = 300$. If the speed or velocity is variable, then V represents the average velocity. This is represented by the equation

$$V \quad \text{or} \quad V_a = \frac{V_0 + V_1}{2} \qquad (2)$$

where V_0 is the initial speed, and V_1 is the final speed. The formula applies only in the case of uniform acceleration.

The speeds dealt with in athletic contests are usually variable speeds. The runner above started the 100-yard dash with an initial speed of zero. He did not, however, accelerate uniformly. He reached top speed at a point 45 to 60 ft from the start and his acceleration represented by ft/sec/sec probably varied from 100 to 0 when he reached top speed. Falling bodies illustrate cases of uniform acceleration.

Acceleration

The rate at which a body changes velocity is called acceleration. If the acceleration is constant the speed acquired is directly proportional to the time or

$$V_1 = at \qquad (3)$$

Where V_1 is the final velocity, a is acceleration and t the time. When the initial velocity is zero, the average velocity may be written by substituting for V_1

$$V \quad \text{or} \quad V_a = \frac{V_1}{2} = \frac{at}{2} \qquad (4)$$

Then, formula (1) $D = Vt$, may be written by substituting for V its value $at/2$. Thus,

$$D = \frac{at}{2} \times t = \frac{at^2}{2} \qquad (5)$$

This relationship of velocity to distance and time may be stated in another way by substituting for t in formula (5) from (3)

$$V_1 = at, \qquad t = \frac{V_1}{a}$$

now substituting for t in (5)

$$D = \frac{a}{2} \times \frac{V_1^2}{a^2} = \frac{V_1^2}{2a}$$

clearing of fractions

$$V_1^2 = 2aD \qquad\qquad (6)$$

From these formulae, if any two of the three quantities are known, the third may be found. The reader must choose that formula that fits the situation under consideration.

Falling Bodies

Many performances in athletics are controlled by the effect of gravity. The laws of freely falling bodies govern the results of these activities. For example, after an implement such as a shot, a discus, a javelin, or a ball is hurled into the air its time of flight, except for air resistance, is determined by the laws governing falling bodies. The broad jumper strives to remain in the air as long as possible in order to gain distance. The diver and gymnast strive for height so that they will remain in the air as long as possible and have time to execute their stunts. The hurdler skims the hurdle as closely as possible in order to get back to earth quickly to continue his run. The baseball player avoids high hops in taking a lead from a base so that he may keep close contact with the ground in order to be able to move back to the base quickly or dart toward the next without delay.

A body falling freely travels at a uniformly accelerated rate of 32 ft/sec/sec in a vertical direction. If the body is going up, it decelerates at the same rate. This is called the acceleration of gravity, and is caused by the force or pull of gravity. Thus, in formulae (5) and (6) a is equal to 32 when freely falling bodies are involved.

For example, if a baseball is thrown into the air in a vertical direction and leaves the hand at a velocity of 70 ft/sec, the moment it leaves the hand, it is affected by gravity and begins to decelerate at the rate of 32 ft/sec/sec until it reaches its highest point where its velocity will be zero. Then, it begins to fall back to the ground with the same acceleration of 32 ft/sec/sec. The time required for its ascent and descent will be equal.

The height to which the ball will rise after leaving the thrower's hand may be found by substituting in formula (6)

$$V_1^2 = 2aD$$

when $V_1 = 70$ ft/sec; $a = 32$.

$$70^2 = 2 \times 32 \times D$$
$$D = \tfrac{4900}{64} = 76.5+ \text{ feet}$$

If the height from the ground is desired, it would be necessary to add the distance of the ball from the ground when it left the hand of the thrower.

Now, if the time t which elapsed from the moment the ball left the hand of the thrower until it reached its highest point is desired, formula (5) may be used.

$$D = \tfrac{1}{2}at^2$$

Where $D = 76.5$ ft; $a = 32$.

$$76.5 = \tfrac{1}{2} \times 32 \times t^2$$
$$t^2 = \frac{76.5}{16} = 4.78$$
$$t = 2.18 + \text{ sec}$$

In the above example, the ball has been thrown exactly vertically. Movement is seldom in an exact vertical direction in practical athletic situations. It is at an angle with the vertical or it is horizontal. If the speed in the initial direction of movement and the initial angle or direction of movement are known, the speed in either the vertical or horizontal directions as well as the distance traveled and the time of flight may be computed. To do this, the vertical and/or horizontal components of the speed must be found. This is done by the application of the relationships of the sides and angles of a right triangle. This involves the use of trigonometric functions. A review of the theory of these functions together with the trigonometric and square root tables is reproduced in Appendix B, page 265.

If the baseball in the above example travels at an angle of 45° with the horizontal and at a velocity of 70 ft/sec in the direction of its release at the moment of release, to what height would it rise and in how many seconds will it reach its highest point? It is first necessary to find the vertical velocity of the ball. By the application of trigonometry this is equal to

$$\sin 45° \times 70$$

From the table on page 267, $\sin 45° = .7071$

$$70 \times .7071 = 49.5 \text{ ft/sec}$$

Now, formula (6) can be applied to find the vertical distance traveled.

$$V_1^2 = 2aD \qquad V_1 = 49.5 \qquad a = 32$$
$$49.5^2 = 2 \times 32 \times D$$
$$D = \frac{49.5^2}{2 \times 32} = \frac{2450.25}{64} = 38.28 \text{ feet.}$$

By formula (5), the time in rising is thus computed:

$$D = \tfrac{1}{2}at^2$$
$$38.28 = \tfrac{32}{2} \times t^2$$
$$t^2 = \frac{38.28}{16} = 2.39$$
$$t = 1.5+ \text{ sec}$$

The height to which an object or a person rises is of paramount importance in sports. It has a double and converse significance. The outfielder in throwing to home plate or to a base, the kicker in football, the shot putter, and the broad jumper are all interested in distance. Since distance which is gained without resistance other than air and the pull of gravity may be obtained only while the body or object is in the air it must be evident from the foregoing that the competitor should strive for height in order to remain in the air as long as possible. There is, however, a margin of utility with respect to height. Any projection beyond 45° with the horizontal would gain height but would lose horizontal distance. In other words, under normal conditions, the angle of projection to gain the greatest distance is 45°. This fact can be demonstrated practically by the use of the common garden hose. By holding the hose at the ground at varying angles with the horizontal, the distance to which the water (under constant pressure) will carry can be observed. Figure 4 illustrates an actual experiment of this type.[1]

---

[1] Cureton, T. K., "Mechanical Analysis of the Broad Jump," *Scholastic Coach*, May, 1935.

It should be evident from the foregoing that in order to gain maximum distance in jumping, throwing, and kicking activities there must be a careful integration between the development of velocity (speed of movement) and height of projection. One cannot avoid the effects of gravity. He should, therefore, apply the laws governing falling bodies to best advantage.

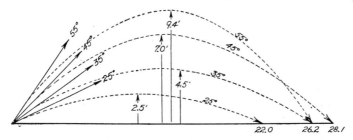

Fig. 4. Experiment showing the distance traveled by a stream of water under constant pressure when projected at varying angles.

A simple demonstration will tend to emphasize the importance of the interacting of gravity and velocity. Two steel balls of equal size and weight are placed on a horizontal platform at the end of a double acting plunger so that both balls are knocked from the platform at the same time when the plunger is released. The plunger is adjusted so that one ball is hit harder than the other. One ball merely clears the

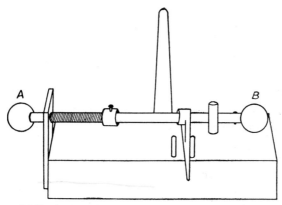

Fig. 5. The law of falling bodies. Steel balls A and B, which are the same distance from the floor, are projected horizontally at the same time but with different velocities. Each ball strikes the floor at the same instant.

edge of the platform as the plunger slides out of it and drops almost vertically. The other is hurled as much as 10 feet from the platform. It will be observed that both balls will strike the floor which is parallel to the surface of the platform at exactly the same time. The one which is discharged with the greater initial velocity lands the farther from the starting point. The significance of this simple fact in athletic activities should be immediately evident to the reader. Figure 5 demonstrates this phenomenon.

In the case of the runner on the track, the base runner in baseball, and the hurdler, it is desirable to avoid rising in the air as much as possible. The objective in these and similar instances is to move from one point to another in the shortest space of time. Therefore, these athletes are not interested in prolonging their flight through the air. It is interesting to note how many base-runners erroneously leap in their last stride to first base or hop as they take a lead off a base and are put out as a result.

In some instances, the football player or the soccer player is interested in kicking the ball high rather than far in order to permit teammates to "cover" the kick. In such instances, height is more important than distance. The angle of kick in these cases would be greater than 45°.

Path of Projectile

The laws governing the path of a projectile, which describes a parabola, explain these phenomena. The following formulae have been derived and will be used here to demonstrate the above situations.

$$R = \frac{V^2 \sin 2\theta}{g} \tag{7}$$

R equals range or distance of flight from the level of release or take-off to return to the same level (horizontal).

V equals initial velocity at point of release in the initial direction of flight.

θ equals angle of projection (with the horizontal)

g equals acceleration of gravity, equals 32 ft/sec/sec.

In the previous example, to find the distance the baseball player threw the ball, substitute in the formula: $V = 70$, $\theta = 45$, $g = 32$, $\sin$ of $2\theta = 1$

$$R = \frac{70^2 \times \sin (2 \times 45)}{32} = \frac{4900 \times 1}{32} = 153 + \text{feet.}$$

This assumes that the ball was thrown and caught at the same level.

If the ball had been thrown at an angle of 75° the distance would have been

$$R = \frac{4900 \times \sin (2 \times 75)}{32} = \frac{4900 \times .5}{32} = 76.5 \text{ feet}$$

If, on the other hand, the ball was projected at an angle of only 30°, the distance would have been

$$R = \frac{4900 \times \sin (2 \times 30)}{32} = \frac{4900 \times .866}{32} = 132.5 \text{ feet}$$

$$\sin 2\theta = .866$$

This indicates that it is better to throw the ball too low rather than too high. Since the ball is also in the air a shorter time when thrown at an angle of 30°, it would be doubly profitable to throw the ball too low rather than too high. The time of flight may be calculated for comparison by using the formula $Tf =$ time in flight, $V =$ initial velocity in direction of release, $\theta =$ angle of projection with horizontal:

$$T_f = \frac{2V \sin \theta}{g} \qquad (8)$$

Where $V = 70$; $\theta = 45°, 30°,$ and $75°$; $g = 32$

$$T_f = \frac{2 \times 70 \times .7071}{32} = 3.09 \text{ sec when thrown at an angle of } 45°$$

$$T_f = \frac{2 \times 70 \times .5}{32} = 2.19 \text{ sec when thrown at an angle of } 30°$$

$$T_f = \frac{2 \times 70 \times .9659}{32} = 4.22 \text{ sec when thrown at an angle of } 75°$$

An analysis of these three situations shows that when the ball is thrown at an angle of 30° it travels 56 feet farther in 2.03 less seconds than when it is thrown at an angle of 75°. When the ball was projected at an angle of 45°, it traveled 20 feet farther than when it was thrown at an angle of 30° but it took .9 seconds longer. A practical question arises in baseball: is it more expedient to throw the ball at an angle of less than 45° or to throw at 45°? Will it take more or less than .9 of a second in the example presented here for the ball to be relayed or to bounce the additional 20 feet? A fast base runner would probably travel 20 feet or farther in .9 of a second. This problem invites scientific exploration

Special Application of Principle of Projectile

Shot Put

Though the laws governing the flight of a projectile describe the action of the flight of an object or body projected through the air, the simple formulae (7 and 8) which have been presented do not account for all phases of the practical situations involved in some sports activities. The shot put and broad jump are two cases in point.

In the shot put, the shot is released at a height of 7 feet or more above the surface to which it falls. Since the angle of projection of 45° in order to attain the greatest distance is predicated on the fact that the implement projected will not fall below the level from which it was projected, the formula $R = V^2 \sin 2\theta/g$ holds for the distance from the point of release of the shot to the point where the shot again falls to this same level. Figure 6 illustrates the situation for the shot

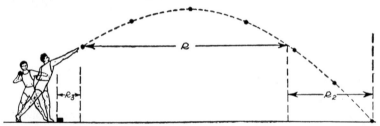

Fig. 6. The flight of the shot. The distances $R + R_2 + R_3$ represent the total distance of the put.

put. R represents the distance calculated by formula (7). In addition, the distance from the point where the shot falls below the level of release to the point where it hits the ground represented by R_2, must be accounted for. The distance R plus R_2 is represented by the formula

$$R + R_2 = \frac{V^2 \sin \theta \cos \theta + V \cos \theta \sqrt{V^2 \sin^2 \theta + 2gh}}{g} \qquad (9)$$

$V =$ the initial velocity of the shot at the point of release and in the direction of the put

$\theta =$ the angle of projection with the horizontal

$g =$ acceleration to gravity—32 ft/sec/sec

$h =$ height of the shot from the ground at the point of release

The distance R_3 is the distance from the inside edge of the toe board to the point in front of the toe board at which the shot was released. This represents the amount of lean and must be measured directly. Cureton[2] from motion picture studies of the shot put found this distance to be consistently 1 foot.

Table I shows the calculated distances in putting the shot when the angle of release and the velocity at release vary.

Using formula (9) and assuming R_3 to be a constant of 1 foot and using 7 feet as height of the shot above the ground at the point of release (Cureton found this distance to vary from 7 to 7.5 feet), it was found the ideal angle of projection θ varies directly with the initial velocity. The accompanying table shows the calculated distances when the angle of projection and the initial velocity were varied. It will be noticed that for distances of 40 feet or more the angle of projection is between 40° and 43°. It should also be observed that the rate of increase in velocity for greater distance is much greater than the increase in the angle of release. The figures in this table emphasize two factors. First, explosive power must be developed. Total body

TABLE I

Velocity of Shot at release	Angle of put at release of shot*							
	37°**	38°	39°	40°	41°	42°	43°	44°
20	18.16†	18.9††	18.6	18.0	17.9	17.8	17.7	17.6
22	19.73	20.96	20.89	20.88	20.72	20.70	20.58	19.78
24	23.61	23.98	23.96	23.91	23.84	23.75	23.65	23.53
26		27.23	27.22	27.19	27.12	27.05	26.94	26.81
28		30.71	30.71	30.68	30.64	30.57	30.46	30.34
30		34.40	34.42	34.42	34.39	34.32	34.21	34.09
32		38.31	38.37	38.36	38.34	38.29	38.19	38.07
34		42.45	42.49	42.54	42.35	42.49	42.43	42.24
36		46.44	46.90	46.95	47.28	47.01	46.87	46.70
38		51.47	51.60	51.68	51.72	51.70	51.63	51.59
40		56.24	56.41	56.50	56.57	56.56	56.51	56.40
45					69.60	70.15	69.62	
50					80.1	84.91	84.65	

* Angle is measured with horizontal.

** Angle represents the optimum angle of put.

† The numbers are given in feet. The horizontal distance from the inside edge of the toe board to the points of release of the shot (which was assumed to be one foot) is not added.

†† The italicized numbers represent the maximum distance to be reached at the velocity indicated.

[2] Cureton, Thomas K., "Mechanics of the Shot Put," *Scholastic Coach,* March, 1935.

strength plus the ability to transform that strength into lightening fast action is by far of greatest importance in putting the shot. Second, the angle of projection should be controlled, varying only slightly with the distance and the velocity.

Broad Jump

The broad jump introduces additional complications due partly to the development of certain techniques that are in harmony with sound scientific principles and partly to the reaction which takes place at take-off because of anatomical structure. It is not possible to accurately calculate the distance for the broad jump by assuming that the path of a projectile is traced by the feet from the place as they leave the take-off board to the spot where they hit the sand pit at the end of the jump.

Because of a hip lock by the iliofemoral ligament, the knee of the take-off leg is forced to bend. Thus, the leg makes a different angle at the take-off than does the center of gravity. Also, at the end of the jump the thrust of the legs forward to gain distance creates a different angle of legs at landing from the take-off angle. This latter fact causes the center of gravity to fall below the level of its take-off height from the ground. It does, however, follow the path of a parabola.

As a consequence, the formula used for the shot put applies for finding the distance traveled by the center of gravity but the distance due to the leg lean at the take-off and at landing must be calculated separately. These two distances can be calculated by using trigonometric functions as indicated below. Figure 7 shows the various distances

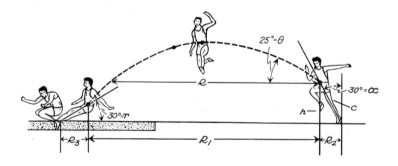

Fig. 7. The flight of the body in the broad jump. The distances making up the total length of the jump are shown by R, R_1, R_2, R_3.

to be figured. It is assumed that the position of the center of gravity in the body is at the same spot throughout the jump.

The distance of the jump is then equal to:

$$R_1 + R_2 + R_3 = \frac{V^2 \sin \theta \cos \theta + V \cos \theta \sqrt{V^2 \sin^2 \theta + 2G\,(H - C \sin \gamma)}}{g} + c \sin \alpha + c \cos \gamma \quad (10)$$

where $\theta =$ angle of projection of the center of gravity

$V =$ velocity of center of gravity at take-off

$h =$ vertical distance from center of gravity to ground at take-off

$g =$ acceleration due to gravity $= 32$ ft/sec/sec

$c =$ distance from foot to center of gravity at take-off. The distance from the center of gravity to point of landing at moment of landing is the same distance

$\alpha =$ angle of lean with vertical at take-off

$\gamma =$ angle of legs at moment of alighting

Using the value of α as 30°, γ as 30°, c as 3 feet and h (by computations) as 2.6 ft, but varying the projection angle for the center of gravity and the V of the center of gravity at take-off, the effect of speed and height on jumping distances are shown in Table II. The above values are representative of some actual jumping conditions. Probably α and γ would not remain constant, but the assumption is made for the purpose of this demonstration, to make clear the effect of various take-off speeds and angles of take-off.

TABLE II

ANGLE OF PROJECTION (θ)

Velocity of CG at take-off	20	25	30	35	40	45	50
20	16.68	17.63	18.47	18.77	18.97	18.84	18.25
25	21.76	24.52	24.81	25.6	26.05	26.0	25.0
30	27.6	30.2	32.6	33.7	34.8	34.7	33.7

As an example, the calculation when $\theta = 30°$ and $V = 25$ are shown below.

$$R_1 + R_2 + R_3 = \frac{V^2 \sin \theta \cos \theta + V \cos \theta \sqrt{V^2 \sin^2 \theta + 2G\,(H - C \sin \gamma)}}{g} + c \sin \alpha + c \cos \gamma$$

$$R_1 + R_2 + R_3 = \frac{625 \times .5 \times .866 + 25}{32} \times .866 \sqrt{625 \times .25 + 2 \times 32 \times 1.1}$$
$$+ 3 \times .5 + 3 \times .866$$

$$= \frac{270.625 + 21.65 \times 15.05}{32} + 1.5 + 2.6$$

$$= \frac{596.46}{32} + 1.5 + 2.6 = 18.64 + 1.5 + 2.6$$

$$= 22.74 \text{ feet}$$

A study of Table II reveals as in the case of the shot put the importance of explosive power at the take-off and the value of attaining height as reflected in the angle of projection. The take-off angle should be emphasized particularly in the broad jump because in actual practice the jumper usually fails to attain an optimum height. It should be observed that the most advantageous take-off angle is somewhere between 40° and 45° from the horizontal. In these computations the greatest distances at each speed were obtained from a take-off angle of 40°.

Rotary Motion

The discussion and formulae introduced up to this point have been related to aspects of linear motion. In many athletic activities, rotary motion must be closely integrated with linear motion to produce top performances. The relation of rotary motion to running has been mentioned already. Other activities in which the principles of rotary motion are involved and are integrated with linear motion are swinging a golf club or baseball bat, kicking a ball, throwing the discus, or a ball, putting the shot, and throwing the javelin.

In other activities, the principles governing rotary motion are the primary factors in the activity, for example in the giant swing, stunts, trampoline routines, swinging activities and many dives.

Rotary motion consists of movement of a body in a circle or arc of a circle and about a center of rotation. It is characterized by its angular speed and the length of the radius of the circle of rotation. The terms *velocity* and *acceleration* are used to describe the speed of rotary motion in the same way that they describe linear motion. They are, however, expressed in degrees of radians. A radian is an arc or a circle equal to the length of the radius of rotation. This arc is the angle made by $180°/\pi$ or $57.29°$. By this relationship the speed of a point in rotary motion can be translated into linear speeds.

Formulae (1) to (6) which were presented to describe linear motion may be applied to rotary motion. V must be expressed in degrees or radians per sec, A in degrees or radians/sec/sec and D in degrees or radians. For example, a diver executes a double somersault in 2 seconds, how fast is he turning?

By formula (1), $D = Vt$

$$D = 720°; \qquad t = 2$$
$$720 = V \times 2; \qquad V = 360°/\text{sec}$$

Much of the application of rotary motion to athletics is related to the movement of a point and conversion of the rotary speed of that point into linear speed. For example, the discus thrower circles in the ring in order to generate speed before releasing the discus. As he turns in the ring, the speed which he generates for the discus is rotary in nature. As he releases the discus, that rotary speed is transformed into linear speed, directed, so the thrower hopes, within the arc which will constitute a legal throw.

The baseball player imparts a certain amount of rotary speed to the baseball by the rotation of his body and the rotation of his arm. By the proper sequence of motions (coaches call it co-ordination or timing), he hopes to transform that rotary speed without diminution into linear speed which will result in a called strike or a put out. The diver desires to control the speed of his rotation in making a somersault so that he will enter the water with his body aligned tangentially to the trajectory of his center of gravity, and, of course, with his head and hands entering the water first.

It is of considerable interest, therefore, to know the relationship between linear motion and rotary motion and the relationship of the movement of a point with respect to the center of rotation. The following equations give these relationships:

$$D_L = D_r r \qquad\qquad (11)$$
$$V_L = V_r r \qquad\qquad (12)$$

D_L = linear distance
D_r = rotary distance expressed in radians
r = radius of rotation in feet
V_L = linear velocity in feet per second
V_r = rotary velocity expressed in radians/sec

For example, assume that the discus as the discus thrower finishes his arm rotation preparatory to releasing the discus is moving at the rate of 25.23 radians/sec and that the center of the discus is 3 feet from the center of rotation. What is the linear velocity of the discus?

$$V_L = 25.23 \times 3 = 75.69 \text{ ft/sec}$$

Now, if the radius were 3.5 feet, what is the linear velocity?

$$V_L = 25.23 \times 3.5 = 88.305/\text{sec}$$

It will be noticed that the linear velocity varies directly with the length of the radius when the rotary or angular velocity remains constant. Thus, with a constant angular velocity, if great linear speed is desired, then the radius should be lengthened as much as possible. The discus thrower at the moment of release should have his arm fully extended.

Conversely, with a constant linear velocity, the angular velocity varies inversely with the length of the radius. For example, if a diver or a gymnast turns too fast or tends to turn too far in executing a somersault from a tuck position he can slow his turning action by straightening out, that is, by increasing his radius of rotation. Assume, in the case of the diver on page 41, that the double somersault was made from a layout position. Assume further that the radius of rotation of a point on his head was 3 feet. The angular velocity of 360°/sec is equal to 6.28 radians/sec. One radian equals 57.29°. The linear speed of the point by formula (12) would be

$$V_L = 6.28 \times 3 = 18.84 \text{ ft/sec}$$

Now, if the diver assumed a tuck position so that the radius of rotation was reduced to 1.5 feet, what would be the angular velocity? Assume that the conditions otherwise are the same, so that the linear velocity of the point remains the same—18.84 ft/sec. Again by formula (12)

$$V_L = V_r \times r; \qquad 18.84 = V_r \times 1.5$$

$$V_r = \frac{18.84}{1.5} = 12.56 \text{ radians/sec}$$

It will be noticed that the angular velocity has increased inversely with the length of the radius. The radius was reduced by one half, and the angular velocity was doubled.

Summary and Principles

1. In throwing, jumping, or kicking activities where horizontal distance is the goal, the body or the object should be projected at an angle of approximately, but not greater than 45°. This statement does not hold when air resistance is a controlling factor.

2. In throwing, jumping, or kicking activities where horizontal distance is the goal, the highest speed possible should be attained at the moment of release or take-off. As speed is developed by a succession of movements of members of the body, the speed of each successive member should be faster than that of its predecessor, and ultimately in the direction of the objective, in order to obtain the best results. The movement of each member should start at the moment of greatest velocity but least acceleration of the preceding member.

3. When the angular velocity is constant, the linear velocity of a point about the center of rotation is directly proportional to the radius. Conversely, when the linear velocity of a point about the center of rotation is held constant, the angular velocity is inversely proportional to the radius.

4. In swinging exercises, shortening the radius of rotation (distance between the center of gravity and center of rotation) on the upswing will accelerate the movement. Lengthening the radius on the down swing increases the linear velocity of the center of gravity at the bottom of the swing. This fact makes it possible to execute the giant swing (see Figure 61, page 195).

5. There must be an integration of forward linear motion with rotary motion in order to obtain the best results in many activities.

The forward movement from the back of the ring to the front in the discus throw must be co-ordinated with the turning movement. The discus must be thrown while the contestant is still rotating.

The baseball player hops or steps forward as he rotates his body and arm in throwing the ball. The shot putter rotates slightly at the end of his hop across the circle. If he hesitates before he begins his rotation, the value of his hop across the circle is lost.

6. When converting rotary motion to linear motion, the greatest speed is transferred when the linear direction is at right angles to the radius connecting the point of release and the center of rotation.

QUESTIONS AND TOPICS FOR DISCUSSION AND REVIEW

1. What is the effect of gravity on a falling body?

2. Give an example of a freely falling body in sports.

3. Of what significance are the laws of freely falling bodies to sports?

4. What is peculiarly characteristic of the acceleration of a falling body?

5. What is the ideal angle of projection of a body in order to gain the greatest horizontal distance? The greatest vertical distance? Why is this true?

6. If the time a body is sustained in the air is of greater importance than the horizontal distance, what should be emphasized? Why?

7. What is the path of a ball thrown into the air?

8. The distance which a body travels is a function of what?

9. Why does not the formula for the flight of a projectile account for the distance which the shot travels?

10. Why does not the formula for the flight of a projectile account for the distance in the broad jump?

11. What is the most significant factor in putting the shot?

12. What one factor should be emphasized in the broad jump?

13. Define rotary motion.

14. What two factors characterize rotary motion?

15. What is the relationship between rotary motion and linear motion?

16. Can the same formulae which were used to describe linear motion be applied to rotary motion? How, or why not?

17. What is the relationship between the linear velocity of a point and the length of the radius of rotation?

18. What is the relationship between the angular velocity of a point and the length of the radius of rotation?

19. In order to convert the greatest amount of rotary speed to linear speed in a given direction, at what point should an object be released?

20. In swinging exercises, why is it possible to attain increase in the speed of rotation on the upswing by shortening the radius of rotation and to increase the speed of movement on the down swing by lengthening the radius of rotation?

PROBLEMS ON MOTION

1. For review of the trigonometric functions, work the following. (See Appendix B for tables and Appendix D, page 293, for answers):

    a. What is the sine of $21°$; $36°$; $49°$; $45°$; $69°$?

    b. What is the cosine of $30°$; $48°$; $87°$; $45°$; $60°$?

    c. What is the tangent of $14°$; $38°$; $73°$; $45°$; $76°$?

    d. What is the cotangent of $17°$; $42°$; $79°$; $45°$; $73°$?

2. If a jumper jumps 2 feet high and takes off at an angle of $20°$ with the horizontal, how fast is he going forward after the take-off?

3. If the shot is put at an angle of $41°$ with the horizontal and with a velocity of 36 ft/sec in the direction of the put, what will be its upward

velocity at the moment of release? What will be its forward velocity? What will be its time of flight from the point of release to the return to the same level at which it was released?

4. How high will the shot in problem 3 go?

5. At the moment of take-off, a broad jumper has a forward velocity of 30 ft/sec. His vertical speed is 10 ft /sec. What is the angle of his take-off? How high does his center of gravity rise?

6. A shot is dropped from a height of 16 feet from the ground. What is its velocity when it hits the ground? How long did it take the shot to reach the ground?

7. If the shot had been dropped from 32 feet above the ground, how fast would it have been traveling when it hit the ground? When it was 7 feet from the ground?

8. If the shot were projected horizontally at a speed of 40 ft/sec from a height of 32 feet, how soon would it hit the ground? How far from the starting point would it hit, in horizontal distance?

9. A runner leaves his mark at an angle of 70° with the horizontal. The starting speed in the direction of his take-off is 15 ft/sec. What is his horizontal speed? If his take-off were at an angle of 50° with the horizontal, what would be his forward speed? How much would his center of gravity rise in each case?

10. A high jumper leaves the ground with a velocity of 12 ft/sec at an angle of 60°. His center of gravity is $3\frac{1}{2}$ feet above the ground at the take-off. What was the total height of his center of gravity above the ground at the peak of his jump?

11. A discus thrower rotates the discus through 600° before releasing it. The distance from the median line of the body (the axis of rotation) to the center of gravity of the discus is 40 inches. The time of rotation is 1.375 seconds. How fast was the discus traveling at the point of release? If the radius of rotation was 36 inches, what would be the velocity?

12. A broad jumper leaves the take-off at an angle of 25° and a velocity of 30 ft/sec. What is the forward velocity? What is the upward velocity? How much does the center of gravity rise?

13. A broad jumper leaves the take-off at an angle of 20°. His forward velocity is 27 ft/sec. What is his upward velocity? What is the velocity in the direction of the jump? How much does the center of gravity rise?

14. A broad jumper rises 1.4 feet during his jump. His forward velocity is 28 ft/sec. What is the upward velocity? What is the angle of take-off?

15. A broad jumper jumps with a forward velocity of 28 ft/sec and with a velocity of 30 ft/sec in the direction of the jump. What is the angle of the jump? What is the upward velocity? How far does the center of gravity rise?

16. A broad jumper leaves the take-off broad at an angle of 20° and jumps 2 feet high. What is his forward velocity?

17. A shot putter puts the shot at an angle of 41° with the horizontal at a velocity of 36 ft/sec. What is the upward velocity? What is the forward velocity? How high does the shot rise?

18. A runner strides 8 feet. He moves at the rate of 30 ft/sec. His foot is in contact with the ground during 2 feet of his stride. How much does his center of gravity rise?

19. A baseball is thrown with an initial velocity of 100 ft/sec and at an angle of 30° with the horizontal. It is caught at the same height from the ground at which it was released. Disregarding the factor of air resistance, how far did it travel? How long was it in flight?

20. A tennis ball is hit at a point 30 feet from the net and 12 inches above the surface of the court. Its speed is 60 ft/sec. At what angle with the horizontal must the ball be projected in order to just clear the net? In order to strike the base line? The ball is hit so that it travels in a direction at right angles to the net.

21. A baseball is thrown at an angle of 45° with the horizontal. It leaves the hand 6 feet above the ground. Its initial velocity is 145 ft/sec. Neglecting all external resistance, how far would it travel? The point at which it hits the ground is at the same level as the ground at the point from which it was thrown.

22. Using the data from Table II, find the distance jumped if a jumper takes off at a speed of 26 ft/sec and at an angle of 41° with the horizontal. 42°? 43°? 44°?

23. What differences would there be in the distances in Table I if a 12-instead of a 16-pound shot were used?

24. A runner with a running start takes 40 equal strides in sprinting 100 yards in 10 seconds. If his foot is on the ground for 2 feet of each stride, how much does the center of gravity rise (and fall) during the rest of the stride?

25. If the runner in problem (24) takes 60 strides and runs 100 yards in 20 seconds, how high does his center of gravity rise?

26. A shot putter puts the shot at an angle of 37° with the horizontal with an initial velocity in the direction of the put of 36 ft/sec. When he releases the shot, his hand (center of gravity of the shot) is 7 feet from the ground and 1 foot in front of the edge of the circle. What is the distance of the put? How high above the ground does the shot rise?

27. If the angle of the put was 45°, 50°, 35°, what would be the distances of the put?

28. From a tower 30 feet high, a man dives into the water. He springs outward and upward at an angle of 30° with the horizontal with a velocity of 10 ft/sec. How far from the edge of the tower (horizontal distance) does he land? How fast is he going when he hits the water? How long is he in the air?

29. A high jumper is 6 feet, 4 inches tall. When he is standing on his toes and his arms are raised upward at the take-off, his center of gravity is 48 inches from the ground. His Western roll style of jumping requires him to raise his center of gravity 4 inches above the bar in order for him to clear it. The take-off angle is 60° with the horizontal. The bar is 6' 4" high. How high does he have to raise his center of gravity to clear the bar? What is the upward velocity? What is the horizontal velocity? What is

the velocity in the direction of the jump? What is the distance of the take-off spot from a point directly below the bar?

30. If the angle of take-off was 70°, find the answers to the questions in problems 29. 57°? 55°?

31. The radius of rotation of a skater who is spinning is 3 feet. Her angular velocity is 1 revolution/sec. She reduces her radius of rotation to 1.2 feet. What is her speed?

32. A diver in executing a somersault from a tuck position is turning at the rate of 2 revolutions/sec. The radius of rotation of a point on the top of his head is 12 inches. Before entering the water, he opens to a layout position with a radius of rotation of the same point of 3 feet. What is his angular velocity in each case? What is the linear velocity of the same point in each case?

4.

Force

Force has the same relationship to athletics that breath has to the individual. It requires breath to maintain life. Since it takes force to create motion or prevent it and since athletics are an activity of motion, there would not be any athletics without force. Force, therefore, is essential to the life of athletics. Force is so vital to athletics that the coach and the athlete should be tremendously concerned with the source, the proper application or use of force, and the conservation of energy, which is a quantitative measure of force. This measure will be discussed in Chapter 6.

Human Force

In the individual, the primary source of force is his strength. The implication here from an athletic point of view is so obvious that it may be overlooked. Strength is derived from a muscle or combination of muscles, and is related directly to the cross-sectional area of the muscle. Therefore, to have strength one must build muscle. And in athletics, in order to have reserve to meet emergencies, it is desirable to acquire strength in excess of that required for the activity. This connotes a conditioning program more strenuous and with a heavier requirement of strength than the activity itself, as a part of the training program. A discussion of conditioning may seem to be far removed from a treatise on the application of mechanical principles to athletics. However, the importance of strength is so vital and actually so neglected that the writer would be remiss if he did not include at least a brief mention of its importance. The reader is referred to the December, 1949, issue of the *Athletic Journal*[1] for additional information on strength and conditioning.

Magnitude of Force

There are two categories to the development and use of force. The first requires an understanding of the factors which describe force or measure its magnitude or quality. Force is the effort which one body exerts on another. This effect may be movement of the one body by the other: for example, the pitcher throws the ball to the catcher. It may be the stopping of one body by another, as in the case of the tackler who stops the ball carrier in football. Or it may be merely resistance against movement. The wrestler in the defensive position on the mat prevents his opponent from moving him. It was pointed out earlier that there may be force without movement but never movement without force.

For those situations where a change in movement is involved, force is a function of the mass of the body to which the force is applied and the rate of change in its movement per unit of time (acceleration). This relationship is represented by the formula:

$$F = ma \quad \text{or} \quad F = \frac{mv}{t} \tag{13}$$

when F = force, v = velocity, t = time force acts, m = mass of body to which the force is applied (weight ÷ 32) a = acceleration

For a particular situation the mass is a constant. Therefore, the acceleration of the body will vary with the force exerted upon it. Remember that acceleration means the *rate of change* in velocity. In athletic situations, the rate of change is the significant factor. It must be almost instantaneous. For example, the pitcher in baseball has a very short time in which to develop a velocity of over 80 ft/sec in the baseball at the moment he releases it. Bob Feller's pitch has been timed at 145 ft/sec. The final speed is imparted with the flick of the wrist at the moment of release. Similar examples are the techniques involved in swinging the bat at the ball, hitting a tennis ball, putting

---

[1] Bunn, J. W., "Why Give Conditioning Exercises for Basketball," *Athletic Journal*, December, 1949.

the shot, broad jumping, rebounding in basketball, striking the handball, spiking the volleyball, kicking the football, swinging the golf
club, and in quick starting and stopping.

There is no opportunity to continue to apply the force for a pro-
tracted period. The application must be almost instantaneous. This,
then, emphasizes the necessity for fast muscular contraction in order
to produce force with an explosive effect. The importance of this
fact can be seen in the following example.

Assume that a ball is delivered to the batter with the speed of 128
ft/sec. What is the force exerted if this speed is developed in $\frac{1}{10}$ sec?
A baseball weighs 5 ounces and mass equals weight divided by gravity
so:

$$m = \frac{5}{16 \times 32}; \qquad F = m\frac{V}{t};$$

$$F = \frac{5 \times 128}{16 \times 32 \times .1}; \qquad F = 12.5 \text{ pounds}$$

Now, if this speed is developed in $\frac{1}{100}$ of a second

$$F = \frac{5 \times 128}{16 \times 32 \times .01} = 125 \text{ pounds}$$

The value of developing explosive power can be seen from these
examples. There is a need for body strength to withstand such strains.
In all fields of sports, it is impossible to avoid the recognition of the
absolute necessity for an exacting training and conditioning program
if one is to excel. Particularly, the development of fast reaction time
to the limit of the potentialities of the individual is essential. It is not
so much how great a force can be mustered but rather how quickly can
it be applied. The necessity for developing the reaction time to the
utmost becomes obvious in view of one of the limitations in human performance. In Chapter 5 this limitation is presented and demonstrated: "In the human body, the available force varies inversely
with the velocity of movement." It can be established mathematically
that optimum speed is one half the maximum velocity. If, therefore,
the speed of contraction is developed to a maximum, one half of this
speed will be higher than will that of a slower, undeveloped maximum.
The reader is referred to Chapter 5 for further explanation.

The lightweight athlete who participates in sports such as football
where body contact is one of the basic conditions of play, is able to

compensate for his weight disadvantage only by developing the explosive aspect of his force to a greater degree than that of his bigger opponent. If the big man is equally quick, then the small man has no mechanical advantage in this category.

Application of Force

The second category of the development and use of force involves the point of application of the force and the direction of the force. This aspect requires an understanding of resultant or the parallelogram of forces, the application of levers, centrifugal and centripetal forces, the force of gravity, friction or shock, impact, and elasticity. Newton's three laws of motion furnish a complete basis for the science of mechanics. They are particularly significant as a forerunner of this phase of the discussion. They are re-stated here for the convenience of the reader, since frequent reference is made to them.

1. Every body continues in its state of rest or of uniform motion in a straight line except insofar as it is compelled by force to change that state.

2. The acceleration (or change of momentum) of a body is proportional to the force causing it and takes place in the direction of the applied force.

3. For every action there is always an equal and contrary reaction.

Parallelogram of Force

The principles of the parallelogram are examples of the application of the first and second laws. The racing start in track and blocking tactics in football can be used to demonstrate these principles. For example, defensive lineman B charges through the line so that he exerts a force of 300 pounds if he hits an opponent directly. Opponent A, with a force of 200 pounds charges the defensive lineman at right angles to his direction of movement. (a) How far will A displace B from his course? (b) If A were to charge at an angle of 30° to the direction which the defensive line man B is moving, how far will A displace B from his course?

If the forces of 200 and 300 pounds are represented by lines of proportionate lengths and these lines are drawn in the directions as indicated, Figure 8 can be used to demonstrate the graphical solution of these problems. The dotted lines in the diagrams are drawn parallel and equal in length to the forces which they parallel. The completed figure is a parallelogram. The diagonal shown represents the direction in which the defensive lineman would be moved and the angle θ represents the amount by which he will be displaced from his original path. This represents a vector analysis of the problem. By means of a scale and a protractor one may get a rough solution to the problem. This is the rule or law of the parallelogram of forces: The resultant of two forces about a point is always the diagonal of the parallelogram from that point.

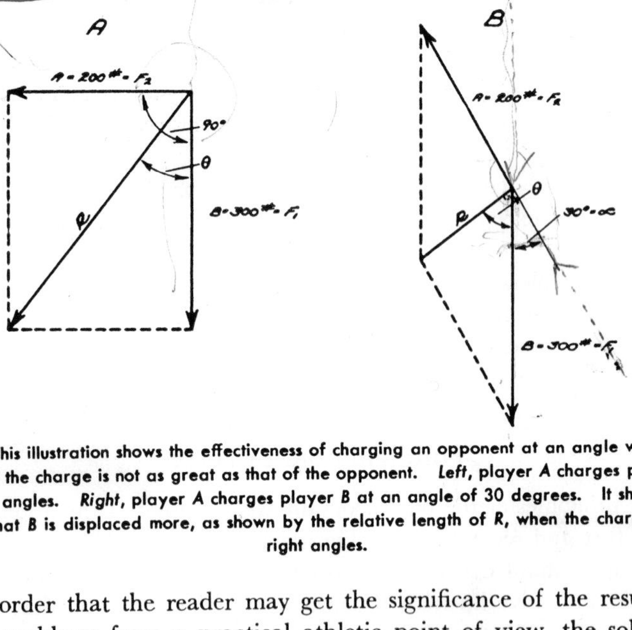

Fig. 8. This illustration shows the effectiveness of charging an opponent at an angle when the force of the charge is not as great as that of the opponent. *Left,* player A charges player B at right angles. *Right,* player A charges player B at an angle of 30 degrees. It should be noted that B is displaced more, as shown by the relative length of R, when the charge is at right angles.

In order that the reader may get the significance of the results of these problems from a practical athletic point of view, the solutions will be worked out mathematically. In example (A) the forces are working at right angles to each other. In example (B) the forces are not at right angles. Since this solution is the more complex, it will be solved first. The formula for finding the R, the resultant force, and the angle of the resultant with one of the forces, is shown by the equation:

$$R^2 = F_1^2 + F_2^2 - 2F_1F_2 \cos \alpha \qquad (14)$$

Substituting in this formula:

$$R^2 = 300^2 + 200^2 - 2 \times 300 \times 200 \cos 30°$$
$$= 90,000 + 40,000 - 120,000 \times .866$$
$$= 130,000 - 103,920 = 26,080$$
$$R = 161.49 \text{ pounds}$$

Now, solving for θ it is necessary to rewrite the formula as follows:

$$F_2^2 = R^2 + F_1^2 - 2RF_1 \cos \theta \qquad (15)$$

Substituting

$$200^2 = 161.49^2 + 300^2 - 2 \times 161.49 \times 300 \cos \theta$$
$$40,000 = 26,080 + 90,000 - 96,894 \cos \theta$$

Transposing and changing signs

$$96894 \cos \theta = 116080 - 40000$$
$$\cos \theta = \frac{76080}{96894} = .7853$$

From the table, page 267

$$\theta = 38°$$

When the forces act at right angles to each other, the problem becomes much simpler. In this case:

$$R^2 = F_1^2 + F_2^2 \qquad (16)$$

So, in example (a)

$$R^2 = 90000 + 40000 = 130000$$
$$R = 360.55 \text{ pounds}$$

Solving for θ

$$\cos \theta = \frac{F_1}{R} = \frac{300}{360.55} = .8321 \qquad (17)$$
$$\theta = 34°$$

The parallelogram in this case (B), however is not a rectangle. Consequently, the triangle formed by the two forces and the resultant is not a right triangle. The law of cosines must be applied. It is represented by the equation:

$$R^2 = F_1^2 + F_2^2 - 2F_1F_2 \cos \alpha \qquad (18)$$

a is the angle formed by the two forces (Figure 8).

If, at any time, more than two forces are involved, in order to find the resultant force, R, for all three, the forces should be dealt with two at a time. For example, if forces F_1, F_2, and F_3 are acting at the same point, R may be found for F_1 and F_2. Then, the resultant for all three may be found by finding the resultant of R with F_3. These calculations may be checked in the laboratory by using the parallelogram force table to demonstrate the balancing of forces.

From the foregoing it is seen that a charging lineman can be displaced more effectively by attacking him at an angle. It is one way in which a lighter player can compensate for his weight disadvantage. If the opponent had met the defensive lineman head on, it is obvious that he would not have stopped him at all. He would have dissipated the force of the charge of his opponent by two-thirds but the opponent would have moved straight ahead.

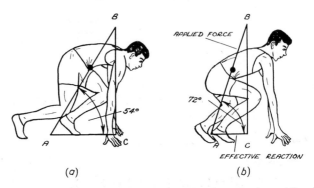

(a)   (b)

Fig. 9. The relative effectiveness of two starting positions in track. A, good "mechanics," and B, poor "mechanics."

The technique of the track start involves a different approach to the application of these same principles. By actual measurement it has been found that a track man pushed with both feet at the start of a race with a force of 397 pounds.[2] In one start the direction of this force was at an angle of 54° with the horizontal. In another, it was at an angle of 72°. Which start was the more effective? These two situations are shown graphically in Figure 9. The track man is, of course, primarily interested in moving in the direction of the

---

[2] Cureton, Thomas K., "Mechanics of the Track Racing Start," *Scholastic Coach*, January, 1935.

finish mark as quickly as possible. This direction is along the X axis. Therefore, when the force of 397 pounds which is directed along the vector representing its magnitude and direction, the effective force becomes in (B)

$$F_x = 397 \cos 72° = 397 \times .3090 = 122.77 \text{ pounds}$$

while in (A) it is equal to

$$F_x = 397 \cos 54° = 397 \times .5878 = 233.34 \text{ pounds}$$

It becomes obvious that on the start one should reduce the angle of projection as much as possible in order not to dissipate the force generated at the start of a race. It should be pointed out that the center of gravity is higher and closer to the edge of the base in the direction of the intended motion (situation A). This corresponds to the principles stated in Chapter 2. Details of the technique of the track start will be discussed in Chapter 7. From these demonstrations one may make applications to other sports and other techniques.

Levers

The proper utilization of the principles of levers opens up another field in the application of force   The body movements are produced through a system of levers. The bones of the body act as the levers. They are acted upon by a force which is produced by the contraction of the muscles. The principle of the lever has its application outside the body also in athletic activities. The techniques of the sport of wrestling are largely based on the principles of levers and leverage.

The lever is a mechanical device to produce turning motion about an axis. It consists of a fulcrum which is the center or axis of rotation, a power arm which is the distance from the fulcrum to the point where the force is applied, and a weight arm which is the distance from the fulcrum to the weight upon which the force is acting.

Levers are of three types and are characterized by the relative positions of the fulcrum, weight, and force. When the fulcrum is located between the weight and the force, it is called a first-class lever. This is the most efficient type of lever. When the weight is between the fulcrum and the force, it is called a second class lever. And when the force is between the fulcrum and the weight, it is a third-class lever.

Levers create a mechanical advantage either for producing strength or speed, unless they are of the first-class balancing type. Most of the body movements are produced through third-class levers. For example, the psoas and iliacus muscles act as a third-class lever in flexing the thigh. The glutii act as a third-class lever in straightening or extending the thigh. The hamstring muscles (the muscles forming the back of the leg), act as a third-class lever in flexing the leg and the quadriceps act as a third-class lever in straightening the leg. Likewise, the action of the biceps in flexing the arm and the deltoid in lifting the arm or abducting it act as third-class levers. On the other hand, the triceps which extend the forearm act as a first-class lever as do also the gastrocnemius and soleus in extending the foot.

Figure 10 shows the three types of levers.

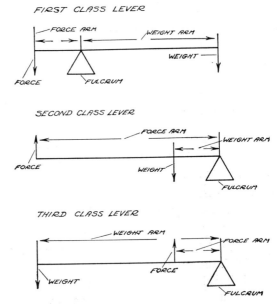

Fig. 10. Three types of lever.

The mechanical advantage of a lever is represented by the ratio of the length of the force or power arm to the weight arm. The longer the force arm the greater is the moment of force about its axis. The shorter the force arm, the smaller is the moment of force but the more immediate is the action. In the case of the levers in the body, the length of the force arm is relatively short. For this reason, the speed of movement as a result of muscular contraction is rapid whereas the moment of force is relatively weak. The moment of a force is equal to the magnitude of the force multiplied by the perpendicular distance from the direction of the force to its axis or fulcrum. An analysis of the diagram of the third-class lever will demonstrate this fact (see Figure 11). It will be seen that a movement of a short distance by the force produces a relatively great movement of the weight. As a consequence, the contraction of the psoas and iliacus muscles which produce a rather limited shortening will flex the thigh through an arc of as much as 135° in running. The distal end of the femur will be moving at a tremendous linear speed in comparison to the linear speed of the point at which the psoas and iliacus are attached to the femur. This, of course, is consistent with the principle in rotary motion that the linear speed of a point in rotation is directly proportional to the distance of that point from the center or axis of rotation (see Chapter 2—Rotary Motion).

Therefore, if one desires to exert tremendous force, he should have his force arm as long as possible. If he is more interested in speed of movement, then the force arm should be relatively short. So far as the movements of members of the body are concerned, the individual has no control over this factor. The attachment of the muscles which are the source of the force exerted is fixed. However, when the lever is used outside the body, this principle becomes important. For example, in wrestling, if one is holding the arm of an opponent down on the mat as a means of preventing the opponent from turning, he will be able to offset the efforts of the opponent more effectively by grasping the arm as near to the hand as possible and holding the arm extended at right angles to the body. The force arm is longest in this position. Therefore, the greatest moment of force can be created and the greatest mechanical advantage secured. On the other hand, if it is desired to turn the opponent quickly assuming, of course, that sufficient force is available, a short force arm is called for. The use of the half nelson is a case in point. Here the force is applied at the shoulder.

In addition to the relative length of the force arm, the direction in which the force is applied affects the efficiency of the effort. In the consideration of levers the force is always assumed to be acting at right angles to the lever. In the case of muscle action, this is seldom the case. For example, the angle of pull of the biceps in flexing the forearm from its fully extended position is practically a straight angle. The effective force is, therefore, very small. For example, a 10-pound weight is being held in the hand with the forearm fully extended.

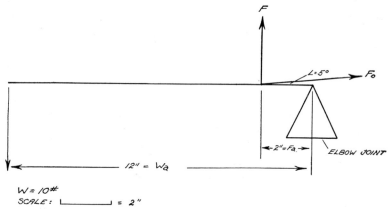

Fig. 11. Diagrammatical illustration of the problem involved when the forearm is flexed from a fully extended position with a 10-pound weight in the hand.

Assume that the angle of pull is 5°, that the weight arm is 12 inches and the force arm 2 inches. What force must be exerted by the biceps to start the flexion of the forearm? When the angle is 30°, what is the force exerted?

$$F \times F_a = W \times Wa \qquad\qquad F = \text{force} \qquad\qquad (19)$$
$$F \times 2 = 10 \times 12 \qquad\qquad F_a = \text{force arm} = 2 \text{ inches}$$
$$F = \frac{120}{2} = 60 \text{ pounds} \qquad W = \text{weight} = 10 \text{ pounds}$$
$$W_a = \text{weight arm} = 12 \text{ inches}$$
$$F_0 = \text{pull of biceps}$$

F here, however, is at right angles to the lever whereas the applied force is at an angle of 5° with the lever. Therefore, the force exerted by the biceps is

$$F_0 = \frac{60}{\sin 5°} = \frac{60}{.0872} = 688 \text{ pounds}$$

When the angle of pull is 30°

$$F_0 = \frac{60}{.5} = 120 \text{ pounds}$$

(It is assumed here that the force arm and the weight arm remain the same as when the forearm is flexed.)

From this example, it can be concluded that it was quite providential that a muscle was made to be strongest under stretch. It certainly needs to be since most situations of muscular actions are of this type. For other situations, the practical advantage of exerting force at right angles to the lever is quite obvious.

Moment of Force

In the discussion of levers the term *moment of force* was used. It is the tendency of a force to rotate a body to which it is applied about its axis of rotation. It was stated that it was equal to the force multiplied by the perpendicular distance of that force from the axis of rotation.

In athletics, the axis of rotation may be the center of gravity of the body, as in the case of the diver or the gymnast doing a somersault or similar stunts. It may be the point of support, as the hands when doing the hand stand or the feet as in lifting. It may be the median line of the body, as in the discus throw or batting. It may be a joint, as the hip joint in kicking or the shoulder joint in swinging the golf club. It may be a bar, as in the giant swing or a point of attachment as the anchor for the flying rings.

If one is interested in overcoming the moment of force or holding it to a minimum, he should maneuver so that the *moment arm* (the perpendicular distance from the force to the axis of rotation) is as short as possible. The *moment of force* is equal to the force times the moment arm. If it can be held at the center of rotation, then there is no moment of force to contend with. For example, in lifting a weight, the axis of rotation is at the feet, which are the point of support. In order to reduce the moment arm the lifter should, if possible, stand right over the weight in order to eliminate the moment of force. If a weight of 200 pounds is to be lifted and the moment arm is zero, there is no handicap to overcome. If the lifter is 1 inch from the weight, the moment arm is 1. But if the lifter is 12 inches from the weight, the moment arm, and thus the moment of force, has been increased 12-fold. It is assumed in each case that the weight is balanced in the same way every time and that the lifter squats each time so that he is using the strong leg muscles to do part of the lifting rather than lifting solely with his back muscles. Incidentally, by this procedure, he protects his back. In the rope climb, the axis of rotation is in the rope or the hands as they grip the rope. If the climber holds his center of gravity directly below his hands he eliminates the effect of moment of force. In layout activities on the bar, the performer attempts to bring his center of gravity directly below the bar, his point of support, in order to lessen the strain of holding his position.

On the other hand, there are situations where it is advantageous to increase the moment arm as much as possible. On the downward path of the giant swing, it is desirable to gain as much speed as possible. Therefore, the body is extended as much as possible so that the moment arm from the center of gravity to the bar is as long as possible. In swinging the baseball bat the fully extended arms give a longer moment arm and produce more linear speed at the end of the bat. Situations of this kind are additional to those already discussed under levers.

Centrifugal and Centripetal Force

Certain forces, developed as a result of rotary motion, are an aid to performance in some activities and in others are a handicap that must be offset. These forces are called *centripetal* and *centrifugal* forces. Centrifugal force is that force which tends to cause a rotating body to fly off at a tangent to its circle of movement or away from the center of rotation. This is considered a fictitious force by physicists. But from a practical point of view, there is a phenomenon which makes it quite difficult to change directions when one is moving rapidly. As one moves in a circle this problem becomes a constant one with every stride. Unless the tendency is offset by either body adjustment or a mechanical device such as a sloping track, one is unable to readily change his path of movement. In athletics, it is essential for success that the athletes have some compensating maneuvers which will permit them to change directions without loss of time or position.

Centripetal force is the opposite of centrifugal force. It is that force which is directed toward the center of rotation. According to the physicist, this is the real force. Centrifugal force has been emphasized here because it describes what actually happens in an athletic situation that creates the necessity for providing some factor (centripetal force) to counteract its effect and re-establish equilibrium.

For example, the problem of centrifugal force presents itself when a runner goes around a track. The shorter the radius of the track the more acute the problem. On the outdoor track with a turn of 100 or more feet, the runners are able to maintain their course by leaning in toward the center. On indoor tracks or tracks with radii of 60 feet or less, the tracks are banked to furnish the force toward the center to prevent the runners from going off at a tangent.

A similar situation exists in baseball. Here, the baserunner must make some abrupt turns. He cannot have the assistance of a banked track. Therefore, he leans far in toward the diamond, depends on his spiked shoes to prevent slipping, and uses the base to push off if he desires to run the shortest distance between bases. Of course, he can take a wide circle when rounding bases and possibly forfeit his chance of gaining an extra base. The football player and lacrosse player have similar problems, though they are often not thought of as analogous to those of the track man.

The same formula is used for determining both centripetal and centrifugal force and is represented by:

$$F = \frac{WV^2}{gr} \qquad (20)$$

F = centripetal or centrifugal force
W = weight of the body
V = velocity in feet per second
r = radius of the circle
g = force of gravity = 32 ft/sec/sec

Outdoor cinder tracks usually have a radius of about 100 feet. Assume the runner is traveling 30 ft/sec and that he weighs 175 pounds. What force tends to pull him out of his lane at the turn or how much force is needed to permit him to follow the turn of the track?

$$F = \frac{175 \times 900}{32 \times 100} = 49+ \text{ pounds}$$

If the radius is 40 feet, what is the force?

$$F = \frac{175 \times 900}{32 \times 40} = 123 \text{ pounds}$$

If the runner is a baseball player who is attempting to make a sharp turn in a radius of 10 feet and is traveling at the rate of 20 ft/sec, what is the force?

$$F = \frac{175 \times 400}{32 \times 10} = 218.75 \text{ pounds}$$

These three examples are worked out to demonstrate the increase in centrifugal force that arises when the radius becomes small. This is the force that tends to pull or throw the athlete off his course when he is turning. As previously stated, to offset this force the runner either leans in toward the point about which he is turning or runs on a banked path. It will probably be more meaningful to the reader to show the amount of lean or bank that is necessary to neutralize the centrifugal force.

The angle of lean of the runner or the slope of the track can be determined by the formula:

$$\tan \theta = \frac{V^2}{gr} \tag{21}$$

$\theta =$ the angle of lean with the vertical or the slope of the track
For the three examples above, θ is:

(1) for the track with 100-feet radius

$$\tan \theta = \frac{900}{32 \times 100} = \frac{9}{32} = .281; \qquad \theta = 16°$$

(2) for the track with the 40-feet radius

$$\tan \theta = \frac{900}{32 \times 40} = \frac{45}{64} = .703; \qquad \theta = 35°$$

(3) For the baserunner who is turning in a 10-feet radius

$$\tan \theta = \frac{400}{32 \times 10} = \frac{5}{4} = 1.25; \qquad \theta = 51°$$

It will be seen that the lean for the baseball player is rather extreme and would probably necessitate slowing his pace or increasing his radius. If he increased his radius to 20 feet, θ would equal 32°. These examples should at least impress the reader with the significance of this force. The principles of Newton's three laws are demonstrated.

Force of Gravity

The effect of the force of gravity, which is represented by a constant acceleration of 32 ft/sec/sec (for all practical purposes), was demonstrated in Chapter 2 on motion. It should be emphasized here that it is the same for all bodies falling freely, ignoring air resistance; that it is

always acting and that it always acts in a vertical direction; and that
it is apparent in all athletic activities and must enter into all calculations when a body is swinging, hanging, or when it is in the air free
of support.

Friction

Friction is the resistance to motion which is created by contact between two surfaces. The magnitude of this resistance is dependent
on four factors—the materials which make up the two bodies, the
irregularities of their surfaces, the force with which the surfaces are
pressed together, and the relative action between the surfaces.

A measure of friction is the amount of force applied to the body
parallel to the surface of contact that is necessary to just start movement or slipping between the surfaces. It has been found that this
force is proportional to the force which presses against the two surfaces.
And most interesting and significant from an athletic point of view is
the fact that the force pressing against the surfaces may be concentrated
at one point or spread out over a large area. The proportional relationship for all practical purposes does not change.

If the force pressing the two surfaces together is represented by W,
and the force necessary to start movement by P, this relationship may
be shown as a ratio:

$$\frac{P}{W} = C \tag{22}$$

C is the coefficient of friction between the surfaces. Observation and
the examples which are presented below demonstrate that the amount
of friction or adhering quality between two surfaces varies directly
with C. The larger C the stronger the adhering qualities of the two
surfaces. Stated another way, the greater the magnitude of the force
necessary to produce slippage, the greater the amount of friction between the two surfaces. By setting up a parallelogram of forces and
finding the resultant (see Figure 12), it is found that this ratio is equal
to the tangent of the angle formed by the vector representing the
resultant and the vector for W. Thus, the ratio may be rewritten:

$$\frac{P}{W} = \tan \theta \tag{23}$$

θ is the angle between the resultant and W. This angle represents the amount by which the surfaces must incline in order to start slippage between them. This angle is called the *limiting angle* or the *angle of friction*.

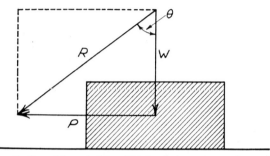

Fig. 12. The application of the principle of friction between two surfaces. W equals the weight pressing the two surfaces together; P is the force necessary to start movement; R is the resultant of the two forces; and θ equals the angle of lean necessary to start movement or "slipping" between the surfaces.

These principles have two quite diverse applications in athletics. The first is the direct application—the problem of slipping. Starting, stopping, changing speed, changing direction are maneuvers which require a firm footing without slipping. They require a gripping effect between the shoes and the surface on which they are moving that will produce a high coefficient of friction. In some sports, spiked shoes are used to accomplish this relationship. Baseball, football, and track are examples. In others, attention is directed to treating the surface and building soles for shoes which have a high coefficient of friction. Treating wood playing surfaces with "gym" finishes, using solvents on rubber soled shoes, putting sticky substances on the soles of shoes are some of the practices which are current.

There is one area, however, that is somewhat neglected. Too little attention is given to the fundamentals of starting, stopping, changing speed, and changing direction that will contribute to maintaining equilibrium—preventing slipping—regardless of the type of playing surface or gripping effect of the shoes worn. The matter of lean referred to above and determined by formula (23) suggests a solution to the problem of slipping when unusual situations are encountered. The principles of equilibrium discussed in Chapter 2 are vital to the problem of slipping. Since the effective force W, in this case the weight of the individual, always acts in a vertical direction, it is well to keep in mind that if this force is kept within the base, the problem of slipping or even falling will be minimized. This, of course, requires squatting to reduce the amount of lean.

Assume that surface conditions are found where the coefficient of friction (C) between the surface and the soles of the shoes was .33. From a formula (23), $.33 = \tan \theta$. From the table $\theta = 18°$. This is about the angle of inclination of a runner in the 100-yard dash. It can be seen, therefore, that very little lean would be possible on this particular surface without slipping or falling. On the other hand, if the coefficient was found to be 1.5 which is not unusual for basketball shoes on a satisfactory playing surface, the angle of lean is 56° (Figure 13 shows a basketball player leaning 18° and 56° respectively).

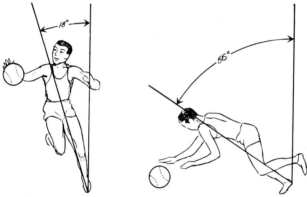

Fig. 13. The angle of lean of a basketball player that is possible without slipping when the coefficient of friction between two surfaces is .33 (left) and 1.5 (right). (See Figure 12.)

This provides better gripping contact than is needed for extreme maneuvers. Certainly, if a player is trained thoroughly in the fundamentals of balance, he will be able to adjust to unsatisfactory playing surfaces, which are occasionally encountered and where it is not possible to create satisfactory footing by artificial methods. He will be able to handle himself even more effectively on satisfactory surfaces.

The second application is based on a deduction from the principles of friction as stated above. Since the friction is the same whether the force which presses the two surfaces together is concentrated at one point or spread over a wide area, it follows that if the total force is spread over a wide area the force will not be as great at any one point (the total force is the same) as it would be if it were concentrated at one point or on a small area.   Therefore, in those sports or phases of sports where contact, such as a blow, a shock, an impact of bodies, or a collision occurs, it may be wise to spread the force of the blow over as wide an area as possible.   This can be accomplished in two ways.   Equipment may be constructed to spread the force of a blow.   Examples are the gloves for the baseball player.   The size of the catcher's mitt compared to that of other players is recognition of this principle.   The catcher sometimes adds a piece of sponge rubber to further cushion or spread the shock.   The sliding pads of the baseball player are another example.   The shoulder pads, hip pads, thigh guards, and head gear of the football player are definitely designed for this purpose.   In this case, pads have been designed not only to spread the force of a blow but also to transfer it from one part of the body to another.   The cantilever idea in shoulder pads is intended to transfer the blow from the more vulnerable pointed parts of the shoulder to flat, protected surfaces.   The 20-ounce boxing gloves for instructional and training purposes are designed to spread the force of a blow over a larger area.

At this point, it may be helpful to call attention to a few of the trends in the construction of some football equipment.   Protective pads are used to spread the force of a blow.   In order to do this effectively the protective materials of which the pads are made must be of more or less unyielding material.   To the extent that this principle is not followed, the protective factor is weakened.   Sponge or foam rubber and materials of this type do not meet the requirement of being unyielding.   Such pads are light, flexible, and comfortable to wear but they lack the safety of the pads made of less flexible materials.   The validity of these statements may be tested by percussion tests on materials with varying qualities of flexibility.

The other aspect of applying the principle is knowledge of the proper fundamental techniques.   Sliding in baseball should include the fundamental movements of a layout which will cause as much as possible of the leg, hip, and back to hit the ground simultaneously.   Such a technique is protection against abrasions even when sliding pads are not used, and helps to keep the spikes from digging into the ground with the attendant danger of serious injury.

The technique of falling on the ball in football should include this principle.   "Tackle" shoulders or so-called "pointers" would be eliminated from this part of football if the player hit flat around the ball. Figure 44 shows a baseball player in correct sliding position to spread force as well as to protect against injury. Judo also applies this principle. The art of learning to fall is a very important factor in sports and one which no coach can afford to neglect.

Impact and Elasticity

So many sports involve the use of a ball and a bat that attention must be given to the principles of *impact* and *elasticity*. The speed and direction of a golf ball when hit by a golf club, the action of a baseball rebounding from a bat, and the action of a tennis ball when hit by a racket are examples of these situations. First of all, the direction of movement of an object such as a ball after it has been struck depends primarily on the angle of contact. This is a further application of Newton's first law. Except insofar as spin, air resistance, and flattening may alter conditions, the angle at which a ball is met by an implement will equal the angle at which it will leave the implement. If the force with which the ball is hit is many times greater than the force with which the ball is spinning, the effect of the spin on the direction of the ball is practically eliminated. The resultant of the two forces is so nearly in the direction of the dominating force that the effect of the spin becomes negligible. Of course, spin that is imparted to the ball by the implement will change the direction of the ball after it leaves the implement.

As an example, if a batter desires to hit a ball to left field parallel to the left field foul line, what will be the angle at which the ball must meet the bat? What will be the angle that the bat makes with the front line of the plate? Assume that the ball is a straight fast ball which is thrown at a right angle to the front edge of home plate.

Figure 14 shows graphically the solution to this problem. The ball from the pitcher makes an angle of 45° with the third base line. Since the ball is to be hit parallel to the third-base foul line, the angle between the pitched ball and the hit ball will be 45°. The line of the bat describes an arc of 180°. 45° of this 180° is accounted for. Therefore, 135° remain. This represents the angle between the pitch and the bat and between the bat and the direction of the hit. Since the angle at which the ball meets the bat equals the angle at which the ball leaves the bat, the angle at which the ball meets the bat equals

$135°/2$ or $67\frac{1}{2}°$.   The ball is thrown at right angles to the plate.   The bat is turned to make an angle of $67\frac{1}{2}°$ with the ball.   Therefore, $90° - 67\frac{1}{2}° = 22\frac{1}{2}°$, the angle that the bat makes with the front line of the plate.   If coaches gave attention to this principle particularly in teaching bunting, much better results might be obtained.

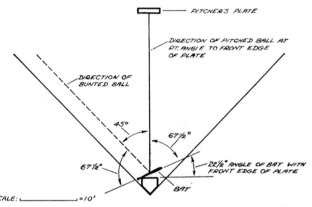

Fig. 14. The angle to hold the bat in order to hit a ball, thrown at a right angle to the front edge of the plate, parallel to the third base line.

The face of the golf club is slanted at an angle in order to give a definite loft to the ball when the ball is hit properly.   If the face of the club makes an angle of 30° with the vertical when contact is made with the ball, at what angle will the ball leave the club? Figure 15 shows this problem graphically.   Since the club head makes an angle of 30° with the vertical, a horizontal line through the center of the ball would make an angle of 60° with the club head.   This is the line of contact of the club head with the ball. Therefore, the ball will leave the club head in its line of flight at an angle of 60°.

Experimentation with the basketball to determine the angle of rebound of the ball when there is no unusual spin on the ball and it does not meet an obstruction such as the basket, verifies the fact that the angle of contact equals the angle of departure.[3]   Using the

[3] Wilson, Floyd, "A Cinematographical Analysis of the Rebounds of an Official Laceless, Last-bilt, and Rubber Basketball from Glass, Wood, and Steel Backboards" (Master's Thesis, Springfield College, 1949).

terms describing light it could be said that the angle of incidence is
equal to the angle of reflection. This same principle holds in
hitting the tennis ball, the hand ball, the squash ball, and so forth.

In addition to direction, the speed of movement of bodies after
impact is a matter of great importance in games. The important
factors which control the results of impact are the degree of elasticity of the implements, balls and bats, which are involved and the
velocity of the ball and the implement which is used to strike the ball.

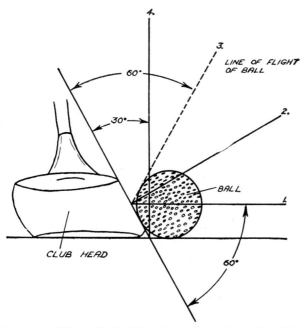

**Fig. 15. The angle at which a golf ball will leave the clubhead when the face of the club makes
an angle of 30 degrees with the vertical.**

The restitution of a body is that characteristic which causes it to resume its original shape after some force has distorted it. All materials
have elasticity. For example, in a place kick, the toe of the kicker may
depress the football as much as one third. The tennis ball seems to flatten
to about one half on impact with a hard driving stroke of the racket.
Even a golf ball shows a surprising amount of distortion on impact with
the club head. This quality of a body is represented by a number called
the coefficient of elasticity. The accompanying pictures of a football, a

golf ball, and a tennis ball are evidence of what takes place (Figures 16, 17, and 18).

Fig. 16. The elasticity of a football.   Note that the toe of the kicker seems to penetrate one-third of the diameter of the ball.

The coefficient of elasticity is represented by the formula:

$$e = \frac{V_2 - V_1}{U_1 - U_2} \tag{24}$$

where e = coefficient of elasticity
  V_1 = velocity of one body after impact
  V_2 = velocity of second body after impact

Fig. 17. A stroboscopic view of a tennis ball at the instant of contact with the racket. Note extreme flattening of the ball. (Courtesy A. G. Spalding & Bros.)

Fig. 18. The flattening of a golf ball is clearly shown at the moment the club head meets the ball. (Courtesy A. G. Spalding & Bros.)

$U_1 =$ velocity of one body before impact

$U_2 =$ velocity of the other body before impact

This formula recognizes the fact that in many of our sports both the ball and the bat are moving objects. If there is only one moving object, then the velocity for one body becomes zero.

The coefficient of elasticity may also be represented by the ratio of the height a body bounces after being dropped.

In this case, e is represented by the formula:

$$e = \sqrt{\frac{h_b}{h_d}} \qquad (25)$$

$e =$ coefficient of elasticity

$h_b =$ height of bounce

$h_d =$ height of drop

The higher the bounce, the greater is the coefficient of elasticity. Likewise, the faster the body moves after impact in relation to the speed before impact, the greater is the coefficient of elasticity (the livelier the body).

The official basketball is standardized in accordance with the length of its rebound. When dropped from a distance of 6 feet, measured from the bottom of the ball, it must be inflated so that it will rebound to a height of from 49 to 54 inches, measured to the top of the ball. In order to calculate the coefficient of elasticity the ball must be measured from the same point. A basketball is approximately 10 inches in diameter. If the bottom of the ball is taken as the common point and if the top of the ball bounces to the maximum height of 54 inches, what is the coefficient of elasticity of the ball?

By formula (24) $e = \dfrac{V}{U}$ (only one body moves), the situation represents that of a freely falling body. By formula (6)

$$V^2 = 2aD \qquad D = 44 \text{ inches}, \qquad a = 32$$
$$V^2 = 2 \times 32 \times \tfrac{44}{12} = 234.66$$
$$V = 15.312 \text{ ft/sec}$$

This equals the velocity of the ball after impact.

$$V^2 = 2aD \qquad D = 6 \text{ feet}, \qquad a = 32$$
$$= 2 \times 32 \times 6 = 384$$
$$V = 19.596 \text{ ft/sec}$$

This equals the velocity of the ball before impact.

$$e = \frac{15.312}{19.596} = .781$$

By formula (25)

$$e = \sqrt{\frac{h_b}{h_d}}; \quad h_b = 44 \text{ inches}, \quad h_d = 72 \text{ inches} = \sqrt{\frac{44}{72}} = .781$$

The question is often asked, "Can a slow ball be hit as far as a fast ball?" If it is assumed that the batter swings the bat with the same velocity at both, meets both squarely with the bat and at the same spot on the bat, and that the ball reaches the same height in its flight, the answer should be obvious. The answer, however, can be calculated by means of the following formula:

$$V_1 = \frac{(m_1 - em_2)U_1 + (1 + e)m_2U_2}{m_1 + m_2} \tag{26}$$

V_1 = velocity of ball as it leaves the bat
m_1 = mass of bat
e = coefficient of elasticity
m_2 = mass of ball
U_1 = velocity of ball before it meets the bat
U_2 = velocity of the bat before it meets the ball

Assume that the ball is thrown first with a speed of 95 ft/sec = U_1 and then 50 ft/sec. The bat meets the ball with a velocity of 40 ft/sec = U_2. The bat weighs 32 ounces and the ball 5 ounces. The coefficient of elasticity of the ball is .5.

$$V_1 = \frac{(.0626 - .5 \times .0098)\, 95 + (1 + .5)\,.0098 \times 40}{.0626 + .0098}$$

$$= \frac{5.4905 + .5880}{.0626 + .0098} = 83.96 \text{ ft/sec speed of ball when leaving bat}$$

when fast ball is thrown.

When slow ball is thrown:

$$V_1 = \frac{(.0626 - .5 \times .0098)\, 55 + (1 + .5)\,.0098 \times 40}{.0626 + .0098}$$

$$= \frac{5.1735 + .5880}{.062 + .0098} = 51.95 \text{ ft/sec speed of ball when leaving bat.}$$

The distance that the ball will travel in each case depends upon the speed of the bat and of the ball as it meets the bat. Therefore, the only possible way to make a slow ball travel faster after it is hit is to increase the speed of the bat so that greater velocity may be imparted to the ball.

Summary and Principles

From an analysis of the foregoing principles and presentations relating to force, several statements may be made in summary that will be a helpful guide to the coach or competitor in adopting and developing sound techniques.

Newton's first law suggests several procedures in athletic performance:

1. In doing exercises that necessitate pulling the body up and then pushing it further upward, there should be no pause between the pull-up and push but rather the movement should be continuous. The breast-up on the rings, parallel bars, and horizontal bar, and the pull-up and push-up in the pole vault are examples.

This principle of continuity of motion also applies to swimming strokes, putting the shot, throwing the baseball, kicking a ball, and throwing the javelin, to name a few. In these activities, there is a gradual increase in the speed, and the movements are taken up in succession in developing force. This gives a basis for principle number 2.

2. The total effective force may be the sum of the forces of each member of the body if applied in a single direction and in the proper sequence.

(a) When successively added, each force should be started at the point of greatest velocity but least acceleration of the preceding force. In many cases, the successive movement would start when the movement of the preceding member was approximately at the end of extension. The final force is usually of an explosive nature because of the short distance through which it acts.

(b) If the forces are applied simultaneously, they will be limited by the weakest force of the group of forces. This point is best illustrated by heavy weight-lifting activities. If the stronger muscle groups (leg and back) are employed to start the movement, then the arms and wrists can follow-up and successfully continue the motion.

Whereas, if the weaker muscle groups (the arm and wrist muscles) attempted to bear the brunt of the starting motion, they would often fail and the weight would drop or the hands would pull loose from their grip.

3. Additional distance from the point of striking a ball may be gained by bending a joint (as bending the knee preparatory to kicking a ball or cocking the wrists before striking a golf ball or a baseball). It gives greater force to the swing by increasing the linear velocity with the same angular velocity of the central rotating body.

4. A body is frequently put in motion by the transfer of momentum from a part to the whole. Mass (m) times the velocity of one part, when the force is transmitted to the whole body, equals the mass times the velocity of the whole.

This principle is employed in gymnastic activities. For example, the legs kick, then stop and as a result, the whole body is brought into motion. One may demonstrate this point by lying on his back on a table with the hips at the edge of the table and the legs extended above the surface of the table with the feet just above the shoulders. A sharp rotation at the hips which stops when the legs make an angle of 30° with the horizontal will cause the body to rise from the table to an upright position.

When a boxer takes a vicious swing and misses, the force of his arm and shoulder movement is imparted to his body so that in some cases he is thrown to the mat.

In kicking a football, the swing of the leg may raise the body off the ground. Here also is a factor of anatomical significance. When the thigh and foreleg are forward and the hamstring muscles are fully stretched with the pelvis rotated backward, the iliofemeral ligament locks the hip. Either the leg movement stops, the opposite knee bends to compensate for the lack of further motion of the hip, the spine bows, or the person leaves the ground from the force of the leg kick.

5. The direction of a body free in the air is determined (except for external resistances—air, water, and so forth) by the direction of the resultant of the forces which set it in motion. No follow-through tactics or movements of members of the body while in the air can change the direction or the height of the center of gravity of the body.

Newton's third law suggests that certain procedures be emphasized in the execution of many athletic movements.

6. When a limb is used to turn the body of another, the individual

turned must resist the force of the thrower by moving the limb against the force. An example of this point is the stunt in dual gymnastics in which one performer turns a somersault by placing his heel in the hands of another with his leg outstretched. As he jumps in the air, the person holding the heel lifts up using the leg as a lever to give rotation to the body of the jumper. Unless the leg of the jumper is held rigid, it will merely rise in the air without giving him rotation.

↘ 7. When blows are struck by an implement held in the hands (for example, a bat, racket, or golf club), the grip must be as firm as possible at the moment of impact. The hands should be placed on the implement in a manner which will permit them to best withstand the force of the impact. If a blow is struck by a member of the body (the hand in handball, the fist in boxing, or the foot in kicking), that member should be rigid at the moment of impact. All of this is predicated upon the assumption that it is desired to impart the greatest amount of force.

↘ 8. If it is desired to absorb the shock of a blow, a fall, a throw, or a kick, the shock should be spread over either as large an area as possible or as long a distance as possible or both.

Since force $F = ma$ (mass $\times$ acceleration)

$$a = \frac{V^2}{2d} \quad \text{so} \quad F = \frac{mV^2}{2d} \text{ or } Fd = \tfrac{1}{2}mV^2$$

It follows, with m and V held constant, that by increasing d (the distance over which the force acts), the magnitude of F is reduced. This, in effect, is what happens when a player in catching a ball reaches out as far as possible to receive the ball and then permits his hands to recoil, when a boxer lets his body retreat with the blow which is struck by an opponent, when a football player rolls after falling on the ball, and when a gymnast takes a roll after alighting.

↘ 9. Reaction to angular movement in athletics is balanced by rotation in the opposite direction. For example, in running, the movement of the left leg in striding forward rotates the hip to the right. This movement is balanced by a forward rotation of the shoulders. If the legs of a runner are heavy in proportion to the arms and shoulders, the arms must swing farther away from the body and possibly more forcefully to counterbalance the rotary force created by the legs. In hurdle races, a wide arm-swing by a runner with very heavy leg muscles is necessary to maintain balance. In a twister dive, more twist occurs when one arm is held fully extended than when both are kept close to the body.

  10. In throwing or pushing activities, one or both feet are kept in firm contact with the ground until the object is released in order that the total effect of the effort may be in the direction of the throwing force. However, the forward momentum of the body may be strong enough to check the reaction from throwing a light object.

Levers suggest many principles. Four are stated below:

  11. The mechanical advantage of a lever is represented by the ratio of the length of the power arm to the length of the weight arm.

  12. The longer the power arm of the lever, the greater the moment of force.

  13. The shorter the power arm in proportion to the length of the weight arm, the smaller is the moment of force but the more immediate is the action. The third-class lever is an example.

  14. To be most effective, the force must be directed at right angles to the lever.

The principles of centrifugal and centripetal force suggest many principles which are adapted particularly to the techniques of diving and gymnastics.

  15. In swinging and suspension exercises, the act of pulling toward the center of rotation along the line of the radius when the center of gravity is under the point of support causes the center of weight to rise much higher than if the force had not been exerted. The uprise on a bar is an example. The time to pull up is when the center of gravity is directly below the bar.

  16. In apparatus-mounting exercises that involve angular motion, the center of gravity should be brought as near as possible to the center of support at the critical moment just before the trunk and legs reach the height of their swing. If, as in the case of the uprise on the high bar, the center of gravity is kept against the bar and between the hands, the centrifugal force is eliminated. Likewise, if one circles or rotates about the bar in this position, the tendency to fly off on a tangent is eliminated.

  17. Mounting movements in swinging exercises on the bars or rings should usually start as the center of gravity passes a point directly below the point of support. The same is true of the shortening of the radius in circles on the apparatus.

  18. On the flying rings, the essential movement is usually at the end

of the swing.   There, gravity is momentarily neutralized by the upward momentum and the effect of centrifugal force can be avoided.

19. In swinging movements, the center of gravity is frequently directed upward in such a way that the arms are relieved of a large part of the weight.   This is accomplished by body swing, just before the end of the swing, that directs the line of force upwards and toward the point of support rather than on a tangent to the swing.

20. The longer the radius of rotation the greater the centrifugal force with the same angular velocity and weight.

21. The greater the centrifugal force the greater the lean or the banking necessary to balance the force.

Several miscellaneous principles on force tend to direct emphasis on fundamentals in athletics.

22. In general, force should be applied as directly as possible in the direction of the intended motion so that as much of the force as possible can be utilized as effective force (parallelogram of forces).

23. The direction of flight of a ball which has been struck depends upon the fact that the angle of reflection equals the angle of incidence. Because of the partial flattening of the ball on the implement (bat, racket, or club) this relationship holds true only in part.   The spin of the ball may also decrease or increase the angle of rebound.   Thus, in the case of hitting a tennis ball, the angle of the racket must account for the angle at which the ball is approaching.   The force with which the ball is hit tends to eliminate the effect of spin and the angle at which the ball is met.   The flattening of the ball tends to cause it to go off from the implement at right angles to it.

24. The coefficient of friction is independent of the area of contact of the two surfaces. The more friction, the larger area

25. The speed of flight of a struck ball depends upon the weight and striking force of the ball and bat and the coefficient of restitution of the ball and of the bat.

QUESTIONS AND TOPICS FOR REVIEW AND DISCUSSION

1. What is the source of force in the human body?   Discuss.
2. How is conditioning related to force?
3. Define force.
4. Force is a function of what two factors?
5. Why is explosive power of such great importance in developing force?
6. Which is more important in the development of force by the athlete—mass or speed?   Why?

7. What are the two categories to the development and use of force? Discuss.

8. State Newton's three laws of motion and illustrate each.

9. What is the application of the principles of the parallelogram of forces to sports? Give several examples.

10. In what two ways may a light football player compensate for his weight disadvantage?

11. What is a lever?

12. How many types of levers are there? Illustrate each.

13. What are the characteristics of each type of lever? When would you use each? Illustrate in sport situations.

14. Most body movements are produced through what type of levers?

15. Of what significance is the fact that muscles are stronger under stretch?

16. What is meant by the moment arm?

17. How is knowledge of the principle of the moment arm utilized to advantage in athletics? Illustrate.

18. What is centrifugal force? Centripetal force?

19. What are some practical problems in sports in which centrifugal and centripetal forces are involved?

20. Define friction. What four factors determine its magnitude?

21. Name two directly opposite applications of the principles of friction to athletics.

22. Explain the principle that "the angle of incidence is equal to the angle of reflection."

23. Of what significance is the above principle in athletics? Give examples.

24. What factors control the results of impact? Of what significance are these in sports?

25. What is meant by the coefficient of elasticity of a body? What effect does it have on results in sports? Where is it applied specifically in the rules of a sport?

PROBLEMS

(Answers to problems are given in Appendix D, page 294.)

1. A broad jumper leaves the take-off board with a speed of 26 ft/sec. He weighs 160 pounds. His foot is in contact with the board for 1/2 second. What is the amount of force exerted? What would be the force if the jumper's foot were in contact with the board for 1/20 second?

2. A 16-pound shot leaves the putter's hand at a velocity of 40 ft/sec. If this velocity is attained in 3/10 second, how much force is applied to the shot? How fast is the shot accelerating?

3. A baseball leaves a bat at the rate of 85 ft/sec. The bat is in contact with the ball for 1/100 second. What force is being exerted by the bat?

4. The velocity of the shot leaving the hand is 25.9 ft/sec. This velocity

is developed through a distance of 5.33 feet in 41 seconds. Find the amount of force applied by the putter by two different methods.

5. A ball carrier weighing 160 pounds runs from 3 yards behind his line of scrimmage at right angles to it. He is going 15 ft/sec when he reaches the line. It takes him $\frac{1}{2}$ second to reach the line. An opponent attacks at an angle of 60° with the ball carrier's direction. The opponent hits with a force of 150 pounds. Will the ball carrier gain ground? What will be the resultant direction of movement? Assume the tackler hits at the center of gravity of the ball carrier.

6. If the ball carrier were running at an angle of 60° with the line and was hit at right angles by the tackler, what would be the result? The speed and force of each is the same as in problem 5.

7. A ball carrier hits the line with his body inclined at an angle of 80° with the ground. His force in this direction is 400 pounds. What would be the force directed toward the goal line? If his angle of lean were 45°, what force would be exerted toward the goal line? How much force is wasted in each case?

8. A runner comes off his mark at an angle of 63°. The force exerted against the starting blocks is 325 pounds. How much of this force is effective force? If the angle is 43°, what are the results?

9. A wrestler is holding his opponent's arm down flat against the mat. The arm is outstretched and the force against the arm is 24 inches from the shoulder. The force is at an angle of 60° with the arm and is equal to 20 pounds. How much resistance will be necessary to just start to move the arm upward?

10. The shot putter holds the shot in his hand and against his shoulder. It is 10 inches from the center of the shot to the elbow joint and 2 inches from the elbow joint to the point of attachment of the triceps muscle. The direction of weight of the shot with the forearm is 55°. The angle of pull of the triceps is 85°. How much force is required from the triceps to start the shot in motion?

11. The attachment of the quadriceps muscle of the leg is 3 inches from the knee joint. In kicking a football, the line of the foot is held at right angles to the foreleg and rigid at the moment of contact. The perpendicular distance from the toe to the knee joint is 18 inches. A 20-pound pull is exerted by the quadriceps muscle at an angle of 10° with the foreleg. What is the force necessary at the point of the toe to prevent the leg from moving?

12. A football player is standing braced and rigid. At which point will it take the least force to push him off his feet: at his center of gravity, above his center of gravity, or below his center of gravity? Why?

13. A 165-pound gymnast is doing the giant swing. On the downward swing he extends his body so that his center of gravity is $3\frac{1}{2}$ feet from the bar. On the upswing he shortens his overall length so that his center of gravity is 3 feet from the bar. What is the moment of force in each case, when the body is in a horizontal position?

14. In problem 13, what is the centrifugal force of the body when it is in

a horizontal position on the down swing? When it is at the bottom of the down swing? When it is horizontal on the upswing? Assume the center of gravity is the same distance from the bar throughout the upswing.

15. A 60-pound pack is carried by being strapped to the shoulders. The pull on the two shoulders is equal. Assume that the full weight pulls against the shoulders. In one case the load is strapped so that the pull is eight inches from the breast joint. In another case, the pull is $3\frac{1}{2}$ inches from the joint. What is the moment of force in each case? Which strapping will require the least effort on the part of the carrier?

16. An indoor track has a 25-foot radius at the ends. It is built to accommodate a runner at the rate of 25 ft/sec. What is the angle at which the track must be elevated to prevent the runner from going off the track? If the runner weighs 185 pounds, what is his centrifugal force?

17. A bicycle has cranks 7 inches long from the axis of rotation to the center of the pedal. If a rider exerts a constant push of 20 pounds vertically through the downward stroke, find the turning moment: when the crank is at the top, when it has turned through 30°, 60°, 90°, 120°, 150°, and 180° from the top position.

18. A player is running so that he has a forward momentum of 250 pounds. He weighs 190 pounds. At what angle must he lean to avoid falling forward if he stops abruptly?

19. The gripping qualities of two shoes show that with 10 pounds of weight in each shoe, it required 8 pounds of horizontal pull to cause one shoe to slip and 15 pounds of pull at an angle of 10° with the horizontal to cause the other to slip. Which shoe has the better gripping qualities? What is the coefficient of friction of each?

20. An individual falls on the football. His center of gravity drops from a height of 4 feet. He weighs 180 pounds. Assume that no force except that from the fall is introduced. If he hits on a point on his shoulder, how great is the force concentrated at this point? His side and the side of his legs and hips hit simultaneously on an area of $2\frac{1}{2}$ square feet. What is the effect of the fall?

21. If an individual weighs 180 pounds and jumps from a height of 15 feet (the center of gravity traveled 15 feet before the feet touched) and alights with a knee bend which permits the center of gravity to move 2 feet in stopping, what is the force of the jump?

22. A thrown baseball is traveling with the velocity of 85 ft/sec at the moment of impact with a bat. The bat has a linear velocity of 40 ft/sec. The bat weighs 32 ounces. The coefficient of restitution of the ball is .50. With what velocity does the ball rebound from the bat, which strikes the ball squarely?

23. The ball in problem 22 meets the bat at an angle of 55° and at a point 6 in. before the center point of the front edge of the plate. The ball first strikes the ground 100 feet behind third base. Is the ball foul or fair? Assume that the spin of the ball does not affect the direction of its flight and that the pitched ball was traveling at right angles to the front edge of the plate.

24. What is the velocity of the ball of problem (22) when it leaves the bat, if the ball is thrown with a velocity of 75 ft/sec?

25. A golf ball is dropped on a concrete floor from a height of 200 centimeters. It rebounds to a height of 84 centimeters. What is the coefficient of restitution?

26. A golf ball weighing 1.62 ounces is struck by a club head moving 162 ft/sec. The ball leaves the club head with a velocity of 238 ft/sec. What is the effective mass of the club head? The coefficient of restitution of the ball is .65.

27. If the length of A's arm is 50 per cent greater than that of B's, prove that A can throw a discus farther from a stand than B can. All other factors are assumed to be equal.

28. Two men are making a giant swing on the high bar. The center of gravity of one, who weighs 180 pounds, is 36 inches from the bar, and the center of gravity of the other, who weighs 150 pounds, is 42 inches from the bar. They are swinging in unison. Which exerts the greater pull on the bar and how much greater?

29. A ladder that is 10 feet long and weighs 40 pounds is leaning against a wall. The base of the ladder is 3 feet from the wall and the center of gravity is in the middle. How much force is exerted against the wall? How much force is exerted against the ground? If the base of the ladder is 5 feet from the wall, what are the forces against the ground and the wall?

30. 120 pounds of force is required to cause the shoes of a 180-pound basketball player to slip. The full weight of the player is directed vertically on the shoes. Another pair of shoes, worn by a player weighing 200 pounds, require a force of 150 pounds before they will slip. Which pair of shoes grips the floor more firmly? What is the coefficient of friction of each?

31. The coefficient of friction of a pair of rubber-soled shoes with a certain maple floor is .75. The player weighs 170 pounds. How much horizontal force is required to cause him to slip? What angle of lean is possible before he will slip?

5.

Special Movements

and Forces—

Factors Affecting Force

There are both internal and external factors that alter the normal resultant of forces produced by the individual in athletics, or affect the magnitude of force which theoretically could be produced. Air resistance, for example, may hinder or aid the athlete. In track, a head wind can make a noticeable difference in the time in running events. Records on the track are not allowed if made with a tail wind of more than 8 miles per hour. In the discus throw, because of the sail effect which the wind has on the discus, a head wind of limited proportions may actually be an advantage to the thrower. In football, the wind is a very important factor because of its effect on the ball when it is kicked. Even in baseball, a strong wind has a surprisingly controlling effect on the flight of the ball. The principles of aerodynamics explain the actions of airborne bodies.

Air Resistance

Air resistance plays such a vital part in the results of many athletic contests that a brief review of the principles of aerodynamics that apply may be of great help to the coach in determining the methods that he advocates to combat or to take advantage of air speed.

The reaction resulting from the diversion of the air stream about a moving airborne body may be expressed by the equation:

$$R = \frac{CpSV^2}{2} \tag{27}$$

where R equals the resulting reaction; C a numerical, non-dimensional coefficient depending on the shape of the body and its attitude to the air stream; p the pressure of the air (15 lb/sq. in. at sea level); S the active surface area of the body over which the air stream passes; and V the velocity of the air stream with respect to the body. The Y component of R creates a lifting effect on the body, whereas the X component has a retarding effect on the body and is called drag.

For a particular example of the effect of the air on a body, the discus,

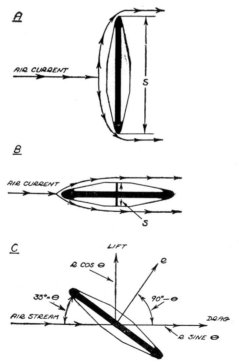

Fig. 19. The effect of wind upon the surfaces of an implement when it is presented to the wind at different angles.

because of its comparatively flat surface, will be considered first.   If it is presented (see Figure 19) with its surface at right angles to the air stream, the whole reaction (R) will be in one direction, along the line of the stream.   The Y component of R in this case would be zero. Thus, the drag (resistance) will be comparatively large per unit area because of the great change in direction, and therefore change of momentum, of the air particles involved in getting around the discus. On the other hand, if the edge of the discus is presented to the air stream, the drag effect will be practically negligible because the change of direction of the air particles is slight and comparatively few are involved. S in this case is represented by the cross-sectional area through the short axis of the discus. R is still wholly in the direction of the air stream with its Y component being zero.

Finally, if the discus is presented at an angle to the air stream, an intermediate value of the reaction (R) would be obtained.   Its magnitude would depend upon the angle.   Air is considered as a fluid, so the reaction (R) will be at right angles to the discus.   If the leading edge is above the trailing edge, the reaction will produce a lifting effect (opposing the force of gravity).   The Y component of R is the lift and is directed upward in opposition to the force of gravity.   The X component is drag and is parallel to the air stream and opposed to the direction of the discus.   The ratio of lift to drag (L/D) is the index of lifting efficiency of a body which is acted on by an air stream.

Because of the fact that S varies with the angle of inclination of the body and V varies with the momentum of the body, it does not necessarily follow that the lift varies inversely with the angle of inclination. Some very revealing experiments were conducted on a discus suspended in a wind tunnel.[1]   The angle of inclination of the discus was varied. The wind was either a direct head wind or a tail wind.   It was found that when the discus was inclined at an initial angle of 35° with a head wind not in excess of 14 m.p.h. the best results were obtained.   Head winds of 7 and 8 m.p.h. were most advantageous.   When the head wind exceeded 14.5 it became a detriment to the flight of the discus. The lifting effect was increased and the discus was held in the air longer but the resistance of the wind reduced the distance covered.

When a tail wind was played upon the discus, the lifting effect was reduced (the vacuum-tail suction behind the discus is very much

---

[1] Taylor, James A., "Behavior of the Discus in Flight." *ICAAAA Bulletin,* February 27, 1932.

less than it is in a head wind). So in spite of the fact that the speed of the discus is increased, the loss of vacuum drives the discus to earth sooner.

Thus, with a head wind stronger than 14.5 m.p.h., the discus thrower would do well to throw across the wind and with the discus at a very flat angle of inclination. If a tail wind is blowing, it would be well to throw at an angle of inclination more nearly vertical.

Figure 20 shows some experimental curves of flight with the plane of the discus at an angle of 35° with varying wind velocities as indicated.

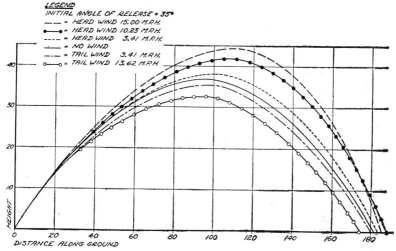

Fig. 20. The effect of wind upon the flight of the discus when it is projected at an angle of 35 degrees. (See footnote, page 78.)

The flight of the football is affected in a similar manner. However because of the difference in mass between the discus and the football the relative ability of the football to penetrate the air stream is much less. It should be pointed out, however, that the mass of the object has no effect on R. Also, because of the shape of the surface of the football, the direction of R is less than 90° with the axis of the ball. Although experimental data is not available to determine the best angle of inclination at which to kick a football under varying wind conditions, in view of the difference in mass between the football and discus and in view of the reduced lifting component, it may be concluded that under the same conditions as those presented for the discus, the angle of inclination of the football should be less than that of the discus. In strong head winds the angle should be as near to zero as possible, with as much spin as possible for stabilization purposes. With strong tail winds the angle of inclination should be more nearly vertical (Figure 21).

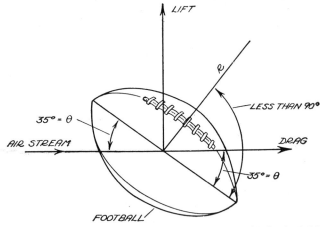

Fig. 21. The lifting component "R" for a football when the angle of inclination is 35 degrees.

Spin or Gyration

Spin plays a dual role in sports. It has a stabilizing effect that holds an object on course or resists a change in the direction of the axis of the body. Motion pictures of the discus indicate that it rotates from 18 to 21 times while in flight and tends to steady the implement without affecting its distance, due to the fact that the forward force is so much greater than the spinning force.

In the case of football, if the spinning is not sufficient to keep the axis of the ball pointed on the course the ball will float or tumble. If too much spin is given to the ball, its effect will cause the ball to curve.

In the case of the baseball, in order to make it curve, the forward velocity of the ball is always less than that of a fast ball and the spin in the direction of the desired curve is always faster than the spin on a fast ball. Here the spin in relation to the forward velocity of the ball is sufficiently great, so that the direction of the flight of the ball is affected. A noticeable curve results.

On the basketball spin is used in an entirely different manner to change the direction of the ball. Here direction is changed through spin not during flight but by use of the floor or the backboard as a secondary agent. Spin and the floor are also used to slow up or speed up the ball.

For example, in passing to a player directly behind an opponent it is possible to bounce the ball on the right side of the opponent and at the same time give counterclockwise rotation. When the ball hits the floor it will bounce sharply to the left to a teammate. In the same manner, on a lay-up shot, when the ball is played against the backboard to the side of the basket, spin is put on the ball in order to carry it across to and down through the basket.

If forward spin is put on the basketball, it will gain speed immediately after hitting the floor on a bounce pass. In this case two forces, that of the spin plus the forward movement of the ball, are combined when the ball hits the floor. If back spin is put on the ball, the ball is retarded in its forward progress when it hits the floor by reason of the reaction due to the back spin. It is a sum of the resultant of forces plus the effect of friction between the floor and the ball. The tennis ball, the handball, and the table tennis ball all react similarly when spin is put on them.

When spin or rotation is used for stabilizing purposes, as in the case of the discus and the football, the conditions for stable motion about a transverse axis may be expressed by:

$$\frac{A^2 N^2}{4B_u} > 1 \tag{28}$$

where A is the axial moment of inertia, B_u is the moment about the transverse axis through the center of gravity and N is the spin in radians/sec.

Water Resistance

Water resistance is a particular problem in swimming. The resistance to the motion of a solid through a liquid increases with its velocity. When a force of a given value is applied to a body to move it through a liquid, the velocity of the body will gradually increase until it reaches a certain limiting value at which the resistance due to friction is equal to the applied force. After that value has been reached, the velocity will remain constant as long as the force is applied. Thus, a body falling through water will have a constant velocity after it has fallen a certain distance.

Most information on resistance comes from the knowledge gained from the study of ships. So important is the problem of water resistance, that speed comes as much from eliminating resistance as from increasing force. There are eight factors which cause a loss of force in swimming. The reduction or elimination of all of them can make a tremendous difference in the efficiency and speed of the swimmer.

1. *Waves.* Wave making is probably the foremost of these resistance factors. The force which makes waves does not propel the body but rather becomes resistance. Wave making is largely eliminated by avoiding up and down movements or rolling during the stroke. It should be pointed out in this connection that the so-called butterfly stroke presently used in the breast stroke causes considerable wave making. However, the force produced is relatively so much greater than the resistance that greater speed accrues therefrom. There is a considerable increase in the energy used.

2. *Eddies.* Eddies are evidence of dissipated force in merely moving water or in changing the stroke. A clash of eddies causes a loss of speed. In order to reduce or eliminate this latter factor, it is customary to plug up the scum gutters of pools which have them and to raise the water to the level of the gutter. The result is that the water of the pool is quieted. There is no return eddy when the water hits the back of the gutter as there is when it hits the side of the pool and tends to rebound back into the pool.

3. *Cavitation.* Cavitation is a loss of suction. It is caused when the propelling member is pulled through the water so fast that a cavity is formed. When this happens there is nothing but space for the propelling member to push against. By Newton's third law it is obvious that there would be reduced forward movement. The action may be likened to slipping which causes a loss of force for propelling purposes.

The old paddle-wheel, propeller-type of river boat experienced the effects of cavitation. If the wheels were rotated too fast, a cavity was created so that there was no water for the wheel to push. The rear oars of a double-oared boat may be useless if they move slower than the front oars. Cavitation does not occur in the flutter kick used in the crawl stroke. The movement here is an alternating movement.

Swirls are set up so that the alternating movement of the legs produces greater power if it is fast enough to take advantage of the swirl.

The factor of cavitation suggests an optimum speed of movement of the arms and legs for the greatest efficiency. This speed is not now known on a scientific basis. It probably does not occur in swimming.

4. *Skin Friction.* There is little scientific information on the study of the reduction of skin friction. The smoother the surface, the less the friction. The hairy body has been shaved to make the surface smoother. Oils of various kinds have been applied to the skin. It has been discovered that silk swim suits cause less friction than wool suits.

5. *Force.* Force used at unproductive angles causes resistance and may be opposed to the intended direction of motion. For example, in the crawl stroke, when the arm is down in a vertical direction, it is most productive of propelling force. When it is straight out in front of the body, it is least productive. If the stroke begins at this point, the force exerted serves only to lift the body from the water, thus producing waves. If the hand is brought to or across the median line of the body in front of the head and the stroke begins at this point, the force directs the body sideways instead of forward.

If, in the breast stroke, the hands are brought together out in front of the head and the stroke begun at this point, the force is directed at right angles to the direction of movement. If the legs are thrashed up and down with the plane of the sole of the feet at right angles to the leg, only up and down motion will be produced.

6. *Starting and Stopping.* Starting, stopping, and lack of smooth progress create resistance. The added effort which is necessary to overcome inertia dissipates force that might be used in developing speed. The breast stroke is the best example of this factor. However, the introduction of the butterfly stroke has cut down the glide time measurably. Lastly, as a result of this fact, the time in the breast-stroke races has been reduced surprisingly.

Smooth progress is difficult to attain in swimming. The physiological steady state for most people is so far below the state of smooth swimming that a glide is necessary. This fact points to the importance of superb conditioning for the champion swimmer.

7. *Internal Resistance.* The effect of tenseness is probably more apparent in swimming than any other sport. This fact is observed clearly

in most beginning swimmers. The tenseness here is usually caused by fear. The aim, therefore, should be to learn to relax in all situations. It has been well said that "the individual who has implicit confidence in his instructor so that he has no fear and can relax, can be taught to swim in fifteen minutes."

8. *Resistance due to Physical Features.* Resistance is proportional to the greatest cross-sectional area of the body. If the width of the leg stroke is kept within this cross-sectional area, resistance will be cut down. Very heavy glutii muscles, which cause the buttocks to protrude, will tend to create greater water resistance. There is also less resistance when the head is kept between the arms on the plunge. It was found that greater distance was attained in this way.

Karpovich[2] studied the propelling force in the crawl stroke and found that force:

$$F = KV^2 \tag{29}$$

where V is velocity of swimming and K is a constant with an average value of .6. K is a factor representing water resistance. It was found that it varies with the skin surface area of the body but involves such factors as skin friction, wave making, eddies, and cavitation.

Available Force

In the human body, the available force varies inversely with the velocity of movement. Thus, when a muscle contracts at its maximum speed of contraction, no effective force for the accomplishment of external work is available. A muscle contracting at half of its maximum velocity will exert only half of its potential force. In the leg-lift strength test to determine the strength of the leg muscles, the muscles are contracting at zero velocity. There is no visible movement. The muscles are exerting their total developed force.

Certain deductions may be made from this principle which give practical significance to it for application to athletic situations. In most athletic activities, speed with the greatest amount of force is desired. It is, therefore, desirable to determine the optimum in speed and force at which each individual can operate most effectively.

---

[2] Karpovich, P. V., "Analysis of Propelling Force in Crawl Stroke," *Supplement to Research Quarterly,* May, 1935.

Howell[3] recognized the principle of available force. He found that there is an optimum load for each muscle, under which it will work at its maximum efficiency. Schneider and Karpovich state that "there exists a certain optimum rate of speed for climbing stairs at which the cost of exertion is reduced to a minimum."[4] By means of integral calculus, this optimum point is found to be halfway between the zero limit and maximum developed limit. If, therefore, the maximum force that can be exerted and the maximum speed are known or can be measured, the halfway point can be determined. If maximum force is desired, a minimum speed or zero speed must be maintained and vice versa, if maximum speed is desired, minimum force will be available for external work.

The above reasoning should partially explain why the golfer obtains better results when he does not swing too fast and why there is a limit to the speed with which the shot putter can move in the final thrust and why the broad jumper may take-off too fast.

Since the amount of force exerted is partly dependent upon the strength of the muscles exerting the force and since strength of the muscle is dependent upon the cross-sectional area of the muscle, it follows that building muscle is a prime essential to top performance where either the optimum or the maximum force is desired. The greater the strength developed the greater will be the optimum point at which the athlete can operate effectively.

This relationship can be expressed by the formula:

$$F_a = F_m \left(1 - \frac{V_a}{V_m} \right) \tag{30}$$

F_a = applied force; F_m = maximum force (zero velocity)
V_a = applied velocity
V_m = maximum velocity (zero load)

Assume that the maximum strength of a muscle is found to be 1000 pounds and the maximum speed of contraction 50 ft/sec. If the speed of contraction is varied by increments of 10, the effective force in each case is shown in the tabulation below. For zero velocity:

[3] Howell, W. A., *A Textbook of Physiology*, Philadelphia: W. B. Saunders & Co., 1911.

[4] Schneider and Karpovich, *Physiology of Muscular Activity*, Philadelphia: W. B. Saunders, 1952, p. 60.

$$F_a = 1000(1 - \tfrac{0}{50}) = 1000 \times 1 - 0 = 1000 \quad \text{when}$$

$$
\begin{array}{ll}
V_a = 0 & F_a = 1000 \\
V_a = 10 & F_a = 800 \\
V_a = 20 & F_a = 600 \\
V_a = 30 & F_a = 400 \\
V_a = 40 & F_a = 200 \\
V_a = 50 & F_a = 0
\end{array}
$$

Assuming that the strength has been developed to a maximum of 1500 pounds, it can be seen that the value of F_a will be increased 50 per cent in each case. Again, this argues in favor of vigorous conditioning exercises in order to build muscle to increase strength.

Human Limitations

Another evidence of the value of building strength is found in experiments with the Sargent jump. It was found that the effective angle at which a muscle operates is dependent upon the strength of the muscle. In other words, in the Sargent jump the stronger the muscle, the greater the crouch to obtain the greatest height in the jump.

This principle is of great significance to the high jumper, the basketball player, and to all in situations where jumping or exerting leg drive is a factor. The boy with comparatively weak muscles should not crouch as low before jumping as the one with strong muscles. The crouch of the runner at the start and the football player before the charge should be regulated accordingly in order to exert the optimum force in starting and charging. On the basis of the above, it is advisable to determine for each boy, by test, the angle of crouch from which he can obtain the best results. Certainly, it is not possible to set a uniform standard for all.

It has been stated previously that the movement of the body is accomplished by force that is developed through the contraction of muscles, which act through a system of levers. It has been shown (see page 51) that the effective force of a muscle is measured at right angles to the lever. It might be assumed, therefore, that a muscle would exert the greatest effective force when it was pulling at an angle of 90° with the lever. This, however, is not found to be true due to a characteristic of muscle. A muscle is strongest when under stretch. Consequently, using the biceps as an example, the biceps muscle exerts its greatest force when in stretch, regardless of angle. But, because of this characteristic of muscles, the greatest effective force may not be exerted when the force is directed at right angles to the lever. As a matter of fact, the greatest effective force is seldom exerted when the direction of the force is at right angles to the lever.

In the human body this is a fortunate circumstance because the construction of the body is such that the muscles are forced to act most of the time at unfavorable angles. It is important to keep this characteristic of muscles in mind when teaching fundamentals in athletics, so that the variation from the principles of physics can be accounted for.

Because so many of the levers of the body are third-class levers, the action of the body is more conducive to the development of speed than strength. As demonstrated on page 51, a movement of a short distance by the power or force arm of the lever (brought about by the contraction of a muscle) creates a movement of a long distance by the weight. This movement, however, is accomplished at the expense of a relatively great force because of the unfavorable relationship between the power arm and weight arm of a third-class lever. As a consequence of this fact, it may not be possible to conform to some of the principles of physics for attaining the best performance in those situations where speed and strength must be equal factors. For example, in the broad jump, the greatest distance should be spanned when the take-off is at an angle of 45°. However, in order to exert sufficient force to attain that angle too much forward speed may have to be sacrificed. As a result, actual distance may be lost.

These peculiarities of the human body are pointed out not to discount the validity of the laws of physics in athletic performance. Rather the purpose is to recognize that there are some conditioning factors due to the compensating characteristics of the body which tend to overcome certain inherent structural limitations. The laws of physics are nonetheless valid and in most cases the above are not limiting factors. In all cases, the effort should be directed to adhere to these laws to the extent that the human limitations which have been enumerated will permit.

Effects of Gyroscopic Action

Twister movements in diving and gymnastics involve principles in translation and rotation which have been developed from a study of gyroscopic behavior. This involves motion in three dimensions which is of great complexity. No attempt will be made in this book to develop these principles. Deductions only will be made here to explain the action in twister movement in diving and gymnastics. Twister movements usually begin before the feet leave their point of support. Some rotation can be accomplished after the body is free in the air.

If the movement is started before the body is free in the air, the rotation will be in the direction of the rotation of those members of the body used to create the twister movement (rotation about the long axis of the body). For instance, turning the head and shoulders gives angular velocity around the long axis of the body in the direction of the turning head and shoulders if the movement is started before the body is free of support. This action is due to the principle of the transfer of momentum from the part to the whole.

If a turn is started before the body is free of support, with the arms outstretched, the speed of rotation will be increased if the arms are brought in toward the body. After the body is free of support, rotation of the arms about the long axis of the body will cause the body to rotate in the opposite direction. Thus, if it is desired to twist clockwise, the arms would be rotated counterclockwise. As the arms are returned to their original position, they are held as close to the body as possible or are moved parallel to the long axis of the body. This is the technique which a cat employs to rotate its body so that it will alight feet first when dropped with its back toward the floor. In the case of the cat, both its front and rear legs are used in counter action to affect the rotation.[5]

Placing one arm in an unbalanced position creates the same reaction as when both arms are rotated about the long axis of the body. The action, however, is not as pronounced. It has also been discovered that forward rotation is faster when a twist is brought into movement. This fact must be compensated for in a dive or the forward rotation will go too far.

Summary and Principles

In summary, the following special principles may be used as a guide in teaching the fundamentals of those athletic activities in which these principles specifically apply.

---

[5] Lanoue, F. R., "Mechanics of Fancy Diving," (Master's thesis, Springfield College, 1936).

1. The laws of aerodynamics control the reaction of air-borne bodies to the air stream which they divert.

2. The reaction produced by the air stream is proportional to the active surface area of the body over which the air stream passes and to the square of the velocity of the air stream with respect to the body. The angle of inclination determines the active surface area.

Thus, a football should be kicked into the wind at a very low angle so that the long axis of the ball is kept perpendicular to the direction of the wind. This reduces the surface area and produces greater distance. When kicked with the wind, the long axis should be pointed in a vertical direction so that the surface area over which the wind passes is as large as possible and the angle of projection should approach 45° to assure the greatest distance.

The discus should be thrown into or across a wind stronger than 14 miles per hour with its broad surface parallel to the ground. It should be thrown at an angle of 35° into a wind less than 14 miles per hour. With a tail wind, the edge of the discus should be more nearly vertical.

3. The spin of an object produces a stabilizing effect upon it. It holds the object on the course and resists forces which tend to change its direction. Insufficient spin will permit the object to tumble as in the case of the football. Too much spin in proportion to the forward velocity of the object will cause it to curve.

4. The reaction of a spinning object after impact with a wall or a stationary surface is dependent upon the direction of spin.

If the spin is directly opposite to the movement of the object, there will be a retarding effect. If the spin is in the direction of the movement of the object, the speed of movement will be increased. If the spin is across the movement of the object, the movement will be at an angle to the direction of movement and toward the direction of spin.

5. In swimming, speed is developed as much by overcoming resistance as by increasing force.

In the formula $F = KV^2$, K is a constant representing water resistance and has an average value of .6. It varies generally with the skin surface area of the body and also involves such factors as cross-sectional area, skin friction, wave making, eddies, and cavitation. Loss of productive force is also caused by applying force at ineffective angles and directions, by lack of smoothness of maintaining a constant effort, and by tension, usually caused by fear.

6. In the human body, the available force varies inversely with the velocity of movement.

In activities in which a maximum of force and speed are desired, the optimum level of performance for each individual is one half the maximum. Since reaction time is more or less constant after a short period of practice, it follows that conditioning exercises to build strength in order to increase the maximum force should be emphasized. If maximum force is desired, speed should be reduced to zero.

7. In jumping activities, the depth of the crouch or the angle formed by the femor (the thigh bone) and the tibia (the shin bone) is directly proportional to the strength of the muscles. The crouch of a football player before charging and that of the runner before starting are also related to this principle.

8. A muscle contracts with more force when first put under stretch. This is important to know in view of the unfavorable angle at which a muscle must apply its force.

9. A muscle will quickly lose its elasticity if it is put under stretch too often and for too long a period of time.[6] This suggests limited practice and no practice immediately before competition in those activities where tremendous effort is required by muscles. Jumping activities on hard surfaces, pole vaulting, shot putting, and broad jumping are examples of these activities.

10. Because the body operates under a system of levers that are largely third-class, its movements are adapted more to speed than to strength.

11. Twister movements which are started before the body is airborne will be in the direction of the movement of those members of the body which are used to create it.

For example, turning the head and shoulders in a clockwise direction around the long axis of the body will give body rotation in this same direction. This action is due to the principle of transfer of momentum from the part to the whole. If the arms are outstretched at right angles to the trunk when the twist is begun, the speed of rotation can be increased by bringing the arms in against the body and parallel to its long axis.

12. Twister movements which are started after the body is air-borne will be in the opposite direction to the movement of the members of the body which are used to create it.

Thus, if the arms are rotated clockwise around the long axis of the

---

[6] Armor, Jules, *The Human Motor*, London: George Routledge and Sons, Ltd., 1920, pp. 94–101.

body, the body will rotate counterclockwise. In the recovery movement of the arms they are held as close to the body as possible or are moved parallel to the long axis of the body. This is the technique that a cat employs to rotate its body so that it will alight feet first when it is dropped from an upside-down position. Placing one arm in an unbalanced position creates the same reaction as when both arms are rotated about the long axis of the body. The action, however, is not as pronounced.

13. Forward rotation is faster when a twister is brought into the movement.

Questions and Topics for Discussion and Review

1. How can a head wind increase the distance of a discus throw?

2. How can a discus thrower take advantage of various wind conditions?

3. What factors tend to make the wind effects on the flight of a football differ from those that effect the flight of a discus?

4. What is the purpose of spin on implements used in athletic activities?

5. How does the use of spin on a basketball differ from that used on a baseball?

6. How is the speed of a solid through a liquid related to resistance?

7. Name eight factors which cause a loss of force in swimming.

8. How can the direction of a force effect the results of a swimming stroke?

9. Explain the statement, "The available force varies inversely with the velocity of movement." Where does this statement have significance in sports?

10. "The effective angle at which a muscle operates is dependent upon the strength of the muscle." Expand this statement.

11. Do human limitations contradict the laws of physics? Discuss.

12. Explain the principles of gyroscopic action.

13. How does a cat always manage to alight feet first?

14. When do twister movements usually begin?

15. What is meant by the active surface area of an air-borne body? How is this area determined and controlled?

16. What is the relationship of the principles of stretch in a muscle to performance? What is the significance of this in athletics?

17. What is the significance of the preponderance of third-class levers in the body.

18. What is the essential difference between the fundamentals in twister movements started before the body is air-borne and those started after the body is in the air?

19. A baseball and a golf ball are hit and they leave the bat and club head with the same velocity, at the same angle, and from the same height above the ground. Will one travel farther than the other or will both travel

the same distance? Why? If one travels farther, which one goes farther?

20. In executing a twist to the right, clockwise, while air-borne what is the direction of the arm movement? Why?

21. A woman who weighs 120 pounds jumps 1.2 feet in a Sargent Jump. She applies force over .6 feet. Her maximum leg lift is 550 pounds. What would be her maximum leg velocity against a zero load?

22. A 160-pound man jumps vertically 2 feet. He accelerates over a distance of .8 feet. At zero velocity he has a leg lift of 1400 pounds. What is the maximum speed of the leg extension under a zero load? What is the maximum speed of the leg extension under a load of 50 pounds?

6.

Work and Energy

In any physical activity, work is performed and energy is con-sumed. The amount of energy possessed by each individual for per-forming work is limited. It is of considerable importance, therefore, from a competitive standpoint, to know the energy requirement for the performance in terms of the methods used. The efficacy of tech-niques can then be determined in terms of both the results accom-plished and the energy expended. It is the purpose of this chapter to present sufficient evidence to give the reader confidence in the pre-ceding materials and in the analyses which follow in Part II. This is a relatively unexplored field, one ripe for research. Data on the energy cost of activity are not extensive.

A. V. Hill[1] measured the energy cost of running the 100-yard dash and Schneider and Karpovich[2] measured the energy cost of pedaling at various speeds with various loads on the bicycle ergometer. These latter figures were determined by first measuring the oxygen consump-tion of the subjects at rest. Then this was subtracted from the oxygen consumption during the period of activity. The reader is referred to Schneider and Karpovich for a detailed explanation of this method. Practically nothing on the comparative energy costs for various tech-

---

[1] Hill, A. V., *Muscular Movement in Man.* New York: McGraw-Hill, 1927.
[2] Schneider, E. C., and P. V. Karpovich, *Physiology of Muscular Activity.* Philadelphia: W. B. Saunders, 1948.

niques is available. It is difficult to measure the amount of work done and energy expended in most activities because they are not readily adaptable to laboratory treatment. At present the instruments that have been developed for conveniently measuring work and energy are limited to the laboratory.

A treadmill is used for measuring the work done in walking and running and the bicycle ergometer is used to measure the work done in bicycling under various load conditions. Without these direct measures work done can be measured only by assuming that certain conditions prevail with consistency. They cannot always be measured with accuracy.

Work done is represented by the formula:

$$W = Fd \qquad\qquad (31)$$

where W = the work done in foot-pounds
$\quad\quad F$ = the force in pounds applied in the direction of the motion or the effective force
$\quad\quad d$ = distance in feet over which the force acts.

When the force and the distance over which the force acts is known, the work done can be found. For example, a high jumper lifts his center of gravity through a distance of 18 inches from the bottom of his crouch to the point where his jumping foot leaves the ground. The force with which he pushes vertically is 300 pounds. What is the work done?

(a) $W = 300 \times 1.5 = 450$ foot-pounds of work

If a shot putter moves the shot through a distance of 5 feet in making his put and exerts a force of 40 pounds on the shot, how much work does he do?

(b) $W = 40 \times 5 = 200$ foot-pounds of work

A high hurdler has his foot in contact with the ground while his center of gravity moves forward 2 feet as he takes off for a hurdle. The horizontal component of the force with which his foot is pushing against the ground is 200 pounds. What is the work done?

(c) $W = 200 \times 2 = 400$ foot-pounds of work

Kinetic Energy

It is quite possible to determine force and distance over which force acts by rough measurements and calculations from analysis of motion pictures (see Appendix C). Then, if the weight of a body moved and the velocity with which it moves is known, the energy expended can be calculated. The formula showing the relationship between W and energy is:

$$W = Fd = \tfrac{1}{2}mV^2 = \text{kinetic energy};\tag{32}$$
$$F \text{ and } d \text{ are the same as in formula (31)}$$

$$m = \text{the mass of the body moved} = \frac{W}{32}$$

$V = $ velocity of the body in the direction of the force

Kinetic energy may be defined as energy of motion, the energy expended as a result of action. It is the energy resulting from the action of a force over a given distance. If in problem (a) above, the jumper weighs 160 pounds and the velocity with which he leaves the ground is 13.42 ft/sec, the kinetic energy equals:

$$KE = \frac{160 \times 13.42^2}{2 \times 32} = \frac{160 \times 180}{2 \times 32} = 450 = Fd$$

The principle of kinetic energy is valuable in checking the validity of the theories and techniques for top performance. It is one thing to be able to present a top performance. It is quite another to perform at the top with the most efficient expenditure of energy. The most efficient expenditure of energy may point the way to even better performance. Cureton[3] has demonstrated this fact in the tables of theoretical specifications for broad jumps of 15, 20 and 25 feet. These tables are reproduced here because they demonstrate a means of checking the energy cost of performance for different conditions.

In each table the distance jumped was held constant. The angle of take-off was varied from 35° to 55° by increments of 5°. A study of these tables reveals two very important facts. First, the foot-pounds of energy required were the least in each table when the angle of take-off was 45°. Second, the velocity of the jumper in the direction of the take-off (the projection velocity) was the lowest in each table when the angle of take-off was 45°. These theoretical values emphasize the value of coaching in accordance with the principles of physics. As shown here, "a slower runner can actually jump farther

---

[3] Cureton, T. K., "Mechanics of the Broad Jump," *Scholastic Coach*, May, 1935.

TABLE III

MECHANICS OF THE BROAD JUMP—THEORETICAL SPECIFICATION FOR THE:

15-FOOT JUMP

Take-off Angle θ	Sin θ	Cos θ	Projection Velocity (ft/sec)	T^* (sec)	t^* (sec)	S^* (ft)	H^* (ft)	Kinetic Energy (ft-lb)	Extra Energy
35	.57	.82	22.7	.80	.40	15	2.6	1202	7.5
40	.64	.77	22.1	.88	.44	15	3.1	1139	1.9
45	.71	.71	21.9	.97	.49	15	3.8	1118	0
50	.77	.64	22.1	1.06	.53	15	4.5	1139	1.9
55	.82	.57	22.7	1.16	.58	15	5.4	1202	7.5

20-FOOT JUMP

35	.57	.82	26.2	.93	.47	20	3.5	1600	7.1
40	.64	.77	25.5	1.01	.51	20	4.1	1515	1.4
45	.71	.71	25.3	1.11	.56	20	5.0	1494	0
50	.77	.64	25.5	1.22	.61	20	6.0	1515	1.4
55	.82	.57	26.2	1.34	.67	20	7.2	1600	7.1

25-FOOT JUMP

35	.57	.82	29.3	1.04	.52	25	4.3	2000	7.1
40	.64	.77	28.6	1.14	.57	25	5.2	1908	2.1
45	.71	.71	28.3	1.25	.63	25	6.3	1868	0
50	.77	.64	28.6	1.37	.69	25	7.5	1908	2.1
55	.82	.57	29.3	1.49	.75	25	8.9	2000	7.1

$* T$ = total time in flight. $t = \dfrac{T}{2}.$ S = distance jumped. H = vertical height the body rises.

and at the expense of less energy with a perfect take-off than a faster runner who deviates from the ideal angle."

McCloy[4] has shown that the power used for performance varies with the cube of the velocity. Power is the basis of energy and is equal to:

$$P = FV \qquad (33)$$

On this basis, the basis of power used, he demonstrated the difference in power units used in running the mile at a constant rate of speed and at a varied rate of speed. Hypothetical rates of speed are taken in each case. Both runners run the mile in 4 minutes and 24 seconds. One paces himself at the constant rate of 33 seconds for each 220 yards or 20 ft/sec. The other varies his pace. The figures for both runners are shown in Table IV.

[4] McCloy, C. H., *The Measurement of Athletic Power*. New York: A. S. Barnes, 1932.

TABLE IV

THE McCLOY POWER TABLE

Table for Man Who Paces Himself

Time by 220's	Speed in Ft/Sec	Velocity Cubed Or Power Used
33	20	8000
33	20	8000
33	20	8000
33	20	8000
33	20	8000
33	20	8000
33	20	8000
33	20	8000
264 seconds	20 average	64,000 power units used

Table for Man Who Does Not Pace Himself

Time by 220's	Speed in Ft/Sec	Velocity Cubed Or Power Used
29	22.7	11697
30	22	10648
32	20.6 (all numbers	8742
34	19.4 are rounded	7301
36	18.3 off)	6128
38	17.4	5268
37	17.8	5640
28	23.6	13144
264 seconds	20 average	68,568 power units used

The power is found by calculating the cube of the velocity for each 220 yards. The significant fact is that although both runners covered the mile in 4:24, the one who ran at a constant rate used 7 per cent less power. A runner with 7 per cent less stamina can by pacing himself match the time of his stronger opponent who does not pace himself but runs as indicated in the table. Another method of analyzing the result is to say that a runner can make better time with the same power (energy) by pacing himself at a constant rate.

These two examples clearly demonstrate to each coach and athlete the importance of careful study and adherence to the laws of physics. They should stimulate others to explore the technique of other activities for further enlightenment and/or verification of their coaching techniques.

Potential Energy

In addition to kinetic energy which is energy of motion, there is potential energy. Potential energy is energy stored up in a body by reason of the position of that body. It represents the possibility of doing work. A person who jumps into the air has expended kinetic energy. When he reaches the highest point of his jump he possesses potential energy in direct proportion to his height from his base. A pole vaulter at the height of his vault has potential energy in proportion to his height above the ground at the take-off point.

Potential energy is of considerable importance in all swinging activities. It is through potential energy that the body develops speed on the downward swing. Potential energy is represented by the formula:

$$PE = Wh \text{ or } mgh \tag{34}$$

when W = weight of the body; h = vertical height

m = mass = $\dfrac{W}{g}$; g = the acceleration due to gravity = 32

In some activities it is often impossible to determine the energy expended by any of the above formulae. Nor do the formulae measure all the energy expended. In the first place, there is expenditure of energy without any motion, at least without any visible sign of motion. For example, in the case of a lay-out from the high bar there is considerable force exerted and energy expended in holding the body parallel to the floor. There is resistance far in excess of the pull of gravity but there is no movement. In football, a player holds his position against the charge of an opponent. Again, considerable force is exerted and energy is expended but there is no movement.

In the second place, and even when there is movement, all the energy is not accounted for by the formulae for kinetic and potential energy. There are internal resistances. In both these instances the energy expended may appear as heat. Heat, if it can be measured, may be converted into a thermal equivalent of work. 0.324 small calories are equivalent to 1 foot-pound of work. Of course, if the amount of energy expended is determined by means of measuring oxygen consumption, the total energy output can be more accurately calculated. There is also wasted energy due to the application of force at unproductive angles and to external resistance, which are not readily determined. For accurate determination of results all these factors must be considered.

Summary and Principles

In summary, the following relationships exist between work and energy:

1. Work equals the force times the distance through which the force acts or $W = Fd = foot$ pounds

2. Kinetic energy equals $\frac{1}{2}$ the mass or weight $\div$ gravity of the body being moved times the velocity of movement squared or $KE = \frac{1}{2}mV^2$

Since $F = ma$; $a = \dfrac{V}{t}$; and $d = \dfrac{V^2}{2a}$

$$W = Fd = \frac{mV}{t} \times \frac{V^2}{\dfrac{2V}{t}} = mV \times \frac{V^2}{2} = \frac{1}{2}mV^2$$

3. $W = Fd = \frac{1}{2}mV^2 = $ kinetic energy $= KE$

4. Power equals force times velocity or $P = FV$, and it has been found that force varies directly with the square of the velocity and power with the cube of the velocity.

5. Potential energy $= PE = mgh$

6. Techniques performed in accordance with the laws of physics produce the best results with the least expenditure of energy.

7. There may be expenditure of energy without motion in athletic activities. This energy appears as heat. 0.324 small calories equal 1 foot-pound of work.

Questions and Topics for Discussion and Review

1. Why are work and energy output not easily measured in sports activities?

2. What are some of the methods used for work done and energy expended?

3. What is kinetic energy? Potential energy? Contrast each.

4. What is the relationship of force to velocity?

5. What is the relationship of power to velocity?

6. From the standpoint of energy consumed, is it more efficient to run at a constant rate of speed or to vary the rate? Why?

7. Does adherence to the laws of physics in performance of sports techniques require more or less energy? Illustrate your answer.

8. Why does not the application of the formulae to calculate energy consumption that are presented in this chapter determine the total energy expended in human activities?

9. How could the energy unaccounted for be determined?

10. Explain the statement, "Energy may be expended without producing motion in athletic activities."

PROBLEMS

(Answers to problems are given in Appendix D, page 294.)

1. A 160-pound halfback accelerating uniformly hits the line 12 feet in front of his starting position with a velocity of 17 ft/sec. How much kinetic energy is expended? Neglect energy lost by heat, internal resistance, ineffective motion, and so forth.

2. If a linebacker weighing 192 pounds starts from a distance of 10 feet from the line and stops the halfback of problem 1 at the line, how fast must he be traveling? How much kinetic energy does he expend? (Assume no lost energy.)

3. A woman weighing 120 pounds jumps 1.4 foot high in the Sargent Jump. She applies force over 0.6 foot. How much energy is expended? What force is exerted? Assume no lost energy.

4. A shot putter puts a 16-pound shot at a velocity of 28 ft/sec from a stand. The angle of put in 38°. He pushes over a distance of 5 feet and lets it go 6.5 feet from the ground. How far does the shot go? How fast does it accelerate? Assume uniform acceleration. What is the energy expended in the push? Assume no lost energy. What force is exerted?

5. Cornelius Warmerdam pole vaulted 15.6 feet. He dropped 16.0 feet (assuming pit is at ground level) after the vault. He weighs 160 pounds. How fast was he traveling when he hit the ground? What was his potential energy at his highest point?

6. From the standpoint of energy consumed, which of the following plans for running a 4-minute, 28-second mile is the more efficient and by how much, in terms of energy saved: (a) run each 220 yard distance in 34 seconds, or (b) run the first 220 in 30 seconds; second 220 in 34 seconds; third, fourth, fifth, and sixth 220's in 36 seconds; seventh in 34 seconds; and the eighth in 30 seconds? The runner weighs 128 pounds.

7. How much energy is required by a 160-pound runner to run the 220-yard dash in 22 seconds? Assume uniform speed and no lost energy. If he runs the first 100 yards in 11 seconds, how much energy is required for the full distance? Assume uniform velocity in each of the two parts.

8. A basketball player who weighs 160 pounds is running at the rate of 25 ft/sec. He stops through a distance of 6 inches. Assuming that the total force of the stop is on the feet, how much pressure must the feet absorb? If, by the use of a deep knee bend, the stop occurs through a distance of 2 feet, what is the force on the feet?

9. A shot putter puts a 16-pound shot at an angle of 41° with such a force that, after the glide, the shot is moving 8 ft/sec. He then accelerates it with a uniform force over a distance of 5 feet to a velocity of 36 ft/sec. What is the amount of force used in this last part of the put?

Part II

Analysis of Activities

Part II

Analysis of Activities

Part II of this book consists of careful analyses of the fundamental techniques of twelve types of athletic activities. These analyses are based upon the principles developed in Part I. The purpose here is to provide a scientific basis for teaching correct form in the execution of fundamental movements in athletics. Such a basis will guarantee (after the performer has mastered the technique) the most efficient and effective results.

No attempt has been made to include all sports or all fundamentals of each sport in these analyses. It is felt, however, that there is sufficient variety in those presented to permit the reader to apply the same procedures to other sports. Also, it will be realized after some reflection that there are many similar elements in the movements in different sports. Therefore, it will not be difficult to transfer the analysis of a fundamental in one sport to another where the fundamental is the same or similar. For example, the principles involved in running, stopping, starting, balancing, lifting, kicking, throwing, catching, dodging, falling, and sliding are essentially the same regardless of the sport.

Cinematographical analyses have been made of the movements in many sports. Such analyses are a means of checking performances against theory. They have been a great aid in teaching and in helping athletes to perfect their techniques. Because of these facts, the method of cinematographical analysis is reprinted for the information of the reader in Appendix C, page 275.[1]

It should be observed that the analyses recognize individual differences and adopt the principles which best fit the individual. One should not conclude, however, that there are so many variables that no two individuals will follow the same pattern. It may be surprising to learn that there is much more similarity than difference in the performance of individuals.

Because the principles have been developed and explained in detail in Part I, these explanations are not repeated in Part II. For each principle involved in the analysis of a technique, the reader will be referred to the page in Part I that explains this principle.

---

[1] Cureton, T. K., "Elementary Principles and Techniques in Cinematographic Analysis as Aids in Athletic Research," *Research Quarterly,* May, 1939.

7.

Analysis of
Track Techniques

An analysis of track is presented first for two reasons. It is a type of activity that permits accurate measurement, so that the validity of the application of the principles of physics can be demonstrated. Also, many of the principles that are applied in track activities can be carried over to other sports. Track, therefore, is an excellent sport with which to introduce Part II.

Starting

In starting, the emphasis is upon getting away from the mark as quickly as possible, and then into a position that will be favorable to developing the desired pace in the shortest distance. Thus, the ideal starting position is the one that permits the greatest amount of force to be exerted over the longest distance in the desired direction, in order to overcome inertia. It must also be the position in which the runner's equilibrium is the least stable in the desired direction, so that he will start as quickly as possible. In other words, the aim is to exert the greatest force over the longest distance in the shortest time.

The position of least stable equilibrium is easily determined. From Chapter 2 it is found that the center of gravity should be as high as possible and over the edge of the base in the direction of the desired movement. Thus, from the crouch start, the hips should be higher than the shoulders so that the center of gravity of the body is thrown forward toward the hands and in front of the feet. With the center of gravity ahead of the feet, a turning movement about the feet is created which is equal to the horizontal distance from the feet to the center of gravity multiplied by the mass of the body. This position takes advantage of the force of gravity in speeding the starting movement.

Another way of describing the position is to say that the angle between the horizontal and a line connecting the center of gravity of the body with a point on the ground midway between the feet should be as small as is consistent with the application of maximum push by the feet at the start. Figure 22 illustrates this position. The angle BAC

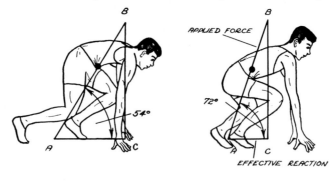

GOOD "MECHANICS"   POOR "MECHANICS"

Fig. 22. Two track starting positions, showing the angle of lean with the horizontal. **Left, the stronger position for starting.**

is more acute in the figure on the left. Likewise, the moment arm in (b) is greater.

The exact position in which the body can exert the greatest amount of force has been the subject of considerable experimentation. White[1] studied hip elevation to determine its effect on starting time in the sprints. In the bunch start, he found that the fastest start was effected when the line of the hips and shoulders was 27° above the horizontal, the hips being higher than the shoulders.

Dickinson[2] studied the relationship between foot spacing, starting

---

[1] White, R. A., "Effect of Hip Elevation on Starting Time in the Sprint," (Master's thesis, University of Iowa, 1940).

[2] Dickinson, A. D., "Relationship between Foot Spacing, Starting Time, Speed, in Sprinting and Physical Measurements," (Master's thesis, University of Iowa, 1938).

time, and final speed in sprinting. He found the bunch start, wherein the toe of the rear foot is opposite the heel of the front foot was significantly the fastest.

Henry[3] in a more recent study seems to invalidate the work of Dickinson. He used foot spacings of 11, 16, 21, and 26 inches respectively. He found that the 11-inch block start resulted in clearing the blocks sooner but with less velocity than was secured from medium stances. The bunch start resulted in significantly slower time at 10 and 50 yards. His results further showed that sprints from the 11-inch stance were actually slower from the very beginning.

Tuttle[4] found that the bunch start permitted both feet to push over a greater distance and develop more power than they do in spread positions. Since the aim is to start quicker and with the greatest amount of force, the position which would provide this result would be (on the basis of the above) one with the hips elevated above the shoulder, the feet in the bunch start position, and the center of gravity ahead of the feet. Such a position is illustrated in figure 23, which is

Fig. 23. Successive stages in starting. Note the continued acute angle of lean with the horizontal to permit direction of push by the feet to be as much forward as possible. (Adapted by permission from Doherty, *Modern Track and Field*, copyright 1953 by Prentice-Hall, Inc.)

drawn diagramatically to show a theoretical position and to indicate the effect of the various factors on the start. The amount of knee bend at the start will depend upon the strength of the leg muscles. The runner with stronger muscles can dip lower but in no case should the dip be extreme.

Additional advantage in starting can be gained by the use of starting

---

[3] Henry, Franklin M., "Force-Time Characteristics of the Sprint Start," *Research Quarterly*, October, 1952, pp. 301–18.
[4] Tuttle and Bresnahan, *Track and Field Athletics*. St. Louis: Mosby, 1937, pp. 471–5.

blocks. Hayden[5] found an advantage varying from 5.4 inches to 4 feet as a result of starting blocks. In the extreme, this could mean more than .1 second faster time in a 10-second 100-yard dash. Blocks provide a firmer base against which to push.

Bresnahan[6] found that speed in starting depends upon which foot is forward in the starting position. Right-handed athletes should start with the left foot forward and left-handed ones with the right foot forward. If this position is reversed, starting is slower.

As the runner starts he should straighten as little as possible in order to follow the direction of his push. Consequently, his movement will be as nearly horizontal as possible. This prevents the waste of force (see Figure 23). It is important that the runners use every available means of gaining speed. Therefore, his arm swing should be as forceful as possible. As the left leg moves forward, the right arm should be brought forward sharply. The principle that the momentum of a part is transferred to the whole applies here (see page 68). In addition, a balancing effect is operative (see page 69).

Since a runner is gaining speed only while his feet are pushing against the ground, he should take relatively short strides when greater acceleration is needed and gradually increase his stride until top speed is attained. Cureton[7] determined that if the first step is less than three feet in front of the starting line faster starting is accomplished. He found this method to be .09 seconds faster than that in which longer strides are taken. The emphasis here is not upon the exact increase in stride, but rather on the fact that pick-up in stride should be gradual. Also, shorter strides should be used while attaining speed. Thereafter, each successive step should be increased by $3\frac{1}{2}$ inches. He also found that reaction time was a very important factor in quick starting. The results of four varsity runners are shown in Table V for the first 20 feet of a start.

Two other related studies tend to verify these results. Lauterbach[8]

[5] Hayden, Thomas C., "A Comparison of the Starting Time of Runners Using Holes in the Track and Starting Blocks," (Master's thesis, University of Iowa, 1932).

[6] Bresnahan, G. T., "A Study of the Movement Pattern in Starting the Race from the Crouch Position," *Research Quarterly Supplement,* March, 1934.

[7] Cureton, T. K., "Mechanics of the Track Racing Start," *Scholastic Coach,* January, 1935.

[8] Lauterbach Ruth, "The Relation between Reflex Time and Running Events in Track," (Master's thesis, University of Iowa).

TABLE V

Subjects	Reaction time to clear blocks (sec)	Running time (sec)	Total timing to 20 ft (sec)
C (distance runner)	.45	1.28	1.74
W (javelin thrower)	.26	1.26	1.52
M (N. E. champion)	.217	1.21	1.427
B (excellent varsity sprinter)	.10	1.21	1.31

studied the relation between reflex time and results in running events on the track. She studied 20 trained and 24 untrained runners and found a correlation of .815 between reflex time and the results in various running events on the track.

Westerlund[9] studied the relationship between running events on the track and the reaction time of the runner. He found a high correlation of .863 between reaction time and speed in running 75-yards. He studied 22 trained trackmen including a world's champion in the 220-yard dash, an NCAA champion in the 220-yard dash and a high school champion in the 440-yard dash. He found the reaction of various groups to be as follows:

Champions	.121
Dash men	.131
Middle-distance runners	.149
Distance runners	.169

The runner should not straighten up until top speed is reached. This keeps the center of gravity well ahead of the feet and gives more turning moment (see Figure 23). Also, the angle made by the line of the center of gravity and the feet with the horizontal is thus kept small. This permits the direction of force to be more horizontal and thus more effective (see page 46 for explanation of components of force). At full speed this angle will be about 70° or 20° from the vertical. Lean is necessary to overcome air resistance and to keep the center of gravity falling outside of the base.

Full speed is gained in about 30 feet. The slowest runners are fully accelerated in 45 feet. Table VI shows the average velocity, and acceleration for 3 sprinters from the start to 42 feet when full speed was attained.

---

[9] Westerlund, J. H., "A Study of the Relationship between Running Events in Track and Reaction Time," (Master's thesis, University of Iowa).

TABLE VI

Distance in feet	Velocity	Acceleration
1	9.5	95
2	13	43
3	15	29.4
4	16	21.5
5	17	15.2
6	17.7	12
7	18.1	9.2
8	18.7	8.0
9	19.0	7.5
10	19.4	7.3
12	19.9	7.1
14	20.6	7.0
16	21.0	6.9
18	21.5	6.7
20	22.0	6.5
22	22.9	6.3
24	23.5	6.1
26	24.2	5.9
28	25.0	5.7
30	25.5	5.5
32	26.1	5.3
34	26.9	5.0
36	27.7	4.0
38	28.0	3.0
40	28.5	1.5
42	28.5	0

Running

Running is a pawing movement. The body is propelled forward by the force of the push backward against the ground. This propelling force and the efficiency with which it is used is the key to the speed that a runner may develop. The available force for running in each individual is constant, from .5 to 1.0 times the body weight.[10] The average is .8 for experienced runners. Little can be done (except

[10] Hill, A. V., *Muscular Movement in Man.* New York: McGraw-Hill, 1927.

to build strength and reduce viscosity) to change internal conditions where a system of third-class levers is at work. But the proper application of mechanical principles can increase the efficiency of running considerably.

In the first place a runner should quickly attain the fastest pace he can maintain for a particular race and hold that pace throughout the race. By this means he obtains the most for the energy expended. Continued accelerating and decelerating is very fatiguing and wasteful of energy. It requires more energy to start, and to change speed, than to maintain speed (Newton's first law—see page 8). Therefore, efficient running consists in keeping the body going after speed has been reached.

The faster one runs the longer his stride. Usually when one runner passes another he does so by lengthening his stride, not by increasing the number of steps. This represents a more forceful push backward by the foot.

The lean of the body is about 20° from the vertical. This lean overcomes air resistance and tends to keep the center of gravity ahead of the striding foot as it contacts the ground. When there is no head wind, a runner at 100-yard-dash speed would create air resistance of approximately 3.58 pounds.[11] This would slow the runner by .28 seconds in a 100-yard dash. With a 30-mile wind, this would amount to .57 seconds. With this wind at his back, he would be aided to the same extent. The wind creates a moment of force forward which is equal to the mass of the body multiplied by the distance that the center of gravity is ahead of the foot which is in contact with the ground (see page 53). If the center of gravity is behind the foot as it contacts the ground, then there is a retarding or backward moment of force equal to the mass of the body times the distance of the center of gravity behind the contact foot. This is a loss of force that might otherwise be used in forward propulsion.

An athlete who runs on his heels (permits his heels to contact the ground first as he strides) is causing his center of gravity to fall behind his contact foot and thus is creating a retarding effect. Actually a deceleration in movement takes place and must be overcome by extra force or else the runner slows down (see Figure 24). For this reason

---

[11] Cureton, T. K., "Mechanics of Track Running," *Scholastic Coach*, February, 1935.

the runner should alight on the ball of his foot. Distance runners whose pace is slower than sprinters usually alight with the knee slightly bent and then permit the heel to hit the surface. These two movements absorb the shock of the foot pounding the surface (trading force for distance—see page 69) and also permit the calf muscles to stretch before contracting to extend the foot for the next push against the track. Such action is less fatiguing to the muscles in the calf of the leg.

Fig. 24. The stride style (runner B) and the step style (runner C). Runner A is a composite of B and C to show the relative positions of the advanced foot with respect to the center of gravity of the body. Runner B shows diagrammatically the retarding effect in running when the foot is in advance of the center of gravity. Runner C shows the position of the foot slightly behind the center of gravity. No loss of speed results from this position.

The push off is with the toe with the foot extended in order to get as much thrust as possible. The leg is fully extended and rigid at the moment of the push in order that the full force of the push back can be converted into forward movement of the body (Newton's third law).

As the foot leaves the ground after a vigrous thrust, the leg immediately begins its recovery for the next stride. To do this with as little effort and as quickly as possible, the knee is bent. The faster the leg moves the more the knee is bent, the higher the foot is raised until the heel practically touches the glutii. By this action the knee moves forward with greater angular velocity because the leg, which rotates from the hip, has a much shortened radius (see page 36).

The faster one moves, the higher the knee should be raised in front. This action delays the placing of the foot to the surface for its next thrust and permits the thrusting leg to reach full extension. It reduces the angle of the leg with the surface and thus increases the effective force of the leg thrust.

The arm motion is opposite to that of the legs. The arms moving across in front of the body act as a counterbalance to the rotation of the hips (see page 69). A runner with heavy hips and legs and light shoulders and arms will find it necessary to carry his arms farther away from the body than he would if there were greater balance between these members (see page 69).

The arms also supplement and aid the leg action. A vigorous backswing of the arms causes the legs to stride farther. When the legs tire, the arm action can help to maintain or give increased speed. Glenn Cunningham, the great miler, once said that his arms were more tired than his legs at the end of a race.

In striding, the center of gravity must rise and fall. However, effort should be directed toward keeping this movement to the minimum consistent with full striding action. The higher the center of gravity rises, the longer the body is off the ground. The forward speed of the runner is decelerating while his body is off the ground.

Hurdling

Hurdling is modified running. It consists of ten exaggerated strides, not ten jumps. The aim should be to raise the center of gravity only enough to clear the hurdle, to bring the striding foot back to the ground as quickly as possible in order to resume regular striding movements. The mechanics of running previously discussed apply to hurdling. The mechanics of going over the hurdle are pointed toward keeping the center of gravity low and resuming the running stride as quickly as possible. In hurdling, the eyes are focused on the top of the hurdle as a means of emphasizing the fact that the hurdler should just skim the top and thereby keep the center of gravity as low as possible.

In going over the hurdle, the foot leaves the ground exactly as in the running stride. For the high hurdle, the take-off point is 6 to 8 feet from the hurdle. As the leg goes up over the hurdle, the body bends forward; this keeps the center of gravity low. As the leg goes down, the trunk is raised. This latter movement raises the hips and trailing leg over the hurdle (see page 19). The trailing leg should be raised as high as possible, consistent with the best body angle off the hurdle, with the toe pointing out and kept as nearly as possible in the same horizontal plane. The importance of stretching exercises is obvious.

The arm swing is the same as in running.   It helps in the forward bend of the body.   The arm swing varies with the build of the hurdler the same as in the case of runners.   If the hurdler's arms are relatively very light, both arms may be brought forward.   This helps in the body bend, though it may adversely affect the balance of the hurdler.

As the leading leg clears the hurdle, it is brought back to the ground faster by raising the trunk and dropping the leg—that is, spreading the ends (see page 19).   This movement will bring the foot to the ground about three feet beyond the hurdle.   The center of gravity will thus be slightly ahead of the foot, which gives forward momentum to the body and thus avoids any further retardation of speed, which began while the body was in flight over the hurdle.

The first stride after clearing the hurdle should be shortened for the same reason as stated in the mechanics of starting (see page 108).   If this stride is too long after each hurdle, as much as 1.5 sec may be lost in a high hurdle race.   Figure 25 shows a series of positions of a hurdler as he takes off, clears the hurdle, and regains contact with the surface.

There is a tendency for hurdlers to overreach in striding in order to be able (in high hurdles) to limit their strides to three between hurdles.   In doing this the foot touches the ground ahead of the center of gravity and time is lost as a result.   The fault usually lies in poor body angle when landing after the hurdle is cleared and from poor body angle between hurdles.   The body is usually too erect.

In order to emphasize hurdling as running, practice during the early learning period may be conducted on a modified plan. The height of the hurdle may be lowered.   The hurdles may be spaced less than ten yards apart.   A loose cross-bar may be used for the top of the hurdle.   This loose cross-bar tends to lessen fear of falling if the hurdle is not cleared.

Fig. 25. Successive stages in clearing a hurdle from take-off to alighting.   Note the relatively small rise of the center of gravity as the runner clears the hurdle.   (Adapted by permission from Doherty, *Modern Track and Field*, copyright 1953 by Prentice-Hall, Inc.)

At first the hurdler may run through the cross-bars until the stride is learned. Later the bar may be cleared. Finally, as form is perfected, the bar should be raised to the proper height and spread to the proper distance. The history of reduction of time in running hurdles is largely one of improvement in form.

Questions and Topics for Discussion and Review

1. What is the purpose of elevating the hips in the track start?
2. Why use the bunch start?
3. Where is the center of gravity when the runner is in the "get set" position?
4. What is the advantage of starting blocks?
5. Of what significance is the angle of inclination of the body in starting and in running?
6. What is the purpose of the arm swing in starting and in running?
7. What is the relationship to the length of the stride and the attainment of speed in starting?
8. What is the relationship between reaction time and speed in running?
9. At what distance from the start is full speed attained?
10. Is a uniform pace or a changing pace more efficient from the standpoint of energy expended? Why?
11. What is the relationship between the speed in running and the length of stride?
12. What should be the relationship of the center of gravity to the position of the striding foot as it contacts the ground? Of what significance is this?
13. Define running.
14. When pushing off in striding, what is the condition of the leg muscles, and of the joints? In what way do these conditions differ from those that obtain when the foot is alighting?
15. Is it good form to run on the heels? Why?
16. Why bend the knee after the foot leaves the ground in the push-off? Is there any relation between speed and knee bend?
17. What should be the position of the center of gravity in running? In hurdling?
18. What is the difference between hurdling and running?
19. What is the purpose of raising the trunk as the hurdle is cleared?
20. Should the foot return to the ground as far beyond the hurdle as possible? Why?
21. Should all strides between hurdles be equal? Why?
22. What is the history of the improvement of time in the hurdles?

Problems

(Answers to problems are given in Appendix D, page 295.)

1. One runner takes a starting position so that the line connecting his center of gravity with the edge of his base makes an angle of 70°. This line

is 20 inches long. Assuming that the position of the center of gravity or the angle does not change when the hands of the runner are lifted from the ground, what is the turning moment created by the position of the body? The runner weighs 150 pounds.

2. The runner of problem (1) now assumes a starting position with an angle of 50° and with the line 30 inches long. What is the turning moment when the hands are lifted from the ground?

3. In striding, a runner's toe is 3 inches back of his center of gravity when his foot hits the ground. The perpendicular distance of the center of gravity from the ground is 40 inches. The runner weighs 165 pounds. What is the turning moment? What is the angle of lean?

4. If, in problem (3), the runner was running on his heels and his center of gravity was 3 inches behind the heel, what is the turning moment? Is it a help or a hindrance to the runner?

5. The better runners exert a propelling force equal to approximately .8 of their body weight. A runner weighs 160 pounds and applies his force at an angle of 39° with the horizontal. How much of this force is effective?

6. In problem (5), the velocity of the runner was found to be 35 ft/sec. Neglecting energy loss from internal and other resistances, what is the energy expended in each stride? Through what distance is the force exerted?

7. If the center of gravity rises 6 inches with each stride, how long is the runner off the ground?

8. In a high hurdle race, if the height that the center of gravity is raised in going over each hurdle can be reduced 3 inches, how much time would be saved in the 120-yard high hurdles? Assume this change involves no loss of time in other aspects of hurdling.

8.

Analysis of

Field Techniques

Eight field events are considered in this chapter: the standing broad jump, running broad jump, high jump, pole vault, shot put, discus, javelin, and hammer throw. The standing broad jump is used as a basis for the analysis of all jumps of this type. The hop, step and jump and the 36 pound weight are omitted. These two are seldom included in track meets and for that reason it is not thought to be of sufficient value to the reader.

Standing Broad Jump

The principles that apply in the standing broad jump illustrate the mechanics that are standard for all jumps. The arms are swung back behind the body as far as possible in a preliminary motion. This is to attain a rhythm of movement for the body. The body bends forward and the knees bend at the same time. More particularly, however, the preliminary swing is to put the arms in a position so a swing forward through as long an arc as possible may be attained. Thus, great momentum (momentum equals mass times velocity) which can be transferred to the body may be built up by the arm swing. The momentum developed by this method aids in adding distance to the jump. The use of weights (to increase the mass) in jumping will clearly illustrate this principle. Two common building bricks held in the hands and released after the feet leave the ground will give as much as a foot in additional distance.

At the moment of take-off the arms should be directly above the head. This gives the maximum effective arc through which the arms may swing. They should be held in this position until the moment of alighting. The bend of the knees before the take-off should not be extreme and should be directly proportionate to the strength of the leg muscles (see page 86). The take-off should be at an angle of 45°. This will mean the greatest effective height for the body (see page 26). The body can move forward only so long as it is in the air; therefore, the take-off is from the toes, which permits the force for the jump to be applied through the greatest possible distance.

In flight the heels should be brought up to the glutii so that, as the legs are thrust forward for alighting, the greatest angular velocity may be attained (see page 36). In alighting, as the feet are thrust forward, the arms are swung down and back. This spreads the ends, rotating the hips, so that the maximum forward reach of the feet is obtained. The legs should be at an angle of 30° with the horizontal in order to get additional distance.

At the moment of landing, the arms should come forward. This gives forward momentum to the body, helps to prevent it from falling backwards, and carries the center of gravity down the line of flight (see page 68) and then forward so that the buttocks will hit the ground just ahead of the heel marks. This movement also absorbs the shock of alighting by substituting distance for force. All movement should be directed in the line of the jump. Any movement at an angle from the line of jump dissipates force and shortens the distance of the jump.

Running Broad Jump

The essential features of the running broad jump are the preliminary run down, the jumping lane, the take-off, the flight through the air, and the landing. Each of these has its mechanics that contribute to the distance of the jump. However, the primary requisite is the development of power. This means speed down the runway and a forceful spring upward from the take-off board. Since speed is so important, it is not surprising that most sprinters become excellent broad jumpers.

The jumper should run increasingly fast so that he has attained full speed at least three or four strides before the take-off. Since the slowest runners can gain full speed within 45 feet, it should never be necessary to run more than 60 feet. To run farther merely invites the possibility of fatigue with its attendant adverse effects on subsequent jumps. Control of the stride is very important; thus the jumper should measure the distance of his run after he has hit upon the correct stride. Since the movement of sprinters from the crouch start is so well controlled, it might prove to be the best method of controlling the stride down the jumping lane. Few jumpers use this method.

From full speed ahead, the jumper must direct his movement from the take-off board upward at the optimum angle of 45°. In order to change the direction of his movement he must prepare for the take-off in the last three strides. To do this he crouches somewhat and his pace is retarded in his effort to gain height. In the world's championship jump of Jesse Owens, he slowed from a velocity of 29.7 ft/sec to 26.7 ft/sec. These velocities were computed from an analysis of the motion pictures of his jump.

At the take-off, the front foot is in advance of the center of gravity at the instant of contact with the take-off board. Owen's foot was in contact with the the board while the center of gravity moved forward approximately 3.5 feet. This is further evidence that there is some retardation at the take-off. Cureton[1] points out that the retardation will not effect the jump providing the ideal angle (45°) is attained.

In the case of the record jump of Jesse Owens, his take-off angle was between 25° and 26°. There are those who feel that, because the body is able to develop more speed than lift, it is not possible to develop sufficient power for a greater angle, particularly an angle of 45°. This theory, however, does not seem valid in view of the fact that the greatest distance can be attained in the standing broad jump by jumping at an angle of 45°. Suffice it to say, the jumper should take-off with as much forward speed and with as much upward thrust as possible for the longest jump. Force times velocity equals power (see page 96). In order to emphasize height in practice, a bar can be set up in front of the take-off board so that the jumper must clear

---

[1] Cureton, T. K., "Mechanics of the Broad Jump," *Scholastic Coach,* May, 1935.

it. The height of the bar can be raised to a point which will require the jumper to approach the ideal angle.

To assist in the upward thrust or lift, the arm should swing upward and the striding leg should swing up as high as possible. (The principle that the momentum of a part is transferred to the whole applies in this case. See page 68). The upward swing of the leg locks the hip joint by reason of action of the iliofemcral ligament. As a result, the take-off knee must bend slightly.

After the take-off foot leaves the board, the leg is bent at the knee so that it may be brought forward faster. With a given force, the angular velocity is inversely proportional to the length of the radius (see page 36). The movement of the legs, called "walk in air," rotates the hips backward and helps the jumper to get more forward reach with the legs. It will give as much as 6 inches additional length to the jump. Realizing this, practically all champions use it. However, Dittrich[2] found no appreciable difference between the "walk in air" and "sit in air" styles of jumping.

Fig. 26. Stages in the broad jump, illustrating the mechanical principles involved. (Adapted by permission from Doherty, *Modern Track and Field*, copyright 1953 by Prentice-Hall, Inc.)

As the feet reach the ground, the arms are brought down and back. This movement, coordinated with the leg movement, aids in the forward reach of the legs. The angle of the legs with the horizontal should be approximately 30°. It would be difficult to keep the body from falling back at landing if this angle was reduced appreciably.

As the jumper hits the ground, the arms are brought forward, the knees are bent, and the body bends forward. This movement brings the center of gravity down the line of flight, gives forward momentum to the body and prevents it from falling back of the heels with the

[2] Dittrich, Francis C., Jr., "A Mechanical Analysis of the Running Broad Jump." (Master's thesis, University of Iowa, 1941).

incident loss in distance. This movement in landing also absorbs the shock of the landing by trading force for distance.

The various stages of a jump are shown in Figure 26. These clearly show the principles and mechanics as stated above.

High Jump

The primary goal in high jumping is, of course, to get the body to as great a vertical height as possible in order to clear a bar. This height depends on three factors. First, the jumper must develop as much lifting power as possible, in order to project the body into the air with the greatest possible initial velocity. The height to which the body will rise is directly related to the velocity with which it leaves the ground. Secondly, the angle of take-off must be as nearly vertical as possible in order to concentrate force upon achieving height; yet the angle of take-off must be sufficient to carry the body from one side of the bar to the other. For an explanation of the mechanical principles that govern these factors, see pages 24 and 25. Thirdly, the distance to which the center of gravity may be raised is limited. In the Sargent Jump, two feet is about the limit to which the best jumpers have been able to project their centers of gravity above their standing positions with arms at the sides. Jumpers must utilize techniques that will overcome this limitation.

The power to spring up derives largely from the speed of contraction of and the strength of the leg muscles, and the strength of the foot to withstand the forceful push-off. Speed is not the most important factor in the high jump. The ability to spring is primary. Lance[3] studied 18 trained and 14 untrained high jumpers. He discovered that the time taken to execute the spring was inversely proportional to the height of the jump. This implies that explosive power in springing is vital in attaining the maximum height in the jump. Consequently, the jumper approaches the bar in comparatively slow loping movements from usually not more than 25 feet away, until he is three or four strides away from his take-off mark. In these last strides he moves rather quickly, with crouch and spring in the last stride in order to be able to stamp the foot hard, so that the push up will be as forceful as possible (Newton's third law—see page 9).

---

[3] Lance, "Relationship Between the Time Spent in Executing the Spring and the Height of a Jump," (Master's thesis, University of Iowa, 1935).

The amount of crouch will be indirectly proportional to the strength of the calf and quadriceps muscles (see page 86).

The crouch and spring before the jump also permit the free leg to swing up hard. At the same time the arms swing up hard. The two movements increase the lifting force of the body—the principle of transfer of momentum from part to whole.

The center of gravity should be directly over the take-off foot at the moment when the greatest upward thrust is exerted. This assures a more vertical direction for the thrusting force. As the jumper approaches the bar, his foot on the last stride before the spring will be ahead of his center of gravity in order to check his forward motion.

The angle of take-off will depend upon the distance of the take-off from the bar. This distance will depend somewhat on the form used by the jumper and the size of the jumper. The distance for good jumping is never over 5 feet. The jumper should take-off as close to the bar as clearance will permit. The closer the take-off is to the bar, the greater is the effective vertical effort, assuming a given force.

Cureton[4] has worked out theoretical tables for 5-, 6-, and 7-feet jumps. These show the distances from the bar, the angle of take-off, the velocity, the time in the air, and the efficiency of the effort. These are reproduced as Table VII for the guidance of readers. By means of motion pictures, cinematographical analyses may be made of jumpers for coaching purposes (see Appendix C, page 275).

To meet the limitations of the human body to project its center of gravity vertically, two steps are taken. First, tall athletes or those with high centers of gravity and those with high leg strength are sought as high jumpers. Studies show that the high jumpers as a group are taller than other track athletes. The second step is to adopt forms for jumping which will necessitate raising the center of gravity a minimum distance above the bar. The mechanics of these forms will be presented briefly. Diagrammatic sketches are shown of each in Figures 27, 28, 29, and 30.

The scissors form of jumping is the oldest and most inefficient. It is now obsolete for competitive purposes but is still useful for jumping low fences and vaulting over obstacles. The approach is from the side. In the last step before the take-off, the foot is far in advance of the center of gravity. This retards the forward movement. Speed is

---

[4] Cureton, T. K., "Mechanics of the High Jump," *Scholastic Coach*, April, 1935.

TABLE VII

A. THEORETICAL SPECIFICATIONS OF FIVE-FOOT JUMP

H Height (ft)	O Angle (degrees) with horizontal	t (sec) in flight	s distance (ft) horizontal	v velocity (ft/sec)	KE Energy (ft-lbs)	Relative Energy (%)
5.0	72	.56	3.25	18.8	823	standard
5.0	64	.56	4.85	19.8	913	+10.9
5.0	57	.56	6.50	21.3	1057	+28.5
5.0	50	.56	8.39	23.3	1265	+53.7

B. THEORETICAL SPECIFICATIONS OF SIX-FOOT JUMP

6.0	75	.61	3.22	20.4	969	standard
6.0	68	.61	4.85	21.2	1047	+ 8.1
6.0	61	.61	6.66	22.5	1179	+21.7
6.0	55	.61	8.44	24.1	1352	+39.5

C. THEORETICAL SPECIFICATIONS OF SEVEN-FOOT JUMP

7.0	75	.66	3.76	22.0	1128	standard
7.0	70	.66	5.10	22.6	1190	+ 5.5
7.0	64	.66	6.85	23.7	1307	+15.9
7.0	58	.66	8.78	25.1	1467	+30.1

not important in the high jump. As the take-off foot is placed, there is some crouch (proportionate to the strength of the calf and quadriceps muscles). The center of gravity is directly over the take-off foot. The take-off is from the foot farther away from the bar. The distance from the bar is just enough to permit the free leg to swing up over the bar without hitting it. The more acute the angle of approach the closer the take-off may be with safety. But the more acute the angle the longer the jumper is over the bar with incident hazard of hitting it.

The free leg and arm swing up hard before the take-off foot leaves the ground. This movement transfers momentum from the part to the whole and thus aids in the lifting force. The free leg straightens out as it goes over the bar. The jumping leg is bent at the knee as it is swung up. This permits faster angular motion (angular velocity is indirectly proportional to the length of the radius). It is then straightened as it goes over the bar and the body is laid out horizontally as well. As the jumping leg approaches the bar the free leg is swung down sharply. This movement raises the jumping leg and helps it to clear the bar.

By straightening out the body as it crosses the bar, the hips are raised (as the ends spread and move down the middle moves up—see page 19). The layout in the scissors jump is never quite complete. As a result, the center of gravity must rise too high above the bar in order for the body to clear. Thus, the scissors form is not as efficient as those which were developed later. The various stages of this jump are shown in Figure 27.

Fig. 27. The scissors form in the high jump.

Eastern Form

The main feature of the "Eastern" form of jumping is the fact that the center of gravity is closer to the bar as the jumper clears it than in the scissors style. Thus, greater efficiency in the jump, in this respect, is attained. The approach is usually from in front but could be from either side or in an arc. The non-jumping leg and opposite arm swing hard out toward the bar to transfer momentum and to rotate the body so that the jumper is laid out horizontally with his back and side to the bar as he clears it. The layout, which is a spreading of the head from the feet, lifts the hips to aid them in clearing the bar.

The knee of the jumping leg is usually bent and tucked under to permit this leg to rotate faster. The arm on the side of the jumping leg is raised and as it clears the bar it is swung down sharply so that the opposite shoulder is rotated away from the bar. The body must travel a considerable distance horizontally in this style of jump in order to clear the bar. As a result the angle of take-off must be correspondingly acute. Since some height is necessarily sacrificed to achieve horizontal distance, the highest jumps are not made with this form.

Fig. 28. The Eastern form in the high jump. Note that jumping leg is away from the bar.

Western Roll

The so-called "Western roll" tends to correct this weakness and, as a result, produces three or four inches more height than the Eastern. The jumper approaches the bar from the side with the jumping leg next to the bar. This permits a much larger angle of take-off so that

Fig. 29. The Western Roll form in the high jump. Note that the jumping leg is next to the bar. The last figure in the sequence is shown to give a front view of the jumper as he is over the bar. (Adapted by permission from Doherty, *Modern Track and Field*, copyright 1953 by Prentice-Hall, Inc.)

more effort is directed vertically, and thus the jumper traverses less distance horizontally in clearing the bar. The free leg kicks up and over the bar. This gives rotation to the body and pulls the hips up. The arm on the side of the free leg also swings up and over. The head and shoulders are over the bar first in this style and the side is toward the bar rather than the back.   After the arm is over the bar, it is swung down to give lift to the other arm.   The jumping leg is tucked to permit faster rotation.

Belly Roll

The "belly roll" style has developed as an adaptation of the western style.   From the viewpoint of the physics involved, it is probably the most perfect form yet devised.   It varies in minor details to give slightly greater lifting force and brings the center of gravity even closer to the bar.   Jumps three to four inches higher than those by the Western roll have been made by this style.   Steers, world record holder in 1941 at 6'11", obtained excellent results with this type of jump.

Fig. 30.   The Belly Roll form in the high jump.   Sound principles of mechanics are best illustrated in this high jump form.   The center of gravity is closest to the bar in this style.   (Adapted by permission from Doherty, *Modern Track and Field*, copyright 1953 by Prentice-Hall, Inc.)

The approach is made from an angle of 35–45° to the bar.   This permits the swing of the free leg and the arms to be directed vertically with no loss for rotation.   The free leg and arm go over the bar first as the jumper more or less straddles the bar.   The body faces the bar and is stretched out horizontally along the bar as it goes over.   The body turns somewhat earlier than in the Western roll.   The jumping leg is bent at the knee as it is swung up to the bar in order to minimize reaction, and then is straightened out as it goes over the bar. The arm and free leg are swung down to give lift for clearance of the jumping leg. Figure 30 shows the various stages of this style of jumping.

Pole Vault[5]

Many principles of mechanics are involved in the pole vault. The event requires the greatest amount of coordination and intricate split-second timing of all track events. As in the broad jump, speed to develop power for the take-off and the take-off itself are of primary importance. The vaulter must develop as much speed as possible in order to swing himself from the ground on to the pole and across the bar. The pole moves through an arc of approximately 60° to a point just short of vertical. The vaulter is handicapped in his running by the fact that he is carrying the vaulting pole.

The vaulter is without the use of his arm swing in running to counterbalance hip rotation. He should approach the vaulting box facing forward. This creates less rotation and concentrates the running effort in the direction of the bar. The pole should be elevated enough to give it balance as it is carried down the runway in order to eliminate as much turning moment as possible. However, it should not be so high as to interfere with placement in the box.

The hands should be above the head when the pole is put into the box and they should be directly above the take-off foot. This position expedites the pull-up. The body will rise faster if pull is exerted when the center of gravity is directly below the point of support (see page 70). The elbows should be bent at the take-off in order to absorb the shock of the reaction of the pole as it is forced against the box (see page 69).

At the take-off the knees are bent to give crouch for the spring upward. The crouch permits the pushing action against the ground to act through a greater distance. If the back is bowed at the take-off, more force can be developed from the swing of the legs. They swing through a greater arc. As the body leaves the ground, the pull upward with the arms is begun. The center of gravity should be directly below the hands. This permits all pulling effort to be directed ver-

---

[5] Ganslen, R. V., "Mechanical Analysis of the Pole Vault," (Master's thesis, Springfield College, 1940).

tically and obviates the disadvantage of the moment arm and wasted force that would be created if the center of gravity were not directly below the hands (see page 53).

After the pull begins, the knees should be flexed to facilitate a faster rotation of the legs upward. At the same time that the legs are drawn up sharply toward the abdomen, the arms should pull very hard. At this point, the angle of the biceps with the forearm is approximately 90°; thus, the action of the biceps is most efficient at this point, from a mechanical point of view.

Fig. 31. Sequence of movement in the pole vault. The mechanical principles of the pull-up and push-up are particularly well-illustrated. Notice that the center of gravity in drawings 4, 5, and 6 is almost directly below the hands. (Adapted by permission from Doherty, *Modern Track and Field*, copyright 1953 by Prentice-Hall, Inc.)

As much speed as possible should be developed at this point and motion should be continued without pause as the body rotates and passes above the level of the hands where the pushing force begins. This is a very critical point in the vault because of the action of changing from pulling to pushing without losing speed. If the action of moving the body up slows or stops at this point, the extra effort to start it moving up again would cost considerably in the height of the vault (Newton's first law).

As the push continues the legs are extended high and then out. The lower hand is released to raise the shoulders. The push continues with the upper hand and the legs are dropped over the bar. The drop of the legs raises the hips (end down, middle up—see page 19) and creates a jackknife effect and gives considerably more height to the vault. Ganslen,[6] however, did not agree with this statement as a result of his analysis of the pole vault.

As the hips clear they drop, the shoulders rise, the pole is released and the chest clears the bar. Figure 31 shows the phases of the vault. Better timing and coordination can be affected if the pole is held at the same place regardless of the height of the vault.

Vaulting is very strenuous and the stretch on the muscles is terrific. The muscles gradually fatigue and lose their elasticity from too much stretch or jarring (see page 90).[7] Therefore, only a few warm-ups and as few vaults as possible should be taken in competition. This suggests moving the bar up a foot at a time at the early heights. It also suggests that practice should not be too concentrated or intense— only two or three times per week and none two or three days before a meet.

Shot Put

Explosive power developed to maximum efficiency through the proper sequence of movements and directed at the correct angle is the secret to a record put of the shot. Power is a function of force times velocity (see page 96). This statement suggests first, speed of muscular reaction and second, muscular strength not only of the putting arm but of the total body for success in putting. Great strength is of little value unless it can act quickly. The reaction time is easily measured, and has been found to change relatively little after even limited practice. Muscular strength is directly proportionate to the cross section of the muscle, and can be built through a vigorous training program.

The sequence of movements, with the mechanical principles involved, can be divided into four phases—(1) the hop, (2) the body rotation, (3) the arm thrust, and (4) the wrist snap.

At the start of the put both feet are together with the putting foot against the back of the circle. This gives the greatest distance through which to build up speed. The preliminary movements of the free leg have nothing whatever to do with the actual put. The center of

[6] Ganslen, R. V., "Mechanical Analysis of the Pole Vault," (Master's thesis, Springfield College, 1940).

[7] Armor, Jules, *The Human Motor*. London: George Routledge and Sons, Ltd., 1920, pp. 94–101.

gravity should be carried as low as possible and the body tilted back. This gives additional distance through which to develop speed as the putting thrust begins.   It also utilizes the strong leg muscles in developing power.

The movement of the body across the circle serves the purpose of overcoming the inertia of the shot (Newton's first law.)   This movement should be done as quickly as possible for the optimum speed for the individual (see page 84).   Once the shot has been put in motion by the powerful leg muscles, it is easier for the arm to keep it moving and to increase its speed on the final thrust.

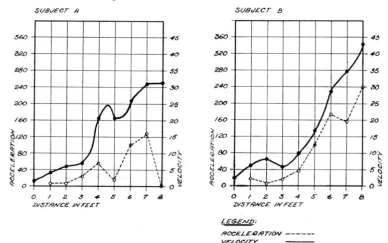

Fig. 32. Velocity curves of shot puts.   A shows a decrease in velocity before the final thrust; B shows a continued increase in velocity throughout the put, which is the ideal for best results.

The important point to remember is that the velocity of the shot from the beginning of the movement across the circle to the release should be continuously increasing.   If the movement stops at any point, the value of the movement has been lost and the putter can put as far by merely standing at the front of the ring and putting.   If the velocity decreases, at any point extra effort is necessary to regain it and the final velocity developed is practically always less than maximum.   This is particularly true if the decrease occurs just before the arm thrust starts.   The graphs[8] in Figure 32 show the velocity curves

---

[8] Francis, Sam, "Mechanical Analysis of the Acceleration and Velocity Involved in the Technique of Putting the Shot," (Master's thesis, University of Iowa, 1941).

of two puts. In *A* there is a decrease in the velocity just before the final arm thrust, and thus the final velocity is barely greater than 30 ft/sec. In *B* there is no such decrease and the final velocity is just under 45 ft/sec. The sequence of movements, then, should be such that just before one member completes its action on the shot, the action of the next should begin; and the succession of actions should take place at an increasingly faster pace (see page 37).

During the movement of the body across the circle, the shot is held stationary against the shoulder with the body pushing it. At this stage of the put, the force is used to move the putter, not the shot. As the hop or glide is executed the feet should stay close to the ground; otherwise, the velocity will decrease. No force can be exerted in moving the body forward while the feet are not on contact with the ground (Newton's third law). Likewise, at the end of the hop, the right foot (right-handed putter) hits and then the left. If both feet hit the ground at once, forward movement is stopped momentarily.

As the putting foot hits at the end of the glide, the center of gravity begins to move forward and upward ahead of this foot and the body rotation begins. The left foot at the end of the glide is placed slightly to the left of the line of movement across the circle in order to permit the body to rotate through a greater arc. The farther the shot is held away from the neck, the greater will be its linear velocity during the period of rotation of the body (see page 36).

As the line of the shoulders approaches a position at right angles to the direction of the put, the arm and leg thrusts begin. It is important that all movements be in the direction of the line of the put. Any deviation means a loss of effective force. Thus, as the arm thrust begins, the shot should be directly in the line of the putting-leg thrust so that the reaction from the push against the ground will be totally effective force.

The angle of projection at release should be approximately 41° (see page 31). In order to learn the proper angle of release, a bar or string may be suspended between standards out in front of the putting circle. The height of the bar or string can be determined by calculating the height of the shot after .3 second when projected at 41°. The velocity has to be assumed or determined by motion pictures. The distance at which the target should be placed from the point of release of the shot can also be determined.

The formulae are:

$$H = V \sin \theta t - \tfrac{1}{2}gt^2 + H_1 \tag{35}$$

$$S = V \cos \theta t + S_1 \tag{36}$$

when $H =$ height shot travels after release

$\quad V =$ initial velocity of projection

$\quad t =$ time of flight $= .3$ sec

$\quad g =$ acceleration of gravity $= 32$

$\quad H_1 =$ height of shot from ground at point of release

$\quad S =$ horizontal distance shot travels

$\quad S_1 =$ distance from front of circle to point at which shot is released

If motion pictures are not available, values may be assumed for H_1, S_1 and V. In measurements that have been made, H_1 varies somewhat between 6.5 and 7.3 feet, S_1 is about 1 foot, and V ranges from 25 to 40 ft/sec. The optimum measurements may also be determined through trial and error. The bar should be placed no further than 5 ft from the ring and closer if it does not bother the putter.

Fig. 33. Sequence of movement in the shot put. Note that in the fourth drawing the line of thrust from the foot to the shot is through the center of gravity of the body at an angle of approximately 41 degrees.

It is important that the putting foot be firmly in contact with the ground during the thrust if the full reaction is to be converted into putting force. The weight of the shot is so great that a slip or the lack of a rigid base to react against means loss of distance (Newton's third law). Moving pictures reveal that it is a common fault of shot putters to lift the putting foot too soon in the reverse movement. Some years ago Munn of Nebraska was able to increase his distance 3 ft by correcting this fault.

At the point of the arm thrust in the put, the increase in velocity begins its sharpest rise; and this should continue until the release of the shot with the extension of the wrist. A study of the velocity curves in Figure 32 reveals the sharp increase in velocity by Subject *B* during this last stage of the put. Subject *A* shows a velocity curve that flattens at the end. This is an indication of lack of effective wrist action and probably means a lack of wrist strength.

It is felt that the increase of present-day distances over those of the past has been due mainly to the improvement of wrist action and to the development of greater wrist strength.

The reverse after the release of the shot is necessary to avoid going out of the circle and to regain equilibrium. The momentum of the body would carry it across the toe board were it not for the reverse.

The sequences in putting are shown in Figure 33, from which the mechanical principles can be observed. Figure 34 shows the position of the shot just in front of the tip of the shoulder. The farther the shot can be held away from the axis of rotation, the greater will be linear velocity for the same angular speed (see page 36). The strength of the putter will determine this distance.

Fig. 34. The desired position of the shot from the neck for developing greatest velocity, providing the strength of the athlete permits.

Discus

Throwing the discus presents a problem in the integration of linear and circular motion. This integration and the fact that all motion is confined to an 8-foot, 2.5-inch circle make the discus a most difficult event. Seldom does an athlete master the technique before his last year in college. It is a four-year course. The problem is to develop as much linear velocity as possible from the rotation in the circle so that the discus can be released with the greatest amount of force. To do this, several mechanical principles must be emphasized and adhered to.

First, the discus should be rotated through as large an arc as possible in order to give time to develop the greatest possible speed. A study of motion pictures of Pete Zagar of Stanford University throwing the discus revealed that the discus moves through an arc of approximately 520° from the end of the back swing to the point of release. To do this, the thrower must place both feet near the back of the circle and rotate his body on the back swing so that he is facing opposite from the direction of movement.

Second, the radius of rotation of the discus should be as long as possible. The linear velocity of a point (the center of mass of the discus) is direcly proportional to the radius of rotation (see page 36). If the thrower is strong enough to hold the discus with the first joint of the fingers, he can get the longest possible radius.

Third, the speed of rotation should be as fast as the thrower can move and still maintain equilibrium. Every man has an optimum speed at which he can operate most effectively. He should build up the velocity of his movement continuously to the point of release. Remember that the greatest force is exerted when both feet are on the ground; speed is lost when the body is free in the air, because there is no support against which to exert force in order to maintain speed. Likewise, if movement stops at any time, the value of previously-developed force is lost.

Fourth, the discus should trail the line of the shoulders in order that the increasing force developed by the rotating body may be imparted to the discus by having the shoulder *pull* it around. In the analysis of the films of Zagar, who was considered to have almost perfect form (he was not big for a weight man), the discus arm trailed the line of the shoulders at all times until release. The angle was never less than 11° (this was at the very beginning of the throw from the back of the circle), and when the arm swing began in the final stage of the throw after the feet were planted following the spin, the angle was 60°. The discus actually traveled through an arc of approximately 150° from the beginning of the arm swing in the final stage to the point of release. There was rotation of the shoulders and hips.

Fifth, the discus should travel during this final arm swing at the intended angle of projection, so that none of the force will be wasted (see page 49). Tests run by James A. Taylor[9] in a wind tunnel (see page 79) show that with a slight head wind (not in excess of 14 miles per hour), the angle of inclination of the plane of the discus for the greatest distance is 35°. For a strong head wind, this angle should be much less, the edge of the discus being presented to the wind. For a strong tail wind, the angle should be greater and the discus thrown so that as much surface as possible is presented to the wind. The sail effect due to the shape of the discus and the speed at which it travels necessitate the variations in the initial angle of flight from the ideal of 45°.

---

[9] Taylor, James A., "Behavior of the Discus in Flight," *ICAAAA Bulletin*, February, 27, 1932.

Sixth, the discus should be released when the throwing arm is in line with the shoulders. The radius of rotation is greatest at this point. Therefore, the linear velocity in the direction of flight of the discus will be greatest at this point. The point at which Zagar released the discus was slightly in advance of the line of the shoulders. The angle was approximately 22°.

Seventh, the spin of the discus tends to keep it on course and keeps it stable with reference to its own axis. Moving pictures show that for true flight the discus makes 18 to 21 revolutions. In order to impart spin, the discus (its center of mass) should be slightly ahead of the center of the hand (about ¼ inch is sufficient).

Fig. 35. Sequence in the execution of the discus throw.

From the standpoint of distance, the thrower must regulate his movements so that when he releases the discus he is up in the front part of the circle. He reverses after release in order to regain equilibrium and avoid stepping out of the circle. Figure 35 shows the sequences in the execution of the discus throw.

Javelin

The javelin throw is one of the best examples in sports for proof of the principles that the total effective force is the sum of the forces of each member of the body if applied in a single direction and in the proper sequence, and of the resultant of forces (see page 67). One can build up force in the run, in the hop, and in the arm swing, but lose the effect of these if final force is not directed exactly in the line of intended flight. If the force is not directed truly, the javelin tends to vibrate in flight. As a result, it will fall far short of the distance it might otherwise have attained.

In addition to care in regulating the direction of the several forces, the angle of flight is important. Approximately a 45° angle will give the longest distance[10] (see page 26). The holding of the javelin does not seem to be of vital or primary importance. The important point is to be able to run fast. Any manner of holding that will permit speed would seem to be acceptable.

As the thrower approaches the balk line at full speed, he must plant his throwing foot for the push-off. This is done by either a hop or a cross-step, which gives time to bring the javelin in position to throw. Most throwers use the hop but the best throws have come from the cross-step as now practiced by the Finns. In either case, as the throwing foot is placed, the body is tilted back with the center of gravity behind the foot. The body is crouched in order to add to the force of the push-off in throwing. As the throwing foot hits the ground, a rocking-forward motion of the body with a driving spring is started.

The arm is drawn far back to get the maximum amount of distance through which to move and develop force. As the body rocks forward, the arm moves in a pitcher's motion except that it is not possible to give the same amount of snap with the wrist and arm as with the baseball because of the greater mass of the javelin.

The body leaves the ground before the javelin actually leaves the hand. The momentum that has developed from the push-off is sufficient to counteract the reaction of the release of the javelin. There is enough difference between the weight of the shot and javelin to permit this without loss. As the javelin is released, the hand and forearm must follow through in the line of flight to avoid any possibility of a change in direction of force at the moment the javelin is released.

As a result of the tremendous throwing momentum, the body is car-

Fig. 36. Sequences in the execution of the javelin throw. Note the angle of the javelin just before release is approximately 45 degrees.

[10] Footrich, William, "Analysis of Javelin Throwing," (Master's thesis, Springfield College, 1938).

ried forward. The feet are reversed, and the thrower should drop low to bring the center of gravity close to the ground to attain balance and stop forward movement to prevent a foul. Figure 36 shows the sequences which demonstrate the mechanics of the javelin throw.

Hammer Throw

The hammer throw, like the discus, offers a problem in the integration of forward linear motion with angular motion to obtain the best results.

The hammer, because of its weight, requires considerable effort to overcome inertia. A high angular velocity must be attained in order to develop a high linear velocity to carry it out the desired distance in competition. As a result, several preliminary swings are necessary before the competitor begins his whirls and movement toward the front of the circle. For clarity it should be explained that angular velocity is measured in *radians* (one radian equals 57.29°) or *degrees per second*. The faster an object rotates, the faster will be its linear velocity at the moment of release. Linear velocity is equal to angular velocity in radians multiplied by the radius of rotation (see page 35).

The thrower takes a position at the back of the circle with his back to the direction of intended flight, his right foot (right-handed person) against the circle and less than a foot to the right of the center. The feet are spread about 18 inches apart with the toes of the left foot in line with the right heel. As in the discus, the hammer should trail the body and be pulled in order that the hammer will continue to accelerate up to the point of release. At the start, it is, therefore, placed on the ground to the right of the right foot (the turning is counterclockwise).

As momentum is gained by the preliminary swings the thrower begins to whirl. Two whirls are taken before the release. Studies of whirling[11] have shown that little or nothing is to be gained by whirling more than twice. The body does not seem to be able to whirl fast enough to develop sufficient additional velocity by whirling more than twice. Also the problem of fouling seems to increase when more than 2 turns are taken (every body has an optimum speed at which it can move most effectively). Velocity curves for the hammer head

---

[11] Buber, Frederic S., "Throwing the Hammer," (an unpublished article).

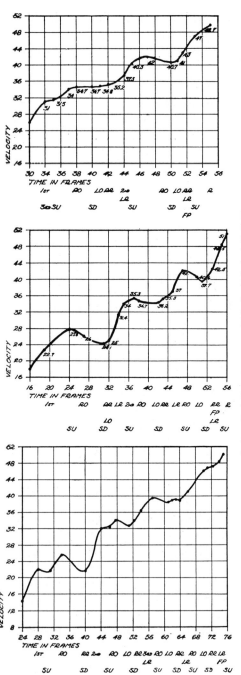

Fig. 37. Velocity curves for two, three, and four turns in the hammer throw. Note that three whirls produce very little increase while four whirls produce less velocity at release than two whirls. (Symbols used: SU = start of upswing of hammer; SD = start of downswing of hammer; FP = start of final pull; RO = right foot leaves ground; RR = right foot returns to ground; LO = left foot leaves ground; LR = left foot returns to ground; R = release of hammer; 1st = start of turn I; 2nd = start of turn II; 3rd = start of turn III. Numbers on curves represent angular velocity of hammer at that point. 16 frames/sec. One turn in 3/4 sec. Two turns in 24 frames.)

taken from a motion picture analysis[12] of two, three, and four whirls are shown in Figure 37. It will be noted that the velocity for three whirls was 51 ft/sec, two whirls 49.7 ft/sec and four whirls 48 ft/sec. The velocity curves also show that there is a gradual increase in the velocity of the hammer to the point of release. They show that the greatest increase in velocity occurs when both feet are on the ground and that the most rapid rise in velocity comes during the final pull when the greatest effort is applied.

The hammer should move in a plane that is at an angle of approximately 45° with the horizontal. The low point of the head of the hammer should be opposite the right shoulder and the high point opposite the left shoulder. Practice swinging in this plane will tend to assure the correct angle of release and a line of flight that will produce the greatest possible distance.

The arms of the thrower should be fully extended at the moment of release in order to create the greatest linear velocity. In the preliminary swing he can gain speed by extending the arm at the downward swing and shortening it on the upswing (see page 36). The centrifugal force from the whirl of the hammer will be so great that the thrower must lean away from the hammer head in order to hold the hammer in its axis of rotation and in order to stay in the circle. After release the thrower should continue his rotation to avoid following the hammer and thus leaving the circle.

QUESTIONS AND TOPICS FOR DISCUSSION AND REVIEW

1. What is the purpose of swinging the arms forward at the take-off in the standing broad jump?

2. Why does the use of weights held in the hands until after the take-off add distance to the jump?

3. Why should height be striven for in the broad jump?

4. How can a thrust of the legs forward at the finish of the broad jump gain additional distance? Illustrate.

5. What is meant by "sliding down the line of flight"?

6. Why is speed not a primary factor in the high jump?

7. Why do tall individuals tend to have an advantage in high jumping?

8. What factors limit the take-off angle in the high jump?

9. What is the purpose of the spring before the take-off in the high jump?

10. What principles can be employed to overcome the limitations of the human body to project its center of gravity vertically?

11. What are the essential differences among the four forms of high jumping that are analyzed in the chapter?

---

[12] Lapp, Vernon, "A Motion Picture Analysis of the Technique of the Throw of National Champions," (Master's thesis, University of Iowa, 1938).

12. After the take-off in the pole vault, what is the most critical point in the vault? Why?

13. Why should the center of gravity of the body be directly below the hands as the pull-up is made?

14. What is the advantage of using the jackknife movement in the vault? What principle is involved?

15. Why are the elbows bent at the take-off?

16. Why should warm-up vaults and total vaults be limited?

17. What two factors are the most important in successful shot putting?

18. What are the four phases in putting the shot?

19. What is the purpose of the movement of the body across the shot-putting circle?

20. Why must the velocity of the shot continually increase from the start across the circle until release for successful putting? What principle is involved?

21. Why should the putting foot be in contact with the ground during the thrust?

22. What practice methods may be used to attain the proper angle of put?

23. What is the advantage of holding the shot as far away from the shoulder as possible?

24. What is the purpose of the reverse after the release of the shot?

25. Name the seven phases in the discus throw.

26. What is the purpose of attaining as many degrees of rotation as possible in the discus throw?

27. What is the value of a long arm to the discus thrower?

28. Why are force and speed lost when both feet are off the ground?

29. Why should the discus be released when the throwing arm is in line with the shoulders? Demonstrate.

30. What is the purpose of the spin of the discus? Normally how fast does it spin?

31. What is the ideal angle of release for the discus? Why?

32. What effect can wind have on the flight of the discus?

33. Of what importance is speed in running in throwing the javelin?

34. What principle is of greatest importance in throwing the javelin?

35. What is the ideal angle of release for the javelin?

36. What is the ideal angle for the release of the hammer?

37. Why should the hammer lag behind the line of the shoulders until the moment of release?

38. What is the proper procedure in making whirls in the hammer throw?

39. How is the centrifugal force of the hammer overcome?

40. What principle is applied to gain velocity in the preliminary swing?

PROBLEMS

(Answers to problems are given in Appendix D, page 295.)

1. The arms of a jumper weigh 15 pounds. The jumper weighs 175 pounds. The arms are swung forward with a speed of 50 ft/sec. If the

moment of the arms is imparted to the body, what velocity of the body will be developed?

2. Demonstrate, by developing a problem, why height is an advantage in the broad jump.

3. If a broad jumper's foot is in contact with the take-off board through a distance of 3.5 feet, if he leaves the board with a velocity of 27 ft/sec., and if he weighs 160 pounds what force is exerted against the take-off board?

4. Assume that a high jumper leaves the ground with a constant velocity and that all other factors are the same, what will be the difference in the height of his jump if one time the take-off point is 5 feet from the bar, and another time it is 3 feet away?

5. If a jumper takes off at an angle of 65° and jumps to a height of 6 feet, 2 inches, what will be his velocity at the take-off? What will be the horizontal distance of the jump? How long will he be in flight?

6. If a jumper is in flight for .868 seconds, and takes off at an angle of 60°, how high will he jump? What is his take-off velocity? What will be his horizontal distance?

7. At what height would you place a target that the shot must pass over after 3 sec., if the shot is released at an angle of 41° with a velocity of 38 ft/sec? The shot is released at a point 6.5 feet above the ground and 1 foot in advance of the inside edge of the toe board? What would be its horizontal distance in front of the ring?

8. A hammer was released with a speed of 70 ft/sec. and at an angle of 45°. How far did it travel? It was released 6 feet above the ground and 2 feet in front of the circle.

9. A broad jumper takes off at an angle of 26° with the horizontal and at a speed of 27 ft/sec. His center of gravity is 3 feet from the ground, and his jumping leg is at an angle of 30° with the horizontal. How far does he jump? How high does his center of gravity rise?

10. When the shot is held against the neck, the radius of rotation is 3 inches. When it is held at the point of the shoulder, the radius is 12 inches. Assume that a constant angular velocity is maintained, what is the difference in linear velocity?

11. It was found that a particular hammer was 3 inches too long. The linear velocity of a hammer of regulation length was 69 ft/sec at release. With the same angular velocity, what would be the linear velocity of the hammer of illegal length? If the hammer is released at an angle of 45° in each case, what would be the difference in distances? Assume all other factors are constant.

12. The firmness of the area where the shot hits the ground is not uniform. At one spot the shot makes an impression whose diameter is 4.5 inches. At another spot, the impression is only 1.5 inches across. What effect does such a ground condition have upon the distance of the put?

13. The landing pit for the broad jump has been raked so that it is 3 inches lower than the take-off board. A jump is measured in a direct line from the edge of the take-off board to the nearest mark on the surface of the pit. What are the errors if the tape shows a jump of 23 feet?

9.

Analysis of
Baseball Techniques

Throwing is probably second only to running as a common element in a wide range of sports. It involves both linear and angular motion. There is angular motion in the rotation of the body about the hips and the rotation of the throwing arm at the shoulder. Linear motion is present in the step forward in the direction of the target (it may be a step and a hop in the case of a fielder), the lean of the body in the direction of the target, and the movement of the forearm and wrist. All of these motions must be carefully integrated so that a smooth rhythmic movement results and the ball can be directed to the target.

Throwing

Just as in the cases of specialized throwing (the shot, discus, javelin, and hammer, which were discussed in Chapter 8, "Analysis of Field Technique"), the problem in throwing a baseball is one of building up power—force and velocity—and imparting it to the ball. However, there is such a difference in mass between the baseball and the shot that we lose sight of the similarity. Baseball throwing differs to the extent that the factor of accuracy is always involved, maximum distance is not usually the goal, maximum velocity is not always desired, and, in the case of the pitcher, a change of direction is often desired. The general mechanics, however, are very similar.

In this chapter pitching will be used for the purpose of discussing the mechanics of throwing, but reference will be made to variations or modifications of the pitcher's throwing style as they apply to other players. The preliminary motions of the pitcher—winding up and stretching—have no relationship whatever to the mechanics of throwing. Each pitcher has his own idiocyncracies in these aspects of pitching. These movements are used either to start a rhythmic motion, to relieve tension, to loosen clothing, or to confuse the batter, or for all of these reasons. One might argue that too much preliminary is a waste of energy that may be needed toward the end of the game. With the exception of those movements that are deliberately designed to confuse or deceive an opponent, they probably have less value than is generally supposed. The fact that such movements have been noticeably reduced in recent seasons would seem to support this conclusion.

To get added momentum, the pitcher may step back with his striding foot and push off it as his beginning movement. As he steps forward, he pivots on his pitching foot which rotates his body toward the batter and permits the arm to draw back in readiness for its forward movement. The farther the arm is rotated back the greater will be the arc and thus the greater the distance through which it can move to develop force. His forward step continues as he pushes back against the rubber. In order to get added force he bends his knee so that he fairly jumps forward from the force of his push back (Newton's third law—see page 9).

As he steps forward, the forward rotation of the pitching arm begins. The force of the step is added to the force of the arm movement and there is a gradual increase in the velocity of movement as each member comes into action. As the upper arm approaches a position straight out from the shoulder, the forearm starts to extend, quickly followed by the snap of the wrist as the ball is released. These two last movements are exceedingly fast and are accompanied by a bending forward at the waist. The ball trails the forearm and wrist up to the time these members start action. Thus the ball is being pulled throughout the movement.

A study of motion pictures shows that the ball leaves the hand just after the upper arm passes the line of the shoulders and as the forearm (in an overhand throw) passes the vertical. As a matter of fact, the ball leaves the hand at a point about on a line with the bill of the pitcher's cap. This is the point at which the linear velocity of the ball is the greatest.

In the push back from the rubber the foot actually leaves the rubber before the ball leaves the hand. This seems to violate Newton's third law. However, the body momentum that has been developed is so great in comparison to the mass of the ball that it is probably sufficient to absorb the backward reaction of the ball without appreciable loss of forward velocity.

Fig. 38. The sequence of movements and the essential stages in the mechanics of pitching are shown in these sketches.

As the pitcher places his foot down in front of the mound, it is to the left (for a right-handed pitcher) of the direct line in which he desires to throw from the mound to the plate. This permits more body rotation in his movement and thus the opportunity to develop greater speed and momentum.

The follow-through adds nothing to the throw. After the ball leaves the hand only air resistance and the force of gravity can have any effect upon it. The follow-through, however, is carried out for two reasons. One, a body in motion tends to remain in motion and the momentum of the throw tends to carry the body with it. It would cause considerable strain and probably injury to the player's arm if he stopped the moment the ball left his hand. The effect (which practically everyone has experienced) of suddenly stopping a fast-moving automobile is analogous to stopping the arm after releasing the ball. The follow-through also has a practical value in that it places the pitcher in position to field the ball should it be hit back at him. Figure 38 shows the essential stages in the mechanics of pitching.

The average pitcher throws a fast ball, a slow ball, and a curve ball. These are usually thrown by means of different methods of gripping the ball and by imparting different directions and speeds of spin to the ball rather than by any difference in the speed of action of the body. This is done so that the batter is unable to detect the type of pitch which is coming until it is too late. There are exceptions to this method, however. Figure 39 shows the methods of gripping the ball for various types of pitches.

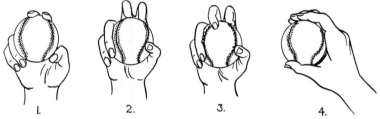

Fig. 39. Various methods for the pitcher to grip the baseball. *1* is the grip for the fast ball; *2* and *3* are grips for the knuckle ball; and *4* is the grip for the slow ball.

The slow ball is usually thrown without the wrist snap. The wrist is held rigid. Also the ball is palmed rather than held at the finger tips. But, regardless of how it is held, the rigid wrist eliminates the increased velocity which the split-second action of the wrist imparts to the ball. The slow ball usually has little or no spin and it often changes direction (breaks). This action is probably due to the lack of spin. Spin creates stability of direction if it is of the proper amount. If there is too much, the object curves. If too little or none, it tumbles. The change of direction depends upon the air resistance that is met.

Even though a curve ball is released with the same total amount of force as a fast ball, it moves forward with less speed than the latter. This is because the total force is applied in two directions, a part of it being spent to impart spin to the ball. This spin is sideways or downwards or a combination of both. It is accomplished by an outward rotation of the forearm and wrist. The degree of curve that the ball takes depends upon the relation of the speed of the spin of the ball to its forward motion. The amount of air resistance at the moment of the pitch is also a determining factor. The ball should be held so that the spin which will create the greatest amount of air resistance may be applied. The grip shown in Figure 39 will accomplish this. The final direction of the ball will be the resultant of the two forces— the spin and the forward force (see page 45). Figure 40 shows the two forces acting upon a curve ball.

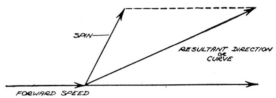

SPIN

RESULTANT DIRECTION
of CURVE

FORWARD SPEED

Fig. 40. The direction of the forces to produce a curve ball, with the resultant direction the ball will take. The forward speed toward the plate is always greater.

The speeds of a curve ball and a fast ball have been calculated from moving pictures of a pitch. An average fast ball travels 94 ft/sec, a curve ball 84 ft/sec. These figures are for major league pitchers. It was found that Bob Feller's fast ball traveled 145 ft/sec. In connection with the speed of pitched balls, Kenny[1] measured by means of motion pictures the relative speeds of overhand, sidearm and underhand pitches. He used 21 pitchers, one third of whom normally pitched by each of the three methods. All threw the three ways in the study.

He found that the overhand pitch was faster in every case except two; the overhand fast ball was 11 ft/sec faster than the overhand curve ball; 2 ft/sec faster than the side arm fast ball; 12 ft/sec faster than the sidearm curve ball; 7 ft/sec faster than the underhand fast ball; and 15 ft/sec faster than the underhand curve ball. He observed that a longer stride was used in overhand throws, which probably meant a more forceful push back on the rubber.

Adams[2] studied the speed of throwing from infield positions to first

[1] Kenny, J. O., "A Study of Relative Speeds of Different Types of Pitched Balls," (Master's thesis, University of Iowa, 1938).

[2] Adams, William J., "Speed of Throwing a Baseball from Infield Positions to First Base," (Master's thesis, Springfield College, 1949).

base. Although his method of timing was not by means of cine-matographical analysis, he came out with essentially the same results. The overhand method gave greater accuracy than other types of throws and practically equal speed. This is interesting because these situations are much different from pitching.

When it is desired to throw the ball a long distance as in the case of an outfielder throwing to home plate and there is not enough throwing power to throw the ball in a direct line, the ball should be elevated. If the greatest amount of distance possible is needed, then the ball should be thrown at an angle of 45°. Increasing this angle reduces the distance rapidly so it is better to throw at slightly less than 45°. The example on page 29 very aptly demonstrates this situation.

In baseball time is equally important, so the ball should not be thrown any higher than necessary to carry the distance. This, in effect, means that there is an inverse relationship between the velocity of the ball and the height it should be thrown from a given distance. It must be remembered that the higher the ball is thrown the longer it takes for it to return to earth. On the other hand, it is probably unwise to bounce the ball to a base or to home plate if it can be thrown through the air the total distance. The moment the ball hits the ground, frictional forces begin to retard its speed. However, at the moment there is no evidence available which compares gravitation retardation with frictional retardation in this case.

Catching

The principle in Newton's first law is involved in catching a ball. Since a body in motion tends to remain in motion, if the ball were stopped abruptly with the hands held rigid the total force of the ball would have to be absorbed by the hands. This may be quite a shock to the hands and often cause painful bruises. Even the protection of a glove is not always a sufficient cushion.

The formula which represents this force is: $Fd = \frac{1}{2}mV^2$ (see page 69). Since the mass of the ball m and the V are constant for each catch, the only possible device for reducing the effect of the force is to change d, the distance through which the force acts. This can be done by letting the hands recoil as the ball is caught. The force of the shock will be reduced by the amount of the recoil. To let the hands recoil 1 foot gives only half as much shock as a recoil of 6 in. A recoil of 2 feet gives only half the shock of 1 foot.

Catching high foul balls behind the plate or high flies between the plate and the mound is a tricky problem unless one knows the direction the ball will take. Such balls are hit below the center of the ball and are given spin so that they will curve toward the pitcher. The catcher must allow for this or he is likely to miss the ball. In many cases it is wiser, where possible, for an infielder to make the catch.

Bouncing balls are moving slowest in a vertical direction at the top of their bounces. Therefore, it is easier to handle the ball at this point. The next best place to catch the ball is at the bottom of the bounce just after the ball hits the ground. The ground has absorbed part of the shock of the downward force.

Batting

In batting, by far the most important factor is that of providing force with the bat to hit the ball. Force is equal to mass times acceleration (see page 43). The mass of the batter is relatively constant. The mass of the bat is the variable quantity. The batter should choose the heaviest bat he can swing without retarding his speed of reaction. In order for the mass to be effective it must move into the ball. This means that the body should not be falling away from the ball. Striding too far locks the hip and causes the body to fall away from the plate (and the ball) with a consequent loss of force. Lou Gehrig, with all his prowess as a hitter, had this bad habit.

In order to develop as much speed in a minimum of time that is available, good reaction time is necessary and an integration and summation of the various movements must be effected. Not much can be done about improving reaction time; for each individual, short practice will develop it to a maximum. Real attention, therefore, must be devoted to the mechanics of proper techniques in batting, to the integration and summation of the movements.

First, as much angular movement as possible should be affected in order to permit the development of an optimum of momentum. This suggests a rotation of the bat as far back as possible preparatory to striking the ball. Balance, however, should not be disturbed and it should not be necessary to turn the head to follow the ball. The eyes do not see when moved rapidly. Seng[3] found that batters did not track the ball to the plate with visible pursuit movements of the head. The primary basis for tracking the ball was by pursuit movements of the eyes, but this movement was not a staccato jerk. In order to swing through the greatest arc under these conditions, the batter should stand close to the plate and take a straight-away stance. Then, in stepping to strike the ball, the foot should step slightly away from the plate. This gives a greater arc through which to swing.

The sequence of movements are as follows: the batter steps first. Seng[4] found that professional batters tended to start the step with the release of the ball. The step finishes approximately 1/24 second before the swing starts. As the foot is placed, the body starts to rotate at the shoulder and hips. Finally, the forearms extend and as the ball is met, the wrists are quickly extended. All this happens much faster than it takes to say it (the duration of the swing tends to be constant regardless of the speed of the ball—between 55 and 80 m.p.h.) but the movements must be in sequence and started at the right moment to assure the greatest effective force. The extension of the forearm and wrists are the most important moves to give increased linear velocity to the bat for the same angular velocity (see page 36). The total time from the beginning of the swing to hitting the ball varies from 1/4 to 1/6 sec in the studies by Seng.

The bat should swing in the plane of the ball so that it can be met squarely. The center axis of the bat should meet the ball at its center. If there is to be any deviation, it is better to crouch and come up slightly on the ball than to stride and swing under.

The ball should be met out in front of the plate just after the arms pass the position where they are straight out from the shoulders so that the bat is at right angles to the line of the shoulders and with the arms fully extended. It is at this point that the greatest forward linear speed is attained. The ball should be met well out on the bat where the linear velocity is greatest. Strategy in hitting—that is, place hitting and such—is not considered here.

In order to meet the ball as indicated, the batter should hold the bat at a very acute angle with the horizontal and with the left elbow

[3] Seng, C. H., "Visual Movements of Batters in Baseball," (Master's thesis, University of Illinois, 1952).

[4] Seng, C. H., "Visual Movements of Batters in Baseball," (Master's thesis, University of Illinois, 1952).

(a left-handed batter) close to the body. This will tend to place the right forearm practically horizontal. The swing must be timed and the amount of rotation determined in accordance with the speed of the ball and the reaction time of the batter. It should be remembered that everyone has an optimum speed at which he can operate most successfully.

The reaction time for the average batter is 1/10 second. Babe Ruth in contrast had a reaction time of 1/20 second which permitted him to swing as hard at fast balls as he did at slow balls. He also had the ideal form according to the principles of dynamics (from a study of motion picture film).

The force imparted to the ball will be dependent upon the firmness of the grip at the moment of impact and the rigidity of the back leg, which is in contact with the ground at the moment of impact. These two must absorb the shock of impact. If the wrists are rigid, the grip firm, and the leg straight, there will not be much recoil and most of the force will be utilized in driving the ball (Newton's third law). If the meaty part of the hands rather than the fingers is placed behind the bat, it can be held more firmly. In bunting the reverse is practiced. The force of the pitch is absorbed by recoil of the bat and a loose grip. This principle is all in accordance with Newton's third law of motion.

Fig. 41. Sequence showing the essential aspects of batting mechanics.

The position of the hands on the bat must be adjusted to the strength of the grip, wrists, and arms, and to the weight of the bat. The individual with a weak grip, wrists and arms should choke the bat and spread the hands. This produces a shorter lever (therefore, less power), but it permits the batter to control his swing more effectively (see page 51). A heavier bat can be swung by a choke grip and spread of hands. Figure 41 shows the essential aspects of the mechanics of batting.

The actual speed at which a batted ball will travel after impact with the bat is dependent upon the coefficient of restitution of the ball and bat, the mass of the ball and bat, and the velocity of the ball and bat at impact. It is seen from this that the variables in any situation are the velocity of the bat and the ball. The weight of the ball and bat as well as their restitution qualities are constant. To hit a slow ball as far as a fast ball, the batter must swing harder (see formula, page 66). The success of the batter in hitting both fast and slow balls is dependent on his ability to quickly adjust to each.

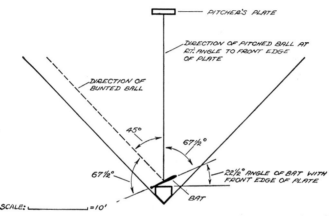

Fig. 42. The angle to hold the bat in order to bunt the ball down the third base line when the ball is delivered at right angles to the front edge of the plate.

Place hitting is dependent upon timing the swing to meet the ball at the proper angle. The principle that the angle of incidence equals the angle of reflection applies. The ball will leave the bat at the angle at which it meets the ball (see page 61). Slight adjustment must be made for curve balls. Assume that the ball approaches at right angles to the front edge of the plate. To bat the ball in a given direction, the bat should be held so that when it meets the ball it makes an angle with the front edge of the plate which is equal to one-half the angle formed by the line made by the thrown ball with the line of the intended direction of flight (see Figure 42). In order to allow for the movement of the bat and the spin of the ball, the bat should be held at a little less than one-half this angle. For example, in bunting the ball down the third base line, the bat should be held at an angle of less than 22½° with the front edge of the plate. The angle with the third base line and the line of the ball is 45°.   It is assumed that the pitch is traveling at right angles to the front edge of the plate.

Running Bases

Running and starting were discussed in Chapter 7.   The same principles hold for base running.   A few specific applications will be made to these principles here.   It is of interest to know that a right-handed batter makes better time running to first base than does a left-handed batter.   The distance to first for the left-handed batter is shorter, however, so he gets there sooner.   Garner[5] studied 35 batters who hit both right- and left-handed.   The average speed to first for the right-handed batters was 21.271 ft/sec while the average speed for left-handed batters was 21.200 ft/sec.   The difference was statistically significant.   The right-handed batters, however, had to run 92.3158 feet while the left-handers ran 88.7080 feet.   An electric timer was used with connections on the bat and at first base.   The advantage of the left-handed batter in running to first is, therefore, due entirely to the shorter distance.

The explanation of this rather startling revelation is in the faster start.   As the right hander hits the ball, the momentum of his swing starts him in motion toward first base.   His equilibrium is upset in that direction.   His right foot steps directly toward first and he pushes off directly toward first with his left foot.   The left-handed batter, on the other hand, must pivot first on his right foot so that he can step toward first.   The momentum of his swing tends to throw him off to the right of the first base line, so that he must swing back into line before starting.   These short delays give the quicker start to the right-handed batter.

In running to first base, the runner should not jump on his last stride.   When he springs into the air higher than his normal stride carries him, it takes longer to reach the base and his horizontal speed is retarded (see page 28).   There are so many close decisions at first that this difference in time may be the difference between safe and out.

The base runner in turning a base to go to the next, should stay in the base line.   He must run farther if he leaves the base in a circular path.   By using the principle of lean to turn, he can stay close to the base

---

[5] Garner, Charles W., "Difference in Time Taken to Reach First Base in Right and Left Hand Batting," (Master's thesis, University of Iowa, 1937).

paths and can turn without undue loss of speed (see page 55). His problem is one of overcoming centrifugal force. Because of the greater power on the push off with both feet, base runners might even profit by turning bases on both feet.

Newton's first law suggests that a base runner would stand a better chance of stealing a base if he could be in motion before the pitch. It would be more effective to start close to the base and be walking toward the next base than to take as long a lead as possible but be stationary (at the moment of the pitch) and facing at right angles to the base, feet spread and crouch low. The effort to overcome inertia is so much greater than the effort to speed up after the body is already in motion. The great George Sisler used this technique with great success.

There are many examples in common every-day experiences with machines which clearly demonstrate this principle. The starting torque to set the motor on the electric refrigerator in rotation is so great and requires so much more electricity to start than to run that the lights are dimmed (when they are on) when the motor first starts. The job of overcoming inertia also causes considerably more noise than mere rotating thereafter. Another common example is that of a car coming up to a stop light. It is barely creeping along but it is moving. Other cars are stopped and waiting for the green signal. The light changes while the one car is still moving. This car is in an open lane but one or two cars back of the lead cars in other lanes. The car which is moving jumps out ahead of all others with comparative ease. Everyone has noticed this phenomenon. Fuel consumption for driving is much greater in the city because of the stop and go actions than on the open road where a constant speed may be maintained.

Taking no lead but walking with the pitch has the added advantage that pitchers are not likely to feel that the runner is planning to steal and, therefore, are more likely to pay less attention to his movements. However, should the pitcher throw to the base the runner is so close he is able to return safely even though his movement was in the opposite direction.

If the conventional lead is taken, the runner should never hop into his lead. He should always have one foot on the ground and take his lead by skip step motions. An alert pitcher will be able to catch a runner who hops, even though he is close to the base. Once the runner is in the air he is unable to start back to the base until his feet return to the ground. If the pitcher throws as the runner starts his hop, the runner is momentarily helpless.

On the basis of this same principle many advocated before the rules prohibited the action that a runner in advancing a base after a caught fly ball start from the outfield side of the base. By this means he could be in rapid motion when the ball is caught. Of course, the runner must time his motion so that he is touching the base as the ball is caught or so that he is a step behind it.

Starting

The position of the fielder as well as the base runner is important from the standpoint of starting quickly. Each must be ready to start in more than one direction and to start as quickly as possible. The track sprinter's start cannot be assumed because this position is designed to move quickly in only one direction. The same fundamental principles can, however, be applied in determining the best position for the baseball player.

Fig. 43. The starting position of a baseball player (left), with movement in different directions.

The player should be fairly high so that equilibrium can be upset easily. The feet should be fairly close together, not farther apart than the width of the hips. Stability is proportional to the width of the base and inversely proportional to the height of the center of gravity above the base (see page 14). Studies have also shown that greater total force can be exerted when the feet are against the ground, and both can be in contact with the ground longer for pushing back when the feet are close together. The weight should be slightly more on the balls of the feet in order to facilitate pivoting to the left or right or back or forward. There should be a slight crouch to permit pushing through a greater distance. In order to exert greater force at the start, it is better to step with the left foot when going to the right and with the right foot when going to the left. Right-handed players would step with the left foot when going forward (see page 108). When going back the step would depend upon the direction in which it is necessary to turn. These small details are important because of the split-second timing which is necessary in baseball, particularly on the part of fielders going after batted balls. Figure 43 shows starting positions for different directions.

Sliding

From the standpoint of mechanics this discussion is concerned only with the aspects of shock and speed. Other factors have to do largely with protection from injury and the strategy of the game. In order to reduce the amount of shock from sliding, the player should slide so that as much of his body as possible is in contact with the ground. The force of the fall is constant but its effect on any one portion of the body is inversely proportional to the area of contact. This suggests that he should lay out flat so that his legs, hips, and back are touching the ground. Such a position also makes it more difficult for the fielder to tag him.

For speed in sliding it is probably faster to slide head first. There is, however, no evidence available to substantiate this point. From the point of view of mechanics, the runner is leaning forward. His center of gravity is over or ahead of his striding foot as he moves toward the base. He is, therefore, in a falling position. The direction of the force from his pushing foot is in the direction of the head. When the runner crouches to slide head first, this force is more nearly horizontal and, therefore, more effective in the desired direction.

If the runner slides feet first, he leans back so that the position of his center of gravity is back of his striding foot. He must crouch to more or less a jumping position. He throws his hands backward. From studies of the broad jump (sliding has some similarity to this) it was learned that there was definite retardation before the take-off (see page 119). All reasoning, therefore, points to the head-first slide as the fastest. Certainly this would be true from a stationary position. Figure 44 shows the two types of slides. It also illustrates the spread of impact.

Fig. 44. Head-first (*this page*) and hook slides (*opposite page*). Note particularly the large area of contact of the body with the ground. This spreads the shock when the body hits the ground.

Questions and Topics for Discussion and Review

1. List the mechanical principles involved in throwing a baseball. Explain each.

2. What mechanical values accrue from the wind-up or stretch motion? What disadvantages, if any?

3. What advantage is given to the pitcher by the rule which permits him to place his striding foot back of the pitcher's plate?

4. What is meant by the expressions, "He pitches from his feet" or "He pitches with his body"?

5. Of what value is the follow-through in baseball?

6. Explain how palming the ball or a rigid wrist can reduce the speed of the ball when all other facts are constant.

7. How can a difference in gripping the baseball affect its action and resultant direction?

8. In which direction will a high foul ball directly behind the plate curve? Why?

9. What is the purpose of recoil in catching a ball?

10. What are the sequence of movements in batting for efficient results?

11. What is the most important factor in batting? How is this attained?

12. How is the impact of the bat with the ball absorbed?

13. Must one swing harder to hit a slow ball as far as a fast ball, all other factors remaining constant? Why?

14. Why is the angle of reflection of a bunted ball more likely to deviate from the angle of incidence than a ball which is hit with terrific force?

15. Other things being equal, which develops the greater velocity in running to first base: the right-handed or left-handed batter? Why?

16. Which is more advantageous in stealing a base; to have a short lead and be moving as the ball is delivered to the plate or to have a long lead and be stationary? Why?

17. How can a base runner shorten his time in advancing a base after a caught fly? Explain.

18. Why is it unwise to jump the last stride in running to first or to hop in taking a lead off of a base?

19. What principles may be employed to advantage in turning a base?

20. Wherein does the application of the principles in starting in track vary from those in starting in baseball?

21. From the standpoint of mechanics, is a feet-first or a head-first slide more effective? Discuss.

22. From the standpoint of mechanics, what is the purpose of flattening the body out on the ground? Discuss.

Problems

(*Answers to problems are given in Appendix D, page* 295.)

1. A baseball has a forward velocity of 75 ft/sec and a velocity to the left as a result of spin equal to 15 ft/sec. What will be the resultant direction of the ball?

2. A baseball has a forward velocity of 60 ft/sec and a velocity to the left as a result of spin equal to 12 ft/sec. What will be the resultant direction of the ball? Will the ball of problem (1) or problem (2) curve more sharply? What angle will the resultant of each make with the forward line of motion?

3. One player throws the ball 90 ft/sec, while a second throws it at a velocity of 110 ft/sec. Each throws the ball from a left field position to home plate, a distance of 210 feet. How high must the ball rise in each case to carry the full distance? Assume the point of release and point of catching are the same elevation. What will be the angle of throw of each?

4. A ball is thrown with a velocity of 130 ft/sec. With what force does it hit the glove if the recoil is 6 inches? 12 inches? 2 feet?

5. A ball is thrown at right angles to the front edge of the plate. The batter desires to hit the ball at an angle midway between first and second. At what angle must the bat meet the ball? Assume that the angle of incidence will equal the angle of reflection.

6. A baseball is moving with a velocity of 80 ft/sec at the moment of impact with the bat. The velocity of the bat is 50 ft/sec. The bat weighs 32 ounces. The coefficient of restitution of the ball is .5. With what velocity does the ball rebound from the bat which strikes the ball squarely and without recoil?

7. If the ball in problem (6) leaves the bat at an angle of 40° with the horizontal, how far will it have traveled when it returns to the same level at which it left the bat?

8. A base runner turns first base at a speed of 20 ft/sec. He turns through a radius of 15 feet. How much must he lean to make the turn?

9. A right-handed batter has a speed of 21.271 ft/sec. He runs 92.3158 feet to reach first base. A left-handed batter has a speed of 21.2 ft/sec. He runs 88.7080 feet to reach first base. Which man reaches first sooner? How much sooner?

10. In problem (8) the base runner weighs 170 pounds. What is the centrifugal force which must be overcome?

11. A player begins his swing 1/6 second before he hits the ball. The ball is traveling 100 ft/sec. How far does the ball travel after the swing starts until it is hit? If the ball is traveling 120 ft/sec and the swing starts 1/4 second before the ball is hit?

10.

Analysis of
Football Techniques

Forward Pass

The mechanics involved in throwing a football are exactly the same as those that apply to throwing a baseball. Because of its size, the grip of the football depends upon the size of the hand of the passer. Those with large hands will grip the ball nearer the minor axis while those with small hands will grip it nearer the end. As in the case of the baseball, if the fingers are placed on a seam or lace the thrower will have a better gripping surface.

Spin is particularly important on the football in order that its stability in flight can be maintained. This is essential for ease in catching and for control of direction. The nose should be pointed up because of the effect of the air on the flight of the ball. If the nose is pointed down, the ball will quickly drop to the ground.

The angle of projection at which the ball is thrown will depend entirely upon the distance desired. Most passes are comparatively short so that little or no angle of elevation is necessary. Speed in getting to the target is usually the essential item. Where distance is desired and there is not sufficient throwing power to carry the distance on a line or at a low angle, then the ball should be elevated toward 45°. For the same force the ball will carry farther at this angle except in a strong wind. In a wind, the angle should be reduced proportional to the velocity of the wind.

Punt

The usual objective in punting is for distance and direction. When this objective changes then the application of the principles of mechanics which govern the punt must be altered accordingly. The presentation here applies primarily to the attainment of distance. Reference will be made to variations.

The power for the kick comes from three movements. There is linear movement which starts the body in motion in the direction of the desired flight of the ball. It comes first from a step and a quick hop and is taken in the desired direction of the kick. The number of steps and the foot used for the step depends entirely upon the developed habits of the kicker. Because of the charge of the opponents, the time for making the kick is limited. Therefore, the slower the kicker, the farther he must be away from the opponent. The stepping technique requires the greatest amount of time for the kick. The subsequent moves are exceedingly fast in comparison.

The second movement is a rotary movement of the kicking leg with the hip joint as the center of rotation. The leg is drawn back as the hop is started. As one foot hits the ground at the end of the hop, the other leg starts forward. The forward speed of the leg is the greatest when the foot is directly below the hip. However, the ball is not contacted at this point because elevation is necessary to attain distance. For the greatest air carry with ideal wind conditions, the ball should leave the foot at an angle of approximately 45°. The example of distance for varying angles of projection on page 28 clearly shows the angle at which the ball should be kicked for the greatest distance.

In order to kick the ball at the proper angle for distance, the ball should be met at a point about $1\frac{1}{4}$ feet from the ground. This gives an angle of the leg with the ground of slightly less than 45°. The ball is dropped approximately vertically (it should be dropped as short a distance as possible). Placing the ball correctly has much to do with the success of the kick. The greater the distance through which the ball drops, the greater will any error in dropping the ball be magnified. The ball will leave the foot at approximately right angles to the leg.

The angle of incidence is equal to the angle of refraction (see page 61). This gives a projection angle of approximately 45°.

The third source of power is the action of the foreleg. As the leg is drawn back the knee is bent. This permits the leg to move forward with greater angular velocity because of the shortened radius. Bending the leg adds force to the kick (see page 68). With the same stepping movement and same speed of rotation of the leg, the amount of the bend of the knee will determine the distance of the kick. For a short kick, the knee should be bent at right angles with the thigh. For a long kick there should be a full knee bend with the heel practically touching the glutii muscles.

The leg should be fully extended when the ball is met and the foot should be extended so that it is parallel to the leg. This gives the longest possible lever (radius) and gives the greatest force to the kick. The leg should be rigid at the moment of impact so that the full force of the kick may be imparted to the ball. This is in accord with Newton's third law (see page 9). The other foot must be planted on the ground for the same reason.

The swing of the leg is toward the median line of the body so that after the follow through the foot finishes in front of the opposite shoulder. The purpose of diverting a part of the force at an angle to the direction of the kick is to impart spin to the ball. Spin is necessary to stabilize the rotation of the ball and to keep it on course (see page 80). Without spin the ball will tend to tumble and too much spin will cause it to curve from the desired direction. The force of the spin is equal to the initial force times the sine of the angle. The ball should be pointed up so that the long axis of the ball with the effect of the spin will follow the parabola of the flight. This angle permits the ball to avail itself most advantageously of the sail effect of air current.

The momentum of the leg as it follows through is imparted to the body as a whole. A powerful kick will cause the body to raise off the ground and to slip forward. Because of the extreme rotation of the kicking leg, the ilio femoral ligament locks the opposite hip. As a result, the knee of this leg will bend in compensation. The head is kept down throughout the kick. If the head is raised, some force is lost, the forward momentum of the body is retarded, stopped, or, in extreme cases, reversed. This represents a loss of force for the kick.

Weather conditions and game strategy make it necessary to change the normal technique for kicking. Sometimes it is desired to give the ends time to get down under kicks when they are unable to cover a normal kick properly. This may call for a high kick. The higher the ball is kicked in the air the longer it takes for it to return to earth. But a higher kick (a kick at an angle of more than 45°) is also a shorter kick. The examples worked on page 29 show the difference in time and distance for kicks of varying heights. To kick the ball higher it must be met at a greater distance from the ground. This increases the angle of the leg with the vertical. This same high kick is used when only a short distance is desired as when the ball is close to the opponent's goal. Also, when there is a very strong tail wind, the ball is kicked higher so that the wind has more time to carry it a longer distance. In this case the long axis of the ball is directed in a more vertical direction to give the wind a greater area of the ball to act upon. When there is a strong head wind, a low kick is called for. The long axis of the ball should be pointed in a horizontal direction in order to reduce the wind resistance by presenting the smallest cross-sectional area to the wind (see page 79 on wind resistance).

Fig. 45. Sequence of movements in punting a football. Pick out the mechanical principles involved by studying each figure.

The Mills system of kicking is devoted to the strategy of keeping the ball away from the opponent and always kicking to out-of-bounds. These kicks are long, low, rolling kicks. The foot is closer to the ground when it meets the ball. More force is, therefore, imparted in a horizontal direction. By keeping the ball low, there is less time for the opponent to get to the ball to prevent it from rolling out of bounds. These low kicks are more likely to be blocked because of the low projection angle. Figure 45 shows the various phases of the mechanics of the punt.

Place Kick

Up to the point of meeting the ball, the mechanics involved in a place kick are the same as for a punt. Body momentum forward is developed from the step and hop. In the case of a free kick, the kicker has time to run several steps. This gives him an opportunity to develop greater momentum and to carry this momentum through the ball by continuing his forward motion. The rotation of the leg and the bend of the knee are the same as for the punt, with two exceptions. The leg is swung directly in the line of desired flight of the ball. This imparts more force in the direction of the kick. The foot is held at right angles to the shin and the ankle is held rigid at the moment of contact. This prevents any recoil action with consequent loss of force in the direction of the kick (Newton's third law).

Since the ball is held stationary on the ground for the kick, conditions for kicking can be held more constant. The axis of the ball is tipped back slightly. This permits the toe to remain at right angles to the shin and still gives the proper lift to the ball. When kicking from a high tee, the axis may be vertical. The ball is high enough off the ground to permit the foot to flex from its right angle position sufficiently to give proper lift to the ball.

The non-kicking foot should be placed about 6 inches back of the point of the ball and to the side of the ball so that the kicking foot will be right in line with the desired direction of flight. Thus, the ball is met immediately after the foot passes the vertical plane of the leg where the linear speed is the greatest. This permits more force in a horizontal direction than in the case of the punt. By placing the non-kicking foot back of the ball, the kicking foot is assisted in giving the desired angle of projection to the ball (see page 61 on the angle of contact and angle of projection).

The ball is met by the toe at a distance of about 1/3 up from the bottom. This makes contact a little below the center of mass of the ball and provides sufficient turning momentum to spin the ball about its minor axis. The spin is necessary to hold the ball on its line of flight.

The head should be kept down or forward as in the case of the punt so that the momentum of the body will carry through the kick. Stroboscopic pictures show the ball collapses to approximately one half its diameter at the point of contact before the ball rebounds from the toe of the kicker. If the kicker is running as in the case of a kick-off, he should plan to continue right through the line of flight of the ball.

Figure 46 illustrates the mechanics of the place kick.

Fig. 46. Sequence in the execution of the place kick. (See also Figure 16, p. 64.)

Drop Kick

The mechanics which were presented for the place kick apply to the drop kick. Since the ball is dropped from the hands in the drop kick, it should be held as low as possible for the same reasons as those indicated in the case of the punt.

The Stance

The principles which determine stability and quick starting must be integrated in designing the stance for a football player. Only those aspects of the stance will be discussed here. First, the assignments of the player must be known.

If a player's assignment is to go straight forward at all times or if that is his primary assignment, then he should use the stance of the sprinter at the start of a race. Bud Wilkinson of the University of Oklahoma uses essentially this stance for his linemen because their primary assignments on all plays are to get to positions for down field blocking. He is primarily interested in a quick get-away straight ahead. Therefore, he sacrifices stability for line blocks and a neutral position for strategy purposes in order to attain his goal (see page 105 for the position of the track start).

If a player has primarily a blocking assignment in close line play, then he must assume a position from which he can move quickly with force but at the same time from which he can maintain a stable position. He must also be able to move in different directions. This requires a position with a fairly wide base, and with the center of gravity lower than in the sprinter's stance. The player, however, must not bend his knees so deeply that he sacrifices force in his charge. The amount of crouch should be proportional to the strength of the leg muscles (see page 86). Robinson[1] found that the three-point stance for linemen was faster. This also gives the player strong stability. If the player has a ball carrying assignment or a blocking assignment to which he moves without interference, then he can take a semi-sprint start position. More of his movement is either straight forward or at an angle forward. The three-point stance with the center of gravity lower and farther back of the hand than in the sprinter's stance, with the weight equally distributed on the feet and hands, and with the hips slightly below the height of the shoulders represents a neutral position.

Figure 47 illustrates the three-point stance.

In all cases, the foot position in the stance should depend upon whether the individual is right- or left-handed. A right-handed person should start with the left foot back whereas left-handed persons should start with the right foot back. It makes no difference for ambidextrous people. Bresnahan[2] found that faster starts were accomplished in this way.

Much has been written about the techniques in pulling out of the line. Becker[3] tested 22 experienced football players and 28 inexperienced students to find whether pivoting on the right, the left or both feet was faster. He found no significant difference. The fact that

---

[1] Robinson, Frank H., "A Comparison of Starting Times from Three Different Backfield Stances," (Master's thesis, Springfield College, 1949).

[2] Bresnahan, G. T., "Movement Pattern in Starting from a Crouch Position," *Research Quarterly Supplement,* Vol. V, No. 1 (March 1934).

[3] Becker, Paul A., "A Study of the Movement Pattern of Football Guards Leading Interference," (Master's thesis, University of Iowa, 1939).

none had ever pivoted on both feet gives credence to the theory that this might be faster with practice. Dickinson[4] found that for the sprinter pushing off of both feet when they were close together was the fastest method for starting.

Fig. 47. The low, stable three-point stance, for stability in blocking and charging.   Check the analysis described on page 166.

Charging

The essential factor in charging is to be able to develop as much power as quickly as possible and apply it in the desired direction.   This suggests making contact as quickly as possible and below the center of gravity of the opponent, getting in close and then applying force upward and to the side.   By getting in close and low, the player is able to direct all of his force more vertically and in a straight line formed by his feet, legs, center of gravity and point of contact with the opponent.   The summation of forces are all in the same direction. Thus, there is no wasted force and the player has a maximum of pushing power (see page 45 on resultant forces).   If, on the other hand, the player is high whether he gets in close or not, he has little more pushing power than his body weight.   The significance of the application of force is borne out by the study[5] of Elbel, Wilson, and French.

Figure 48 shows two types of charge.   Player A in Figure 48 is in a strong charging position while B is weak from the standpoint of developed power and applied force.   This technique is consistent with

[4] Dickinson, A. D., "Relationship Between Foot Spacing, Starting Time, Speed in Sprinting and Physical Measurements," (Master's thesis, University of Iowa, 1938).

[5] Elbel, Edwin R., Donald Wilson, and Clarence French, "Measuring Speed and Force of Charge of Football Players," *Research Quarterly* (October 1952), 295.

the preceding discussion of stance. Klumpar,[6] in studying open field blocking, found that regardless of what coaches advocated the success of open field blocks included essentially the items mentioned above. He found particularly that making contact low or dipping under the stiff arms of the opponent was essential to a successful block.

Fig. 48. Two charging positions. *A* is a strong position from the standpoint of developing power and applied force; *B* is a weak position.

In order to make quick contact, the shoulder or arm extension of the shoulder should be used by the offense while the hands and arms may be used by the defense. Contact can be made quicker in each case because these members are closest to the opponent. However, the defensive player must be careful not to violate the other principles stated above just because the rules permit him to use his hands.

Tackling

The primary aim in tackling is to save distance and to prevent the ball carrier from advancing after contact. This means developing enough momentum to offset the momentum of the ball carrier. Since momentum equals mass times velocity, the light player must hit faster

[6] Klumpar, Emil, "Analysis of Blocking in Football," (Master's thesis, University of Iowa, 1939).

to overcome the advantage of the heavier player. If the tackler can develop equal or greater momentum than the ball carrier, then he should tackle him right at the center of gravity and head on if he is to save distance. If this is not possible, then he should tackle at an angle and below the center of gravity. This is all a matter of resultant of forces (see page 48).

Fig. 49. Three types of tackling technique.

The angle tackle will lose some distance but is a method for the lighter and less powerful player to use in order to stop his opponent. Tackling low gives the tackler the advantage of a moment arm (the distance of the point of contact from the center of gravity), and the effective use of his available force. A high tackle is not as effective for the same reason that a high charge is not as effective. A powerful ball carrier could run right over a much less powerful tackler who used a high tackle. The work of Anderson[7] in analyzing tackling in football substantiates the mechanics of tackling as presented here. He studied the films of 200 successful and unsuccessful tackles, both head on and at an angle. He wanted to find exactly what players did in

[7] Anderson, Richard F., "Analysis of Tackling in Football," (Master's thesis, University of Iowa, 1939).

relation to what coaches say they do. He found that the practice did not agree with the theory in many instances. For the purpose of this presentation, we summarize his findings as the discovery that successful tacklers hit at the center of gravity or lower, crouched before contact, and took short driving steps.

To prevent the ball carrier from evading a player who is a potential tackler, the principles of equilibrium apply. Assuming that the ball carrier is in a position to dodge, change pace, and so forth, the tackler must be able to meet these tactics by stable balance. As he approaches (approximately 5 yards), he must widen his base, crouch (lower the center of gravity and bring it within the base) and shorten his stride. All these movements produce stable state of equilibrium in contrast to running headlong forward where the center of gravity is high and outside the base. Figure 49 shows tackling techniques.

Tactics of Ball Carrier

1. *The Straight Arm.* The tactics of the ball carrier in the use of the straight or stiff arm should be to capitalize on the momentum of his opponent. To do this, he applies the principle of Newton's third law. As the ball carrier makes contact with the potential tackler, he should make his arm straight and rigid. He should not attempt to push the would-be tackler aside. Rather, he should use the momentum of the would-be tackler to propel him, the ball carrier, around his opponent. In other words, the ball carrier rides his opponent to get out of his path. By keeping his arm stiff, he not only keeps his opponent at arm's length, he also uses the full reaction of the force of his opponent. Much of the practice in running through a maze of posts is misdirected because the emphasis is on the push of the ball carrier. He will be successful in this tactic only if his momentum is considerably greater than that of his opponent. In that case he probably would not need to use a straight arm—he could run right over his opponent.

2. *Dodging.* Dodging consists of quickly changing the direction of the motion of the body. By Newton's first law, a body continues in its state of uniform motion in a straight line except insofar as it is compelled by force to change that state. Movement consists of upsetting the equilibrium of the body in the direction of motion. In dodging, then, the first consideration must be to re-establish stability momentar-

ily. The body must be stopped going in one direction before it can change its direction. In the case of a player dodging, the body is usually stopped by action from within the body. This consists of throwing the foot or feet ahead of the center of gravity and leaning away from the direction of the original motion. This action brings the center of gravity within the base. The knees are bent to drop the center of gravity near the base. The amount of lean and dip depends upon the speed with which the player is moving. The lean cannot exceed an angle whose tangent is equal to the coefficient of friction of the two surfaces—in this case, the surface of the ground and the cleats of the shoes of the players. The dip should not be so low that the player cannot spring quickly and forcefully in another direction. The amount of crouch is proportional to the strength of the leg muscles. If it is necessary to crouch lower, then subsequent movement will be slower.

Now, the force which starts the body off in another direction comes from the push off from the foot or feet and the acceleration of gravity which plays a part when the equilibrium of the body is again upset. More force can be exerted by both feet, close together. Therefore, the player will make a faster get away in the new direction if he uses both feet to stop and start. Some of the most outstanding backs in the country have discovered this technique and use it to great advanage.

3. *Change of Pace.* Change of pace consists of accelerating and decelerating. Slowing up is accomplished by putting the foot ahead of the center of gravity, leaning back and crouching as described under dodging. In this case, the body is not brought to a stop and it continues in the same direction. Speeding up consists of exactly the opposite. The center of gravity is thrown outside the base, the player leans toward the direction of motion and increases the force of his push back. Short steps are necessary in each case in order to exert more force against the ground to stop or to start.

4. *Running Hard.* A ball carrier has occasion when he hits the line or when he is trapped to try to gain as much distance as possible before he is stopped, or to try to break away with hard driving movement forward. He is interested in such cases in building up as much momentum as possible. Since momentum equals mass times velocity, he must build up as much velocity as possible as quickly as possible. The mass, his weight, divided by 32, is constant.

From a standpoint of the principles of dynamics he should do two things. He should bend farther forward at the waist. This concentrates his mass near the center of gravity with the consequent concentration of force and throws his center of gravity lower and farther forward which lessens the chance of being thrown back. Second, he must move with shorter steps which will permit him to accelerate faster (see page 108).

Falling on the Ball

Falling on the ball consists of two factors—assuming a position to get control of the ball and taking a position to reduce the shock of diving on the ball and avoiding injury. If one dives so that he surrounds the ball with his arms, legs and abdomen, there is little chance of losing control. If he dives so that he hits flat on his arms, side of body, and legs at the same time, he will have spread the shock of the fall so that there is little chance of injury (see page 60). The shock from a fall is inversely proportional to the area of contact. This is the principle used in judo.

Few players can do an artful job of falling on the ball, and yet it is of fundamental importance in football. Because of the lack of understanding of the principles involved and lack of mastery of the fundamentals, a certain fear exists among players. Many unnecessary injuries occur from falling on the ball as a result. Many opportunities to recover a loose ball are also lost.

There is another technique involving a different principle and is sometimes advocated also. This consists of rolling as one dives on the ball to further reduce the shock. The principle is trading force for distance on the basis of the formula $Fd = \frac{1}{2}mV^2$ (see page 69). It is the same principle which is used in catching a ball. This technique in football invites injury and it is not recommended.

Catching the Ball

The principles involved in catching a football are no different from those involved in catching a baseball. The reader is, therefore, referred to the discussion on catching the baseball (see page 147). The importance of making a basket with arms and body for the ball and trading force for distance is even greater than in baseball. This is because of the resilience and the shape of the football.

1. What difference is there between the mechanics of throwing a football and throwing a baseball?

2. What determines where the football is gripped?

3. Why is the angle of projection of the football important?

4. What are the three essential movements from a mechanical point of view in kicking a football?

5. List the mechanical principles involved in punting. Discuss each.

6. Why does the leg swing across the median line of the body in punting the football?

7. What causes the body to be raised off the ground at the completion of a punt?

8. What is the purpose of keeping the head forward during the execution of a punt?

9. What is the value of a high kick? A low kick?

10. What is the difference in punting and place kicking from the standpoint of mechanical principles?

11. At the kick-off, why is it desirable to continue motion in the direction of the ball as it is kicked?

12. Why should the ball, in the place kick, meet with the toe at a point below the center of gravity of the ball?

13. What factors determine the stance which a football player assumes?

14. What would be the advantage in getting low and in close to an opponent so that the charge is more vertical than horizontal? Illustrate.

15. What is the difference in the principles applied by the offensive and defensive players in charging?

16. How can a lighter player compensate for the difference in weight of his opponent in order to stop the opponent by tackling him? If he is unable to develop equal momentum, what should he do? If momentum is equal, how should the tackle be executed?

17. What principle is involved in tackling a ball carrier who is in the open?

18. What principle is involved in the use of the straight arm?

19. What two major divisions of mechanics are involved in the technique of dodging?

20. Why is it suggested that one may change direction more quickly in stopping and starting by planting both feet and pushing off with both?

21. What two aspects of equilibrium are involved in dodging?

22. Define change of pace.

23. Of what does "running hard" consist?

24. What technique should be used to apply the principles which will result in running hard?

25. What is the mechanical principle involved in falling on the ball? Illustrate.

26. What two techniques may be used in applying the principle? What are the advantages and weaknesses of each?

27. Why is it more important to apply the principle of recoil in catching a football than it is in catching a baseball?

PROBLEMS

(Answers to problems are given in Appendix D, page 295.)

1. A kick carries 60 yards where it is caught at the same level from which it was kicked. The ball was kicked at an angle of 43° with the horizontal. How high did it rise? How long was it in the air? Assume no help or retardation from the wind.

2. Another kick carries 60 yards where it is caught at the same level from which it was kicked. The ball is kicked at an angle of 30° with the horizontal. What is the difference in velocity with the kick in problem (1). Which kick is in the air longer?

3. Assume that the kicks in problems (1) and (2) were made from 10 yards behind the line of scrimmage. Will the ends be able to reach the safety as he catches the ball if both travel at the rate of 30 ft/sec? They start from the line of scrimmage and 2.5 seconds elapse before the ball is kicked.

4. A ball carrier is running so that as he hits the line with his shoulder, the angle which the line of his body makes with the horizontal is 75°. On another occasion, when he hits the line, his angle is 40°. He weighs 190 pounds. His speed is the same in each case. Will it be more difficult to stop him in the first or second instance? How much more effort will it take to stop him in his strongest position? Assume the distance from his feet to his shoulders to be 5 feet on each occasion.

5. A lineman gets in close to his opponent and low so that when he makes contact and charges, he charges through a distance of 1.5 feet. He weighs 210 pounds and moves with a velocity of 28 ft/sec. How much force does he exert?

6. On another occasion, the lineman in problem (5) moves with the same speed but because he is unable to get as close and as low his charge is through a distance of only 8 inches. Which charge is more effective and by how much?

7. An open field runner stops by crouching and planting his right foot forward. He then pushes off from this foot with a force of 175 pounds through a distance of 2 feet. He weighs 180 pounds. With what speed is he moving?

8. The same runner in problem (7) stops by setting both feet and pushes off with both feet with a force of 375 pounds. This time, his feet are in contact with the ground while his body is moving 1.5 feet. Which method of dodging produces the greater speed?

11.

Analysis of
Swimming Techniques

Resistance or loss of propulsive force plays such a major role in swimming that one might well devote more attention to those aspects of the techniques which would eliminate resistance as to work on increasing the amount of force. Certainly, a great deal more energy would be available for investing profitably in a race. The reader is referred to page 81 in Chapter 5 where a detailed treatment was devoted to this problem. The factors which cause loss of force are merely enumerated here for ready reference during the analysis of various swimming strokes.

These factors are *wave making* caused largely by up and down movements; *eddies* or *swirls* caused by merely moving water or changing the stroke; *skin friction* caused by rough skin, hair, swim suits; *cavitation* which is loss of suction; *force* used at unproductive angles; lack of smooth progress, particularly that due to an uneven stroke; *internal resistance* due to tension, and resistance due to the shape of the body or shape caused by movement.

Karpovich[1] found that skin friction was the most important resistance factor. The type of bathing suit is more important than the

---

[1] Karpovich, P. V., "Water Resistance in Swimming," *Research Quarterly,* October, 1933).

quality of the material. A suit which is loose about the back and tight about the legs may considerably increase the resistance. He found no difference in resistance between a silk suit and a swimmer in the nude but an increase in resistance when a woolen suit is used.

He found that resistance for the glide on the back is greater than for the glide in the prone position. Turning the head for breathing increases the resistance slightly. But merely lifting the head so that the eyes are just above the water level does not appreciably change the water resistance. "Hydroplaning," an exaggerated lifting of the head and body as in the breast stroke, increases resistance.

The resistance is greater during the attempt to gain a certain speed than during the maintenance of the speed. This suggests that a swimmer should maintain a constant speed during a race for the conservation of energy. Because of the high resistance factor, this is even more important in swimming than in running where it was quite significant (see page 97).

There is a definite relationship between the cross-sectional area of the body and the resistance. In this connection, the movements of the legs and arms should be kept within this area in their stroking movements. For example, the leg kick in the crawl should be confined as much as possible within this area. In other words, the leg stroke should not be too wide because of the resistance factor.

Eddy resistance and wave making resistance affect swimmers just as they do ships. The formula for the resistance or drag on ships indicates how complicated and how important this factor is in the propulsion of ships. It is:

$$D = C_d \frac{PV^2}{2} \Delta^{\frac{2}{3}} \left(\frac{\sqrt{lg}}{V} \right)^{2d} \left(\frac{W}{PVl} \right)^e$$

where D = drag, C_d = coefficient of drag, P = density of water, Δ = wetted volume, l = length of individual, W = viscosity of liquid, $\sqrt{lg}/V^{2d}$ = Froude's number for wave making

$$\left(\frac{W}{PVl} \right)^e = \text{Reynold's number for skin friction.}$$

Crawl Stroke

There is much speculation about the technique of the crawl stroke. This is due largely to the fact that various theories have not yet been thoroughly investigated. The effects of resistance as related to the various body movements are not known. However, the mechanical aspects of swimming are quite simple. They involve the application of force through the arms and legs and the direction of this force in order to get the most effective use of the force.

Karpovich[2] found that efficient swimmers derived approximately 70 per cent of their propelling force from the arms and 30 per cent from the legs. Poorer swimmers derive 77 per cent of their propelling force from their arms. This is due to poor leg action.

In contrast to these findings, Cavill, in testing the value of the arms and legs in the crawl stroke, swam with his legs tied together and made his best time.

To eliminate as much as possible of the lost force due to resistance in the crawl stroke, the swimmer should:

1. Eliminate body rotation. That is, he should not roll from side to side as he alternates his arm stroke.

2. Keep his head down so that no more that the eyes are above water.

3. Not turn the head to the side any farther than necessary to breathe.

4. Maintain a constant pace.

5. Keep the leg stroke within the limits of the greatest functional cross sectional area of the body. In other words, as much stream-lining as possible should be effected.

6. Wear tight fitting silk-like suits.

7. Eliminate all movements which will cause the body to go up and down and make waves or eddies or swirls. These consist of side movements of the arms in the stroke, or motions directed downward which do nothing more than lift the body out of the water.

In order to get the most effective use of the available force in the stroke, the direction of movement of the arms and feet in stroking should be to the rear, pushing directly back against the water. The reaction then will be forward and equal to the push back (Newton's third law—see page 9).

Specifically in the case of the arms, the pulling stroke should not start until the arm is approximately at an angle of 45° with the horizontal. The angle of the hand permits the stroke to begin before the arm reaches a 45° angle. The greatest effective pulling force is derived when the arm is vertical. At this point all of the force is

---

[2] Karpovich, P. V., "Analysis of Propelling Force in the Crawl Stroke," *Research Quarterly Supplement,* May, 1935.

effective. At 45°, .7071 of the available force is effective (see page 267—sine 45°). If the propelling stroke is started sooner than this, more force is wasted. For example, if the propelling stroke were started when the arm is at 30° with the horizontal, one one-half of the available force is effective (see Figure 50).

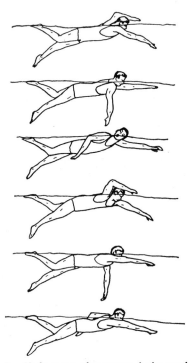

If the arm is fully extended forward and the stroke begins at the surface of the water, all the force at this point is directed downward. It not only wastes force, but it lifts the body out of the water and causes waves, which create resistance which must be overcome with additional force. If the arm crosses the median line of the body and then the stroke begins, the body will be propelled sideways, and turned away from the desired direction of movement.

The arm, therefore, should enter the water at an angle downward and be pulled straight through and directly under the body. The pulling stroke should begin at approximately 45° and continue to approximately 45° with the horizontal in the rear. In other words, the working stroke is a little more than 90°. The arm should be fully extended in order

Fig. 50. Sequence of movements in the crawl stroke.

to get the advantage of a larger lever. Alley found that the force of the normal arm stroke was greater than the bent arm stroke.[3] The elbow is bent at the end of the arm stroke so that a full arm stroke may be attained.

If the arm is pulled through the water too fast, there would be a loss of force due to cavitation—a loss of suction. Propulsion comes from tail suction. There is, however, no evidence that the arm can be pulled through the water so fast in the normal racing stroke to produce

[3] Alley, Louis E., "An Analysis of Water Resistance and Propulsion in Swimming the Crawl Stroke," *Research Quarterly*, October, 1952, page 253.

slip or cavitation. Each swimmer should experiment with different rates to test this point.

By bending the wrist when the arm is at an angle with the vertical, the flat surface of the hand will be at right angles to the direction of movement. This provides greater effective propulsive force. The hand literally pulls the body through the water. It is not known whether it is more effective to stroke with the fingers spread or with them tight together. More tail suction may be developed by spreading the fingers.

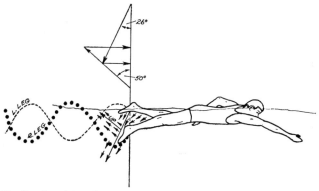

Fig. 51. The direction of the effective propelling force of the feet through the up and down movements of the legs in the crawl stroke.

There is some question about the speed of the leg kick. A two-beat stroke may be more effective than a six-beat stroke. In any case, cavitation does not occur in the flutter kick because of the alternating movement. The alternating movement of the legs produces greater power if made at the right speed to take advantage of the swirls which are set up. This is one case where swirls may be used advantageously.

The feet are the propelling agents in the leg kick. On the down stroke, the knee is bent slightly so that the top of the foot pushes back against the water. The foot must be hyper-extended so that the back of the foot may be as nearly perpendicular to the direction of movement as possible. If perpendicular, all of the force is effective force. The principle of the parallelogram of forces is involved (see page 45). Extreme flexibility in the ankle is an asset to the swimmer using the flutter kick.

On the up stroke, the sole of the foot gives the force through ankle movement. The ankle moves from a flexed position to extension.

The foot slaps at the water.   The knee is kept straight on the up stroke so that the foot may be kept nearly at right angles to the direction of movement.   Supple ankles are necessary for a successful leg kick (see Figure 51).

The foot action resembles the double fish tail action of a fish with the exception that the fish's tail moves horizontally while the swimmer's foot moves vertically.   The width of the leg stroke should be kept within the greatest cross section area of the body to cut down resistance (about 18 inches).   Cureton[4] found that leg action from the hip gave more propulsion (about 50 per cent of power of leg kick comes from the hip) and also that 48.4 per cent of the kick is useless in propulsion. He found that the upkick may be stronger as the angle of the foot is more nearly at right angles with the direction of motion (50°, whereas on the down kick the angle is only 26°).

Back Crawl

Fig. 52. Sequence in the back crawl.

The principles governing the action of the back crawl are similar to the regular crawl except that the arms move in a more nearly horizontal plane rather than a vertical plane.   The arms enter the water at an angle of approximately 45° with the body, and the effective stroke cuts through approximately 90° as in the case of the front crawl. The side movement of the arms may not be as effective as a vertical movement.   The facts, however, are not known.   If too much roll is required to attain the movement of the arms through a vertical plane, so that resistance is increased out of proportion to any gain in effective propulsive force, it would be uneconomical to use the vertical movement.

[4] Cureton. T. K.. "Mechanics and Kinesiology of Swimming," *Research Quarterly*, December, 1930.

The principles of the leg kick are exactly the same as for the front crawl except that the action is reversed (see Figure 52).

Breast Stroke

The principles of the arm action in the breast stroke are similar to those for the crawl stroke. Both arms work in unison, but they should not be brought together in front of the head. The effective stroking angle is from 45° in front to 45° behind. However, the arms should enter the water at an angle considerably less than 45°. The arms should also be fully extended to get the advantage of a long lever as in the other strokes.

In the leg kick, movements should be such as to reduce resistance to a minimum and to develop a maximum of power. To reduce friction, the thighs should be held as nearly horizontal as possible. They should not be spread at too wide an angle. The purpose of this is to keep the thighs within the body area. Also, the effective stroking angle is approximately 45°, so a wide spread would represent added resistance. The knees should be flexed extremely as the thighs are spread. This facilitates the movement in the spread of the thighs—the shorter the radius, the greater the angular velocity for the same force (see page 36). With the knees flexed they are kept within the body area to the reduction of resistance.

After the knees are extended, the ankles must be flexed so that the feet, which serve as the paddles, can be held as nearly as possible at right angles to the direction of motion. Flexibility of the knees and ankles is essential to a powerful stroke. Allen[5] found that the greatest power was developed from the stroke when the knees and ankles were flexible and not held immobile. The frog kick in the breast stroke is very powerful. Allen found that it pro-

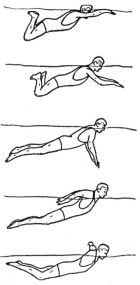

Fig. 53. Sequence in the breast stroke.

[5] Allen, H. R., "Mechanics and Kinesiology of the Frog Kick as Used in the Breast Stroke," (Master's thesis, Springfield College, 1933).

duced two or three times as much propulsive force as the flutter kick. However, this is necessary because of the greater resistance involved in the frog kick. Resistance varies according to the square of the velocity.[6]

To get continuous motion and thus more efficient investment of energy the leg and arm movements should alternate. As the arms stroke, the legs should recover. The resistance is greater when the body is accelerating. More speed has been derived from the present racing form in the breast stroke in spite of the increased resistance. Of course, it is at a much greater and less efficient expenditure of energy. Very good condition is required (see Figure 53 for arm and leg positions in breast stroke).

Reverse Breast Stroke

The principles of the reverse breast stroke are the same as the breast stroke. In the reverse breast stroke, however, the arm and leg stroke are simultaneous. This stroke is not a speed stroke, but rather a resting stroke. The cadence is quite slow with a long glide between strokes.

Side Stroke

In the side stroke, the arms should pull in vertical planes in order to direct all the force backward opposite to the direction of movement. The under arm should move directly below the body and the other arm as close to the body as possible, so that little or no force will be wasted in turning the body to one side or the other. The arms should be fully extended in order to gain the advantage of a long lever or radius of rotation. The power stroke again begins at 40° to 45° with the horizontal.

The principles of the leg kick are similar to the leg action in the crawl stroke. The legs move laterally rather than vertically and there is only one leg kick for each arm stroke. The legs do not alternate as

---

[6] Karpovich, P. V., "Water Resistance in Swimming," *Research Quarterly,* October, 1933. *See also* Tews, R. J., "The Relationship of Propulsive Force and External Resistance to Speed in Swimming," (Master's thesis, University of Iowa, 1941).

in the flutter kick but come together and each always works in the same direction. The kick is a scissors kick. The leg drawn to the rear uses the front of the foot as the propelling surface. The knee is slightly bent as in the crawl stroke. The leg which is drawn forward uses the sole of the foot as the propelling surface. The leg is extended with the ankle flexed during the stroke. All this gives the best direction to the applied force. If the swimmer is towing someone, the bottom leg should be forward to avoid interference.

In order to get continuous motion, the legs and upper arm recover while the under arm strokes.

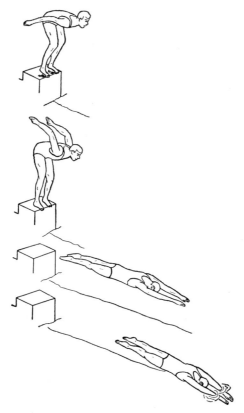

Fig. 54. Sequence of movements in the proper racing start. Note the position of the heels in the first two drawings. This permits quicker starting by throwing the center of gravity outside the base.

Starting

As in running, starting consists of upsetting the equilibrium and exerting the greatest amount of force through the longest distance. The feet are together, the toes are over the edge of the starting box and the weight is on the balls of the feet. An advantage in starting is accomplished if the swimmer rocks back on his heels at the start. This action throws the center of gravity forward outside the base and starts the body to fall by reason of the pull of gravity. Experiment shows that it gains a faster start. It permits as much as a three foot advantage in the start. This is a considerable advantage in many swimming races. Therefore, the technique is worthwhile mastering. Figure 54 shows the principle involved in this maneuver.

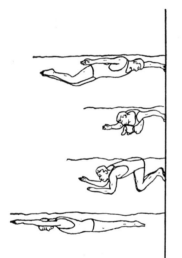

The feet are in good position for a powerful push-off. The knee bend should be in proportion to the strength of the leg muscles. The arms should be swung forcefully forward above the head to add force to the push back of the feet and to give momentum to the body. This is in accordance with Newton's third law and the principle that momentum of a part is transferred to the whole. The body should be fully extended and should leave the starting box in almost a horizontal plane. This

Fig. 55. Sequence of movement in the racing turn. Note that the head is between the arms to reduce resistance.

projects the body the greatest distance before the water is entered.

The angle of entry into the water should be as acute as possible in order to direct the force as nearly horizontal as possible. This angle will depend upon the height of the starting platforms above the surface of the water and the power of the push-off of the swimmer. Each swimmer, therefore, must determine his own angle by trial. In any case, he should avoid hitting the water with the flat surface of the body. The hands should hit the water first. The head should be kept between the arms to reduce resistance (see Figure 55).

Racing Turn

Three principles are involved in the racing turn. The body should turn through as short a radius as possible because the shorter the radius, the faster the angular velocity with the same force. The push-off should be with knees bent in proportion to the strength of the leg muscles. The push-off drive would seldom, if ever, therefore, start with the hips against the pool. The knee bend would rarely be greater than a right angle. The push-off should be in a horizontal direction in order that the force may be made most effective. The head should be between the arms to reduce resistance and add to the distance of the push-off (see Figure 55).

QUESTIONS AND TOPICS FOR REVIEW AND DISCUSSION

1. Why is resistance in swimming such an important factor?
2. What are the factors which create resistance in swimming? Which is the most important?
3. Which creates greater resistance—the glide on the back or on the front?
4. Why is so much resistance created in the execution of the breast stroke?
5. What is the relationship of acceleration to resistance? What are the implications of this relationship?
6. What is the relationship of the cross sectional area of the body to resistance? What are the implications of this relationship?
7. What per cent of force in swimming is derived from the arms? The legs?
8. What specifically should the swimmer do to reduce resistance in the crawl stroke?
9. What is the pulling stroke for the arms? Why?
10. Should the fingers be held together or spread during the stroke?
11. Is it possible to develop cavitation in the flutter kick? Why?
12. Which is more efficient, the up kick or down kick of the legs? Why?
13. What should control the length of the leg kick?
14. At what point should the arms enter the water in breast stroke? Why?
15. What factors govern the spread of the legs in the breast stroke?
16. What is the difference between the action in the breast and the reverse breast strokes?

17. What is the advantage of dropping the heels as the push-off starts in the racing start? Explain the principle involved.

18. What determines the angle of entry into the water?

19. Why keep the head between the arms when entering the water?

20. Explain the principles employed in the racing turn.

PROBLEMS

(Answers to problems are given in Appendix D, page 295.)

1. What is the water resistance of a swimmer who swims 100 yards in 50 seconds? For this swimmer $K = .65$.

2. The angle of the down kick of a swimmer in the crawl stroke is 26° with the horizontal. The angle of the up kick is 50°. Assuming that the force of the kick in each direction is the same and is exerted through the same distance, which kick produces more propulsion? How much?

3. One swimmer begins his arm stroke in the crawl when his arm is at an angle of 45° with the horizontal and finishes at an angle of 45°. His hand exerts a force of 10 pounds through the stroke. The distance from his shoulder to the center of application of his force is 24 inches. How much work is done in each arm stroke?

4. Another swimmer begins his stroke at an angle of 30° and finishes at an angle of 45°. He exerts the same force as the swimmers in problem (3) but his power arm is only 20 inches long. Which swimmer does the more work with each arm stroke and how much?

5. A swimmer in the breast stroke exerts a force of 12 pounds with each arm through his stroke of 30 inches. He weighs 160 pounds. What is the kinetic energy expended? How fast is the swimmer moving?

12.

Analysis of

Diving Techniques

Certain principles are fundamental to most all dives. These principles will be discussed and related to specific dives and specific situations where they apply. Many of these principles were determined by Lanoue[1] in his study of the mechanics of diving. Groves[2] studied the jackknife, back, and forward one-and-one-half dives and discovered these same principles.

1. *The height to which the diver rises in the air is governed by the amount the spring board is depressed and the angle of take-off.* The amount by which the board is depressed depends upon the amount of force which the diver is able to bring to bear on the board in a vertical direction. Force is equal to mass times acceleration. The mass is constant for each diver so that the only opportunity to increase the force is to increase acceleration. This can be accomplished only by a higher spring on the approach. The higher the spring the greater will be the speed when the diver hits the board. Consequently, everything depends upon the ability of the diver to get height on his

---

[1] Lanoue, F. R., "Mechanics of Fancy Diving," (Master's thesis, Springfield College, 1936).

[2] Groves, William H., "Mechanical Analysis of Diving," *Research Quarterly,* May, 1950, page 132.

approach spring. This height may be increased by a sharp swing up of the arms as the diver springs. This arm movement gives momentum to the body and increases the push against the board to produce a greater reaction in the upward movement, giving more height. A knee bend (equal to the strength of the leg muscles) will increase the push back against the board on the spring.

When the diver lands on the board to depress it, he should also have his knees bent and his arms ready for the sharp swing upward as on the approach spring. As the diver leaves the board his legs must be extended and his body rigid so as to produce the maximum reaction upward (Newton's third law—see page 9). Unless this last principle is followed, the advantage of the height attained on the approach will be lost.

The diver should hit the board near its end in order to take advantage of as long a lever as possible. This aids in the attainment of the desired height. The standard diving board is adjustable as to length. The diver should test the board in order to get the right length of lever for his needs.

If there were no lean then the diver could get his maximum height, but if there were no lean the diver would return to the board. Consequently, there must be some lean on all dives. The greater the lean, the less the height of the dive.

2. *The amount of lean depends on the amount of turn that is desired.* This fact must be recognized in judging dives where distance from the board when entering the water is one of the points on which a dive is judged. One cannot go straight up and expect to turn. Even in dives such as the swan and jackknife which have a minimum of turning, there must be some lean. Lanoue[3] found that the flight of the dive which is a parabola is dependent upon the angle of take-off (lean). The lean increases somewhat with the amount of turning which is desired and, of course, for safety in clearing the board. Lafler[4] found that the amount of lean varied with the amount of turning. For example, he found the greatest amount of lean in the two-and-one-half somersault. Here the lean from the vertical was 27°. In contrast, the angle of take-off in the jackknife dive was only about

---

[3] Lanoue, F. R., "Mechanics of Fancy Diving," (Master's thesis, Springfield College, 1936).

[4] Lafler, Josephine, "Mechanical Analysis of Diving Techniques," (Master's thesis, University of Iowa, 1943).

half as much. It was 14°. Figure 56 shows the lean for divers as indicated. These were taken from films of the actual dives. It will be noticed that the center of gravity is ahead of the feet in each case. The distance of the center of gravity ahead of the feet determines the turning moment (see page 53).

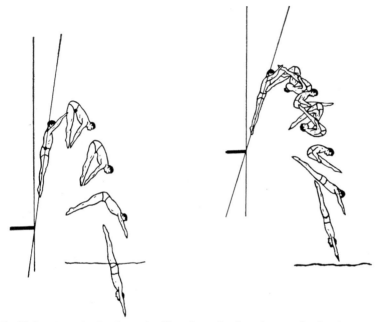

Fig. 56. Two dives, showing the angle of lean for each. (Lean is proportional to the amount of turning desired.)

3. *All turns start as the diver leaves the board.* This is another way of saying that the path of the center of gravity cannot be changed after the feet leave the board. Throwing the feet back as they leave the board will give more turn. In order to throw the feet back with force, the feet must push forward on the board with an equal force (Newton's third law).

4. *All twister dives start their turn before the diver leaves the board.* Arm movements may be used after the feet leave the board to create twist. In these cases the movement of the arms in one direction about the long axis of the body will cause rotation of the body in the opposite direction. By the application of this principle the diver is able to

make complicated combination movements in his dives. For example, he can make a somersault of different types with a half twist by the use of the arm movement following the somersault.

The diver should remember that when twisting movements are employed in a dive, the turning speed is increased. Consequently, he must adjust for this increased speed of rotation in order to prevent his body from turning too far. He does this, of course, by lengthening his radius of rotation (see page 36).

5. *The speed of turning is controlled by the length of the radius of rotation about the center of gravity.* For example, the body will turn the slowest when the body is in a lay-out position. The radius of rotation is the greatest in this position. It will turn the fastest when the body is in the tuck position. The speed of rotation will be medium when the body is in the pike position (see page 36). In the case of the twister dive, the arms act as the radii. Extended, they create the longest radius. As they are drawn toward the body, the radius is shortened and rotation speeds up. In somersault dives, the timing of the turns is controlled by the application of these principles so that the diver may enter the water at as nearly a vertical angle as possible. If the diver finds that his turn will be completed too soon, he straightens out. If his turn is too slow, he tucks his body to speed up his turn. Also, by the application of these principles, he is able to put together combinations of movements.

6. *The jackknife dive applies the principle that governs the movement of the ends and the middle* (see page 19). After the diver leaves the board and as he reaches the height of his spring, he bends to bring his head toward his feet. As he does this, the hips move up. Then, he extends his body, the feet move up and the hips move down.

A thorough understanding of these principles by the beginning diver would do much to speed up and perfect his development. Many of these points are not only misunderstood but are doubted by divers. A careful analysis of moving pictures of dives will clearly demonstrate their validity.

Questions and Topics for Discussion and Review

1. "The height of the hurdle is related to the height of the dive." What is the principle involved which makes this statement true? What condition is it dependent upon?

2. If the diver does not lean, what will be the result of the dive?

3. What determines the amount of lean in a dive? Why is this true?

4. What is meant by turning moment?

5. When do turns start in a dive? Why?

6. What is the principle which creates twister movements after the body is free from support in the air?

7. What effect do twister movements have upon turning?

8. What controls the speed of turning after the diver leaves the board? What is the principle involved?

9. What is the relationship of twister movements to arm movements?

10. What principle controls the movements in the jackknife dive?

PROBLEMS

(Answers to problems are given in Appendix D, page 296.)

1. The arms of a diver weigh 25 pounds. As the diver poises to spring, he swings his arms upward with a velocity of 60 feet per second. What velocity does this give to the diver who weighs 165 pounds? How high will this cause the body to rise if all effort is in a vertical direction?

2. A diver leaves the board at an angle of 15° with the vertical and with a speed of 20 ft/sec. How high will he rise?

3. The distance of the center of gravity from the feet of a diver is 36 inches. He leans 20° in his take-off. What is his turning moment if the diver weighs 160 pounds?

4. If a diver leaves the board with a lean of 25° from the vertical, raises to a height of 5 feet, how far will he be from the end of the board when his center of gravity returns to the same level at which it left the board?

5. A diver is in a lay-out position so that his radius of rotation is 3 feet. He is turning at the rate of 2 revolutions per second. Now, if he takes a tuck position with a radius of rotation equal to 15 inches, what will be his rate of rotation?

13.

Analysis of
Gymnastic Activities

Gymnastic activities are so numerous that it will not be possible to analyze each. A selected group which is representative is chosen to show the application of the principles involved. From these the reader will be able to analyze similar activities. The successful execution of gymnastic activities more than any other sport, except diving, depends entirely upon following absolutely the principles of dynamics. A thorough understanding of these principles and their application on the part of the coach will make his teaching more meaningful to the student.

Three factors are primary to the successful execution of any gymnastic activity.

1. *Strength in the arms and shoulders above that of the average individual is necessary.* Even though one mastered the principles involved, he would not be able to execute them without sufficient strength. For example, to execute the upstart—in addition to shortening the radius of rotation of the body, bringing the center of gravity to the center of rotation, and swinging the legs at the proper moment— requires considerable strength to hold the body close to the bar as the legs swing down and the body rotates about the bar.

2. *The center of gravity must always be controlled.* Either it must

be kept within the base where equilibrium is involved (see page 16), it must be brought close to the center of rotation when it is desired to neutralize the turning movement of the body (see page 53) or it must be extended from the point of support or center of rotation when greater turning force is needed (see page 54).

3. *Exact timing for the starting of each movement is absolutely necessary.* Waiting too long or starting too soon at any one point in the execution of a stunt means failure for the whole performance. For example, in swinging exercises if a movement is started before the body reaches the end of its swing not only will it be practically impossible to carry out the movement, it may not be possible for the performer to hold to his support.

Balancing Activities

The essential feature in balancing activities is to keep the center of gravity within the base or directly over the center point of support. When this is done, there is no moment of force for turning the body. The base should be made as wide as possible to increase the stability of the body. This can be done by spreading the hands in the case of the hand stand. In the head stand, the hands should be placed as

Fig. 57 (*left*). Mechanics of the head stand. Note the wide base and the compensating bend in the body to maintain the center of gravity within the base. Fig. 58 (*right*). Balancing on one hand. The fingers must be spread as much as possible to increase the area of the base.

far as possible in front of the face (see Figure 57). Spreading the fingers also gives a better base for each hand. Where the body is balanced over one hand, spreading the fingers is the only means of widening the base (see Figure 58).

If one is making a hand stand on a bar, the hands may be spread apart, but the strength of the grip substitutes for the fact that the hands and fingers cannot be placed flat or the fingers spread.

In order to keep the center of gravity over the center of the base one must make compensating movements to effect any unbalancing moves. For example, if the feet move back, the body may be arched to throw a compensating weight in the opposite direction or the head and shoulders may be moved by bending the elbows. If one walks on the hands or turns about, the weight must be shifted to the hand which is in contact with the support as the other hand is lifted so that the center of gravity is over this hand.

The art in performing balancing techniques is in being sensitive to the position of the center of gravity and being able to make quick, fine adjustments to maintain the balance. This art becomes even more refined if one is balancing on a swinging support such as a trapeze or flying rings.

Swinging Activities

In swinging activities the principles of angular rotation, centrifugal force, and the moment of force are the main factors. Whether one swings from a high bar, parallel bars, or flying rings, the principles are the same.

 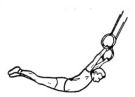

Fig. 59 (left). To gain height on the upswing the radius must be shortened by bringing the center of gravity close to the center of rotation. Fig. 60 (right). To gain momentum on the down swing, the body is extended as far as possible from the center of rotation. The principle here is the opposite of that shown in Figure 59.

1. To gain height on the upswing, the radius of rotation should be shortened (see page 36). To do this, the body is pulled toward the point of support as the body passes a point directly below the point of support. The elbows are bent, the knees and thighs are flexed. Thus, the center of gravity is brought nearer to the center of rotation (see Figure 59).

2. To gain momentum on the down swing, the radius of rotation should be lengthened (see page 54). To do this, the body should be fully extended at the height of the swing by shooting the legs up-

ward and outward from the point of support. This throws the center of gravity the farthest possible distance from the center of rotation. Then, the body should be held rigid and permitted to fall freely. These movements should be repeated until the desired arc of swing is attained (Figure 60).

To perform the giant swing on the high bar, one continues to swing until enough momentum is built up to carry the body directly above the bar where it is fully extended. The down swing is performed as before. The only means of shortening the radius on the upswing is to extend the neck, flex the wrists and pull the body up as far as possible without flexing the elbows, thighs or knees. This is done by arching the back and drawing the shoulders toward the bar. If a full free down swing has been attained, these maneuvers coupled with the sharp pull-up when the center of gravity is directly below the point of support will produce sufficient shortening to overcome the downward pull of gravity and to swing the body to a vertical position above the bar. Figure 61 shows the various stages in the giant swing.

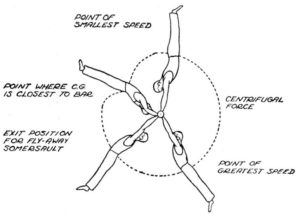

Fig. 61. Various stages in the giant swing. The art of shortening and lengthening the radius of rotation is clearly shown.

3. In all types of mounting exercises which involve swinging or angular motion, the center of gravity should be brought as near as possible to the center of support or rotation at the critical moment (see page 70). The critical moment varies with the exercise. This action eliminates the centrifugal force or the tendency for the body to fly off on a tangent. For dismounting, the opposite tactics are prac-

ticed plus the use of Newton's third law.   Several examples are given
below to demonstrate this principle.

(a) To do a *hip swing up,* one merely uses the upswing and does
not need much momentum.   The action is largely a pulling action directed toward the supporting hands.   The thighs are flexed so that
the feet are shot in a vertical direction with the thighs close to the bar.
At the end of the upswing, the center of gravity is held against the
bar and above it.   The legs continue around the bar until equilibrium
is attained.   Figure 62 demonstrates the various stages of the hip
swing up.

Fig. 62. The hip swing up is accomplished by holding the body close to the bar and pushing
the feet vertically above it.   Effort is at a minimum by elimination of a moment arm.

(b) The *front uprise* or upstart is executed on the down swing.
The center of gravity is brought against the bar from below at the end
of the upswing.   On the upswing, the thighs should be brought up
along the bar.   At the end of the upswing, the legs are extended out
and down.   Before this action starts the center of gravity must be
held against the bar to eliminate a moment of force.   This is the critical moment in this exercise.   Considerable strength is required to
hold the body against the bar from below until the upper half can
rotate above the bar.   Consequently, the front uprise becomes a more
difficult maneuver than the back uprise, where the body is brought to
the bar from above.   Figure 63 illustrates the various stages of the
uprise.

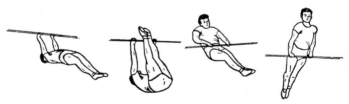

Fig. 63. The front uprise.   Note that the body is held against the bar to eliminate as much
moment arm as possible.

(c) To *circle from the front uprise,* the bar must be kept against the body at the center of gravity. The trunk and head must be pulled across the top of the bar. As the head starts down, the neck should be extended and the shoulders raised to increase the radius of rotation on the down swing. As the legs go around, the head is thrown back and the shoulders draw back to shorten the radius on the upswing. The legs should be swung down sharply. Figure 64 shows the various stages of the circle from a front uprise.

Fig. 64. Execution of a circle from a front uprise.

(d) For a *front drop off,* the bar should be held against the thighs and the body rolled forward. The moment of force which is equal to the horizontal distance from the center of rotation to the center of gravity times the mass of the body will give the body sufficient angular momentum to carry the body around (see Figure 65).

Fig. 65. Sequence of movement in the front drop off.

(e) For a *back drop off,* the back should be arched to hold the body to the bar and to start a backward circle. The foot is swung to give angular momentum. After the body leaves the bar, a tuck will increase the angular rotation so the landing will be on the feet. The tuck should not be begun before the body leaves the bar or rotation will go too far. Figure 66 illustrates the back drop off.

Fig. 66. The back drop off.

(f) The *dismount* from hanging by the knees consists of the application of the principle of Newton's third law. If the legs are extended sharply as the body hangs, the reaction of the thighs against the bar will give sufficient angular momentum to the body so the performer will land on his feet. The same principle is followed for a dismount from a sitting position on the bar. In this case, when the body drops back to a horizontal position, a sharp extension of the legs gives a similar reaction against the bar and turns the body to land in a standing position. Figure 67 shows the stages in the dismount from hanging by the knees.

4. In exercises on the flying rings the essential movement in the exercise is usually made at one end or the other of the swing. At these

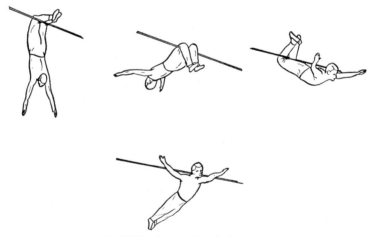

Fig. 67. The dismount from the knee hang.

points, the center of gravity is momentarily neutralized. The momentum of the upswing has spent itself and the force of gravity has not yet started the downward movement. The body is held suspended in the air. There is no centrifugal force. As a result, all effort can be devoted to the exercises. If the essential movements take place during the swing, the body may not be strong enough to withstand the centrifugal force, the force of gravity and the force required for the exercise. As a result, the exercise is a failure, the performer may lose his grip, be thrown violently to the floor, and suffer serious injury.

The front uprise on the rings is performed at the end of the upswing. The feet are swung high above the head. The hands are spread so that rotation is about the shoulders. As the body reaches the end of the swing, the hands are brought to the hips and the body pushed up between the rings so that the arms are fully extended. Figure 68 shows the front uprise on the flying rings.

Fig. 68. The front uprise on the flying rings.

If a circle is made, the body is held with the center of gravity at the point of support. The rings and hands are held tight against the hips.

Dismounts and cutaways are all performed right at the end of the swing. To try to perform them at any other point, the body would be thrown by the effect of centrifugal force. Figure 69 shows the cutaway from the flying rings.

Fig. 69. The cutaway from the flying rings.

Activities on the Parallel Bars and Horse

Exercises on the parallel bars which are performed with a swing involve exactly the same principles as covered in the preceding discussion.   In these exercises also, the center of gravity must be kept over the point of support.   For example, in performing a cutaway or cutoff, the center of gravity is kept over the point of support.   This eliminates a moment of force (see page 53).   The cut-off is made at the top of the swing where centrifugal force is eliminated.

In the uprise as the upswing reaches its highest point, the arms pull to bring the center of gravity over the point of support.

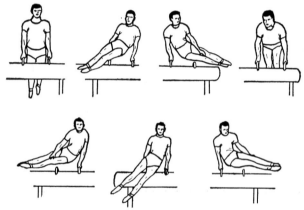

Fig. 70. Rotary exercise on the horse.   Note that the center of gravity is always over the point of support.

In rotary exercises on the parallel bars or the horse, where the support is shifted from first one hand to the other, the center of gravity is always kept over the center of support.   This is accomplished by throwing the shoulders back when the feet are forward, or vice versa, and by throwing the shoulders to the left when the feet are to the right and vice versa.   The center of gravity must always be moved first in the direction of the desired movement.   In exercises of this kind, the shift of the point of support is always made when the body is at the top of its swing.   Figure 70 shows a rotary exercise on the horse.

In the execution of vaulting exercises, similar principles are employed.

Tumbling Activities

Tumbling activities apply a variety of principles. Heidloff[1] emphasizes ten principles. Typical activities will be analyzed to demonstrate most of these principles.

Drop to Back Roll. The performer is standing erect at the start. The knees are held stiff. Then, the body bends at the waist and the body is permitted to fall backward, equilibrium being destroyed. Just before the seat hits, the body is straightened. This action relieves the force of the fall by producing a rolling movement. Force is traded for distance, and straightening the body throws the center of gravity back of the seat or outside the base. This maneuver upsets the equilibrium and gives momentum for the roll. The moment of force is equal to the mass times the moment arm, which is the horizontal distance that the center of gravity is beyond the axis of rotation—in this case, the seat. The legs are drawn to the chest, an act which shortens the radius of rotation and speeds up the roll. The hands are placed down as

Fig. 71. Sequence in the drop to back roll, showing the mechanical principles involved.

the body rolls and are used as the new point of support and center of rotation. The hands push against the mat after the center of gravity passes the point of support and the reaction from this push turns and lifts the body to standing position (Newton's third law). Figure 71 illustrates the stages in the drop to a back roll.

If a head stand is to be made at the end of the roll, the body is extended. This action slows the turn. Equilibrium is a function of the width of the base. The hands are placed as far back of the head as possible to give a wide base and to be ahead of the center of gravity to stop the roll. The feet are extended above the base. Another condition of equilibrium is to keep the center of gravity within the base.

---

[1] Heidloff, R. E., "Logical Application of Physics to Selected Tumbling Stunts," (Master's thesis, Springfield College, 1938).

The Snap Up or Neck Spring.　The snap up is accomplished by the application of the principle that the momentum of a part imparts momentum to the whole (see page 68). The legs whip forward. This motion brings the hips up and then the head (pressure from the hands aids in the movement). The knees are flexed so that the body lands on its feet. The center of gravity is behind the point of support, therefore, the moment of force tends to pull the body backward. If there is not sufficient forward momentum to overcome the backward moment of force, the knees are flexed and the body bent at the waist to shorten the moment arm. The arms are swung forward to increase the forward momentum and the center of gravity slides down the line of motion (see Figure 72).

Fig. 72. Sequence in the neck spring.

The snap up on the parallel bar, while not a mat activity, is a perfect example of the application of the transfer of the momentum from the part to the whole. The movement starts with the shoulders and back on the bars. The legs are flexed on the abdomen. The legs start their movement from above the hands and kick back and slightly up. As the legs are extended, the shoulders are forced up (see page 68). The body is pulled to a vertical position by the hands on the bars. As the legs extend the knees must not flex again. This would produce angular motion and the body would not be lifted, but would only rotate about the hands.

The Handspring.　In the handspring the swing up of the back leg gives momentum to the body for the turn. The knees are flexed, thus shortening the radius of rotation and speeding up the turn (see page 36). As the center of gravity passes the vertical position, the hands push against the mat. The reaction is to raise the center of gravity and give more force to the turn (Newton's third law). As the feet hit, the body follows the same line of motion as in the snap up. If the turning momentum has been too great, a front roll may be taken to avoid falling forward on the face—in other words, the principle of rolling with the force or trading force for distance is employed (see Figure 73).

Fig. 73. Stages in the execution of the handspring.

Dual Activities

Dual activities for the most part apply the principles of equilibrium, levers, and moments of force and rotation.

Fig. 74. Balancing in dual activities.   Note that the lean of one gymnast is offset by the lean in the opposite direction of the other to keep the center of gravity over the base.

A.   B.

Fig. 75. Turning exercises.   Note that the turning force is applied at right angles to the limb and near its end.   These actions give greater turning moment and require less effort.   The leg must be held rigid.

Fig. 76A. Principles in lifting exercises.   Above, a weak position; the lifter is too far from the weight, and too much lifting is required by the back muscles.

1. *Balancing or pyramid exercises.*   In balancing or pyramid exercises the weight must always be distributed so that the center of gravity falls within the base.   For example, as one performer stands on the thighs of the other and is held by the legs or hands as he leans away, the other must lean in the opposite direction to establish equilibrium (see Figure 74).

2. *Turning exercises.*   In turning exercises where a limb is used as a lever, the amount of force is proportional to the length of the lever. For example, if the leg is extended horizontally from the hip, less force will be needed than if the performer stands in the hand of the turner with the thigh at right angles to the foreleg or with the leg extended more or less vertically.   In each case, in order to impart a maximum of force, the limb must be held rigid so that there will be a minimum of

Fig. 76B. (Above), a strong position for lifting excercises, with the moment arm reduced to a minimum. Most of the lifting is done by strong leg muscles, because of the crouch and rigid back.

recoil. The force should be directed at right angles to the limb in order to be most effective (see Figure 75).

3. *Lifting exercises.* Where heavy lifting is required, the point of support should get as nearly as possible over or under the center of weight. This eliminates the moment of force and reduces the effort necessary to raise the body. The force in lifting can be largely borne by the legs if the knees are bent and the back held erect. The greatest force is required to start the object in motion (Newton's first law.) Once the object is put in motion, there should be no stopping until the

desired height is attained (see page 67). Figures 76A and 76B illustrate the principles in lifing exercises.

No matter what the exercises, these are the usual principles which
are involved in dual activities.

Trampoline Exercises

Trampoline activities are very similar to diving activities and to
some mat exercises. Thus the trampoline affords a sensitive means
of validating the principles which were applied to diving. In particular, these principles which determine the height attained from
springing, the effect of lean, the path of the center of gravity, twister
movements, and Newton's third law may be readily observed.

The height and effect of lean are easily checked in the simple exercise of "working" the bed of the trampoline. The control of the
body in this exercise is necessary before others can be executed successfully. The effect of the crouch before the spring, the sharp swing
up of the arms to produce more push back against the bed—which in
turn produces more reaction upward—can be readily checked through
the observation of repeated springs from the bed of the trampoline.
Likewise, the added force gained each time when the body drops from
a greater height and the comparative reaction when the body is held
rigid as the bed springs back from the depth of its depression can be
observed. All these factors, of course, demonstrate Newton's third
law, of action and reaction.

The slightest lean is reflected in the movement of the body to a
spot forward, backward, or to the side of the spot from which the feet
left the bed of the trampoline. Leaning the head forward so that the
center of gravity is thrown forward very slightly will effect this change.
A slight push back by the toes as the body leaves the bed so that the
direction of force is slightly forward will move the body forward. One
can readily get the "feel" of this reaction as he "works" the bed. One
must keep the center of gravity directly over the base and must direct
it absolutely vertically in order to return to the same spot on the bed
from which he sprang. In other words, a slight lean in any direction
causes the body to travel in that direction. The principle that all essential movements start as the body leaves its point of support can be
readily observed in trampolining (see page 88).

The trampoline is so sensitive in comparison to the springboard that it is a very satisfactory laboratory for testing many of the principles which govern gymnastic activities. The fact that an activity (such as springing, for example) may be repeated indefinitely adds to the value of the trampoline in this respect.

Drops. The various drops require a vertical rise of the center of gravity. Lean will start a turning movement. The spring from the drop position must likewise direct the center of gravity vertically or a turning movement will be started.

(a) *Seat Drop.* For the seat drop, the legs are flexed at the hips to a right angle position with the trunk. The trunk is vertical. The center of gravity should be directly over the spot where the feet left the bed. To recover, if bounce is not high enough for the legs to remain straightened, they should be flexed to get them under the body (see Figure 77).

Fig. 77. The seat drop on the trampoline. The secret is to keep the center of gravity directly over the spot from which the feet sprang from the bed.

(b) *Back Drop.* For the back drop, the legs are extended upward at right angles to the trunk. A 90° rotation of the trunk is effected. The back hits flat with the center of gravity hitting over the spot where the feet left the bed. If the legs were tucked, too much rotation would occur from the shortened radius. The recovery to the feet is effected by tucking the legs to speed the rotation. When the body reaches the top of the spring on the recovery, the legs are straightened to stop the rotation (see Figure 78).

(c) *Front Drop.* For the front drop particular care must be exercised to avoid leaning forward. This would cause a dive forward. The center of gravity must be directed vertically so that the center of

gravity when the body hits the mat will be over the point where the feet left the bed. The body is horizontal when it hits the bed. Tucking the legs on the return to the upright position speeds rotation (see figure 79).

The essential movements in each of the drops start as the body leaves the bed. The trampoliner may move from one drop to another. He may reverse or partially reverse his position on the bed. The essential movements for these new positions must begin before the body leaves the bed and are made in

Fig. 78. The back drop on the trampoline. The center of gravity is kept over the take-off spot. Rotation is through 90 degrees with the legs at right angle to the body.

the direction of the desired move.

Somersaults. For somersaults there must be a lean forward or back to get the center of gravity ahead of or behind the feet in order to produce a moment of force. For the front somersault the feet push forward as they leave the bed to get the backward reaction for the turn. They push backward for the back somersault to get the forward reaction for the turn.

If the body is tucked, the turn will be faster and the spring from the bed need not be as high as when the body turns from a layout position where the rotation is slowest. The effect of all of these factors can be readily observed on the trampoline. Figure 80 shows a back somersault from a layout position. In like manner, twists and gyroscopic

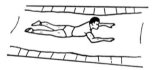

Fig. 79. Front drop on the trampoline. Holding the center of gravity in a vertical line is essential in all "drop" exercises.

Fig. 80. The back somersault on the trampoline.

movements can be demonstrated. The principles are the same as for diving.

Questions and Topics for Discussion and Review

1. In general, what three factors are necessary for the successful execution of gymnastic activities?

2. Why is it so necessary to execute gymnastic activities exactly in accordance with mechanical principles in order to perform successfully?

3. What is the essential feature in balancing activities? Why?

4. What are the main principles involved in swinging activities?

5. How can one utilize the principles of angular rotation to effect a complete circle in swinging activities?

6. What problem arises if the center of gravity is not brought over the center of support in mounting exercises?

7. What is meant by the critical moment in the execution of various exercises? Illustrate.

8. How is Newton's third law applicable in the dismount from a bar when hanging by the knees?

9. Why is the essential movement in exercises on the flying rings performed at the end of the swing? Would this point in the activity be considered the critical moment?

10. What difference is there in swinging and rotary activities on the parallel bars and the horse from other swinging activities?

11. Enumerate the principles involved in executing the hand spring.

12. Where is the critical moment in the hand spring?

13. Where is the critical moment in the snap-up on the parallel bars?

14. How may Newton's second law be illustrated on the trampoline?

15. How may Newton's third law be illustrated on the trampoline?

16. Why is it necessary for the limb which is being used as the lever to be held rigid in dual turning exercises?

17. Why is less force needed for turning in dual exercises if the leg which is used as the moment arm is fully extended horizontally from the hip than if the thigh is a right angle to the foreleg?

18. What is the essential feature to emphasize in lifting heavy weights? Why?

19. How is it possible to lift largely with the legs instead of the back?

20. What main principles are involved in dual activities?

Problems

(Answers to problems are given in Appendix D, page 296.)

1. The center of gravity of a gymnast on the flying ring at the top of his swing is 10 feet above the position at the bottom of the swing. The radius of rotation is 20 feet. The gymnast weighs 160 pounds. What is his centrifugal force at the bottom of his swing?

2. As a gymnast's feet hit the mat in turning a hand spring, the line from his center of gravity to his feet makes an angle of 30° with the floor. He

weighs 150 pounds. The distance between his feet and his center of gravity is 36 inches. His linear speed as a result of the hand spring is 20 ft/sec. Assuming that he maintains a lay-out position and that there are no other factors to aid him in gaining his balance than the force of his spring, will he fall back or gain his feet? At what angle must he light to exactly counterbalance the force of his turn?

3. A gymnast weighing 192 pounds is doing the giant swing. His center of gravity is 4 feet from the bar. What is his centrifugal force at the bottom of his swing?

4. Another gymnast weighing 175 pounds whose center of gravity is $3\frac{1}{2}$ feet from the bar is also doing the giant swing. Which develops the greater centrifugal force, this gymnast or the one in problem (3)?

5. The radius of rotation of a tumbler in a lay-out position is $2\frac{1}{2}$ feet. In the tuck position it is $1\frac{1}{2}$ feet. His speed of rotation is 2 turns/sec from the lay-out position. If he springs 6 feet into the air from the bed of the trampoline will he be able to complete a somersault from the lay-out position? How many could he make from the tuck position?

6. In dual gymnastics a somersault is executed by means of exerting a turning moment on the outstretched leg which is 3 feet long. If the turn is made with the turning lever only 20 inches long, what is the amount of force needed compared to the first method? It is assumed that all other factors are the same.

7. One gymnast is standing on the thighs of another. The top man weighs 160 pounds and his center of gravity is 2 feet outside the point of support of the bottom man who weighs 200 pounds. How far must the center of gravity of the 200-pound man be from his point of support in the opposite direction to maintain equilibrium?

14.

Analysis of
Basketball Techniques

While there are many theories about basketball and many techniques practiced, the principles of dynamics which govern the actions of the body are invariable. Therefore, whatever the theory may be, it should be in harmony with these principles.

Foot Work

Quick starting and stopping, change of direction, feinting, maneuvering, and change of pace form the basis of successful basketball. These tactics are all problems in the control of the center of gravity and application of force. The analysis is not unlike many aspects of the presentation of the tactics of the ball carrier in the chapter on football (see page 170). At least the objective is the same—to out-maneuver an opponent.

For quick starting the foot position should be such that push may be exerted most effectively by both feet. The sprinter's start position cannot be taken because action is required in all directions. But the feet should not be too widely spread. It is better to have one foot slightly ahead of the other. Thus, no matter which way the player turns he has an assimilated track position, which study has demonstrated gives the fastest start. The base need not be wide nor does the center of gravity need to be low (starting is faster with the center of gravity unstable) as in the football stance, since the contact and charging feature is absent. The position, however, must not deviate too widely from the stopping position or too much valuable time will be lost in recovery. Some adjustment is, however, possible in the recoil from the stop.

Quick stopping, on the other hand, requires a low position for the center of gravity to reduce or eliminate the turning moment forward. It requires that one foot be placed ahead of the center of gravity for the same reason. A scoot or low hop with the bend of the knees (which drops the center of gravity) provides better body control and places the player in a position to start off in another direction by push-

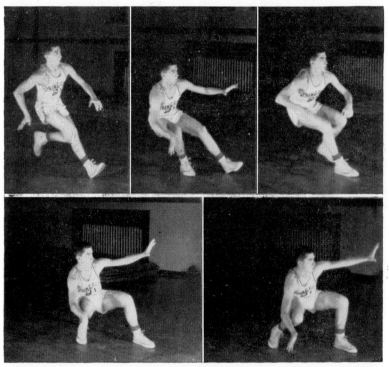

Fig. 81. Sequence in the execution of a stop after rapid motion. Notice that by knee and body bend the center of gravity drops. The center of gravity is also thrown to the rear as far as possible by the action of sitting on the heel.

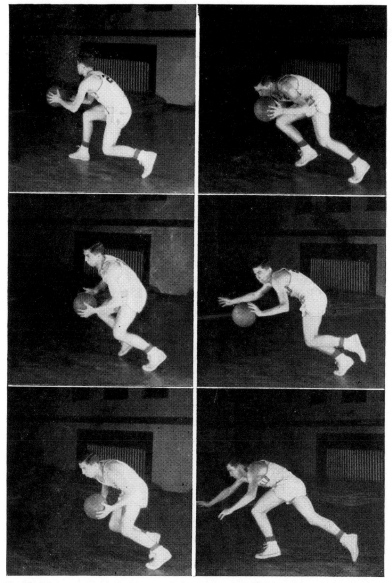

Fig. 82. Feinting movements before a dribble. The secret of deception and fast starting is to throw the center of gravity forward as the player steps back.

ing from both feet, which is faster. The speed with which a player is moving may require a very low stop from which a recoil is necessary for quick starting. The low crouch in stopping also relieves the force on the feet because here force is traded for distance. If there were no give in the knees and at the hips, the feet would be subjected to a terrific pounding. Figure 81 shows the stages in the execution of the stop.

Feinting, which consists of head, body, arm and/or foot moves, is designed to deceive an opponent and cause him to act to his disadvantage. These are not likely to be effective if the center of gravity is thrown outside the base or too near the edge of the base in the direction of the feint. The time required to recover equilibrium and start in another direction will offset the advantage otherwise gained by the feint. Therefore, there must always be a compensating move which maintains equilibrium. For example, if a player who has the ball steps back with the hope, as the result of a previous maneuver, of causing his opponent to move toward him to attack the ball so that he, the player with the ball, may dribble by, he must compensate for this move. This is done by bending forward at the waist as the foot drops back. In this way, the center of gravity is kept toward the forward edge of his base and permits him to move in that direction more quickly (see Figure 82).

A head and shoulder feint in one direction is compensated for by a dip of the opposite knee. This permits a quick push in the opposite direction of the feint. The center of gravity, by reason of the dip of the knee, is prevented from moving in the direction of the feint. One compensates for a thrust at the ball, a step by one foot, and an arm reach by a bend of the opposite knee, which prevents the center of gravity from moving forward. If, as a result of this maneuver, it is necessary for the defensive player to turn and move in the opposite direction from that of his thrust, he should throw his center of gravity outside his base and directly backward by a deep knee bend of the back leg as the forward leg pushes in that direction. A good illustration of the position of the center of gravity in this maneuver is shown in Figure 83.

Change of pace consists of an alternation of slowing down and speeding up. To slow down, one foot is put down ahead of the center of gravity and the body straightens, but the knees may bend slightly.

Fig. 83. Reversing direction of movement after a thrust forward. Time is saved by starting the body backward by throwing the center of gravity outside the base before the step is taken.

To speed up, the body is inclined forward, the center of gravity is thrown ahead of the forward foot, and the legs extend as they push off for speed.

If the change of pace is indulged in by the dribbler, the speed of advance of the ball is controlled by the angle at which the ball is pushed to the floor. For speed, the angle of the line of movement of the ball with the floor is reduced. To slow up, the angle of the line of the ball with the floor is more nearly a right angle.

Jumping

Several principles govern the jump. In the first place, a player will jump higher if he steps or hops before he takes off. Such a maneuver overcomes the inertia of the body and starts it in motion (Newton's first law). It also permits him to push off of the floor with greater force which in turn will give greater height (Newton's third law). The stamp of the foot by means of the hop before the jump not only increases the force of reaction between the foot and the floor but the stamp stretches the muscles of the foot. This gives a more forceful elastic rebound. A muscle will contract faster and with greater force immediately after being stretched (see page 90 and Cureton, T. K., "Mechanics of the High Jump," *Scholastic Coach*, April, 1935).

By the same token a slight crouch of the knee and hip permits a more forceful action of the muscles which control these joints. The amount of the crouch will depend upon the strength of the muscles. Boys with weak leg muscles should not take as deep a crouch as those with strong leg muscles.

At the take-off, the arms should swing up hard to give momentum to the jump. If the take-off is from one foot, the thigh of the free leg should swing up hard for the same reason. Just before the maximum height is reached, the leg should be extended downward sharply. The arm not used in reaching or tipping should be swung down in the same manner. This raises the position of the center of gravity in the body and thus gives more reach to the tipping hand.

All force and movement should be directed as nearly vertical as possible. The more nearly vertical all forces are directed, the greater will be the effective force for the jump. Any sideward swing of the free arm, for example, will waste a part of the force which is exerted. Figure 84 illustrates the various principles involved in jumping.

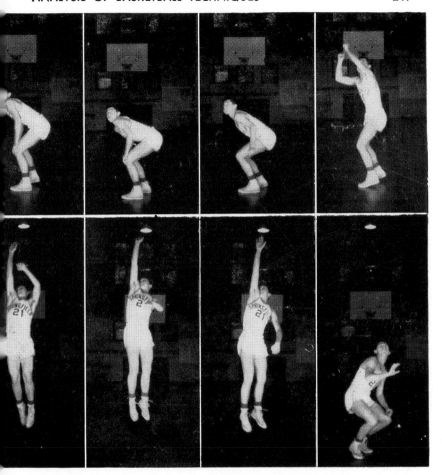

Fig. 84. Sequence in jumping to tip the ball, demonstrating the principles involved.

All these principles should be followed whether the jump is after a held ball or whether the player is jumping to tip the ball at the basket. These principles suggest that a player at the basket should stay back far enough to be able to take a step before jumping. Maneuvering to get a position from which this can be done is quite important.

The movement of the jumper is confined when he is in the jumping circle. However, by standing at the very edge of the circle, the player will have sufficient space to take a short quick catch step before jump-

ing. Few if any players have developed this technique. Most, because of the universally bad practice of officials in tossing a ball, jump
from a stationary position and attempt to "steal" the ball. Actually,
as the ball is thrown up (if the official throws it high enough) the
player should take his preliminary step so that he can develop maximum force for his jump.

Jumping is of great importance in basketball and merits the special
attention of players and coaches alike. The ability to out-jump an
opponent is the difference between ball control and the lack of it on
many occasions. A fraction of an inch increase in the jump can be
the difference. When it is realized that as much as three inches may
be added to the jump by the position of the center of gravity in the
body, the importance of concentration on all the principles which
govern the technique of the jump can be understood.

Passing

The principles of throwing the baseball that were presented in the
analysis in Chapter 9 apply to passing the basketball. A few points
need special emphasis because of the size of the ball and the peculiar
characteristics of the game.

Because of the large cross-sectional area of the basketball the effect
of air resistance is quite pronounced. As a consequence, the spin of
the ball must be carefully controlled to prevent wide divergence from
the intended direction. For long passes, passes of 40 ft or more, the
ball should be thrown with backskin directly opposite to the direction
of flight. If spin across the direction of flight is imparted to the ball,
it will oftentimes curve so far out of its direct line as to be out of
reach of the receiver. This, of course, depends upon the speed of
spin in proportion to the forward speed of the ball and the distance
of the pass (see page 80). Figure 85 shows the action of the ball
as the result of spin of different directions.

Quickness in the movement of the ball is an important factor in
basketball. Except for long passes, great force is not necessary. As
a consequence, the problem of imparting maximum force is not significant with the exception noted. Attention, therefore, should be
given to those factors which contribute to speed of movement of body
members.

Two points are important. The wrist snap is the primary source of force for passing the basketball. The other body movements which are used in throwing are relatively slower. Film studies of the shot put and baseball throw show that the wrist snap is the fastest movement in the sequence of body movements.

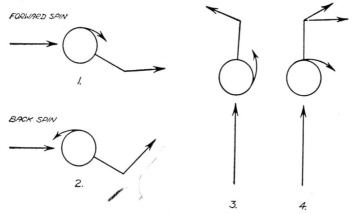

Fig. 85. The effects of spin on the basketball in determining the direction of the ball after it hits the floor. In 1, with forward spin the ball does not bounce as high but moves forward faster. In 2, reverse spin causes the ball to bounce upward sharply and to have its forward movement retarded. In 3, counterclockwise spin causes a bounce to the left, while in 4, clockwise spin causes a bounce to the right.

In order to eliminate or reduce the other and slower body movements to a minimum in passing the ball short distances, the ball is held with the wrists cocked and ready for the release of the ball. In the two hand pass, for example, the ball should be held back against the chest with the elbows bent. Only the quick partial forward extension of the forearm and the wrists is necessary to develop sufficient force for the pass (see Figure 86). For the one hand pass, only a slight amount of upper arm rotation is necessary, and no body rotation. Therefore, the upper arm is held almost at right angles to the body, and the forearm is in a position slightly back of vertical with the wrist cocked. These are the positions for the forearm and wrist when they start their movements in the normal throwing movement as discussed under

Fig. 86. Position of the basketball for quick short passes. The ball is held back against the body so that quick extension of the arms is all that is necessary to execute the pass.

baseball (see page 140). Thus, for the purpose of quickness that portion of the throwing movement which contributes the greatest speed but the least force is emphasized for the short pass. See Figure 87 for the sequence of movements in executing the one-hand pass.

Fig. 87. Sequence of movement in the execution of the one-hand pass.

In the case of the hook pass, a new element is introduced. The hook pass in addition to other movements involves a circular movement of the arm in a plane which is perpendicular to a sagittal section of the body. In order to offset the centrifugal force developed from this movement, the hand is laid around the ball with the ball rolled back on the forearm. In this way, the ball can be controlled better and prevented from flying off at a tangent before the desired release point. Figure 88 demonstrates the method of holding the ball for the hook pass.

The bounce pass is used to get the ball by an opponent by means of deflecting the ball off the floor. In the pass, the principle of spin plays an important part. If one desires that the ball gain speed after hitting the floor, forward spin is imparted to it. If he desires that the speed be retarded and the ball bounce high, backspin is put on the ball. Backspin is used when bouncing the ball in front of a fast-moving player. The forward speed of the ball is retarded and it bounces higher so that the receiver is able to catch the ball and still maintain his speed.

Fig. 88. The position of the basketball on the hand and arm when making a hook pass.

Spin across the direction of flight of the ball is also used in bounce passes. This is done when it is desired to pass to a teammate who is directly behind an opponent. The ball can be bounced to the side of the opponent and by means of the spin be deflected directly to the teammate (see Figure 85).

Because of the fact that bounce passes travel a greater distance (not on a direct line between passer and receiver) and because of the bounce element, more bad bounce passes are made. Raws[1] discovered this fact in a study of Big Ten Conference games. He also found that direct passes were used 84.3 per cent of the time and that of these, 72 per cent were short passes.

_____

[1] Raws, Raymond S., "A Comparative Study of the Bounce Pass and the Direct Pass in Basketball," (Master's thesis, University of Iowa, 1939).

Shooting

The amount of arch with which to shoot, whether to shoot direct or to bank the shot, and whether to impart spin to the ball have long been matters of controversy. All these can be answered by a consideration of some of the trigonometric factors involved. In addition, the dynamics need some attention.

The amount of arch to put on the ball is a problem of accuracy, strength, and defense. If a player was absolute in his accuracy, then the amount of arch would be that necessary to clear the upraised hand of the opponent and the near edge of the rim of the basket. If the opponent were close, more arch would be necessary than if he were some distance away from the shooter. The arch in this case would be inversely proportional to the distance of the defensive player from the shooter. Figure 89 shows this situation diagrammatically.

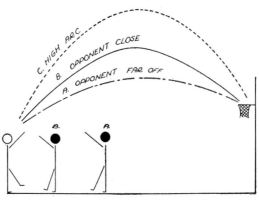

Fig. 89. Three types of basketball shooting arches. A requires the greatest accuracy but the least amount of strength. B must be high enough to clear the guard's hands. C shows the high arc requiring the greatest amount of strength but the least accuracy. In each case the ball traces a parabola.

Few if any players are accurate enough to fit into this category. Therefore, the problem becomes one of trigonometry that involves strength. The basket is 18 inches in diameter. If the ball is dropped from directly above the center of the basket, the full area and diameter of the basket is projected at a right angle to the line of flight of the ball. If the ball is shot at an angle of 60° with the plane of the rim, only .8661 (see Appendix B) of the diameter is projected at a right angle to the line of flight.   If it is shot at an angle of 45°, then .7071 is available as a target.   If the angle is dropped to 30°, the margin is reduced to .5.   This ratio is actually the sine of the angle which the line of flight of the ball makes with the horizontal plane of the basket, multiplied by 18 inches, the diameter of the basket.   Thus, as the angle is reduced, it becomes evident that the chances of the ball hitting either the front or back edge of the rim and bouncing away from the basket increases proportionately.   Therefore, the lower the angle of flight of the ball, the greater must be the accuracy of direction.   All this emphasizes a rather high arch of the ball.   A study of the film of the underhand free throw of a group of Springfield College varsity players shows that the ball leaves the hand at an angle of about 30° from the vertical or 60° from the horizontal.   The ball travels in a parabola. The basket is above the point of the release of the ball.   The angle at which the ball would enter the basket would thus be something less than 60° with the plane of the basket.   Figure 90 shows the flight of

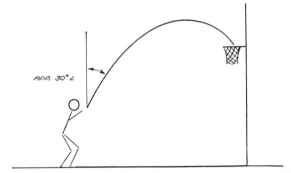

APP. 30° L

Fig. 90. The flight of the ball on a free throw.   Note the approximate angle of the ball with the vertical as the ball leaves the hands.

the ball from the free throw line with the various angles illustrated. Mortimer[2] studied basketball shooting and found that an angle of 58° with the horizontal, with the ball traveling at a speed of 24 + ft/sec, would probably produce the greatest accuracy.

The horizontal distance of the ball from the basket is the same from any one spot regardless of the arch.   The deviation of the ball to the right or left, therefore, would be the same regardless of the arch.

[2] Mortimer, Elizabeth M., "Basketball Shooting," *Research Quarterly*, May, 1951, p. 237.

However, the higher the ball is arched, the longer its parabolic path. More power is necessary to project the ball through the high arch. A player who is not strong in the wrists will find it necessary to press beyond the realm of accuracy for him when shooting long distances, 20 feet or more, if he arches the ball too high. Not only will his shots deviate more from right to left because of varying force in the right and left hand in an effort to cause the ball to reach the basket, but his accuracy with respect to long and short shots will decrease also. Therefore, the amount of arch for each individual will vary with the strength of the individual. Each should emphasize as much arch as possible, consistent with his own strength.

The degree of accuracy which is necessary in shooting may not be apparent to all coaches and players. The following examples will serve to emphasize its importance. A player whose shot deviates 4° to the right or left from a distance of 20 feet from the basket will miss the rim entirely. The ball will be 16¾ inches off line when it reaches

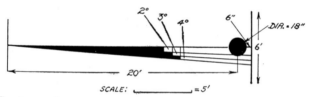

Fig. 91. The degree of accuracy necessary in shooting from twenty feet is shown diagrammatically. A deviation of 4 degrees will miss the basket entirely. With a deviation of 3 degrees the edge of the ball will hit the edge of the rim. A deviation of 2 degrees will just score a goal if the shot is neither long nor short.

the basket. The ball will miss the edge of the basket by almost 3 inches. If his shot deviates 3° he will just hit the rim on the outside without any chance of making the basket. A shot which deviates 2° will probably score a goal but his shot can be neither long nor short. If the reader will use the trigonometric functions in Appendix B he may check these statements. Figure 91 illustrates this situation. If a player shoots from farther than 20 feet, the margin of error allowed becomes increasingly less. Figure 92 shows the degree of accuracy in shooting from different distances. The figures represent shooting in competition.

The ball should be shot with backspin. Such spin serves two primary purposes: 1) it helps the ball to maintain its direction by preventing it from drifting; and 2) it retards the ball's rebound from the board and causes it to drop more sharply (that is, the angle of rebound is less than the angle of approach), which draws the ball down to the basket and lessens the chances of its rebounding too forcefully. In addition, backspin retards the speed of the ball when it hits the rim, thus adding to the possibility of its dropping through the basket rather than bounding away. In general, backspin tends to compensate for too much speed on the ball in shooting.

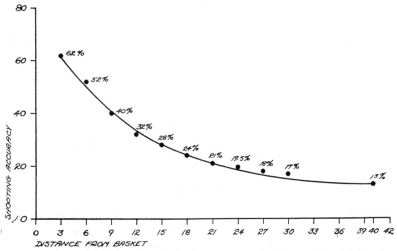

Fig. 92. A curve showing the relation of shooting accuracy to the distance of the shot from the basket. The percentages represent shooting in competition.

The speed with which a ball rebounds is dependent upon the coefficient of restitution of the ball, its mass and the speed with which it is traveling. All these are constant except the speed. It follows, therefore, that in order to prevent a fast rebound, the ball should be shot as softly as possible, that is, with as little velocity as necessary.

From the foregoing it would appear that from the point of view of dynamics, all shots should be banked shots. This fact is enforced somewhat by two other facts. A tabulation of shots indicates that more shots fall short than long. This is probably caused by the fact that most players are taught to use the nearest point on the rim as a target. With this as the focus, the distribution of shots will be short of and beyond this point. As players tire, they begin to fall short of their target. It would appear, therefore, that one should emphasize overshooting with the use of the backboard. Thus, short shots would fall into the basket and long ones, particularly with the help of back spin, would drop in from the backboard. Certainly, the target should not be the front edge. A study on shooting at a target in the center of the basket showed that scores improved 20 per cent over the aim at the front of the rim.

A study which placed spots on the backboard 6 inches apart and one foot above the rim of the basket showed that players who used the spots as targets improved faster than those who shot at an unmarked board. Those who used spots improved 10.8 per cent after four weeks practice. Those who shot without spots improved 4.4 per cent. Removing the spots later did not affect accuracy. The image had been set. Surprisingly, little improvement was shown after four weeks of practice. This tends to indicate that a four-week practice period was sufficient for optimum results.

Much of the shooting is muscle control. Thus shooting with eyes closed will test muscle control. All factors of a mechanical nature which can be applied to assist shooting should be utilized.

Energy

Much has been written about the strenuousness of basketball. A study of the recovery from various activities showed that players recovered from playing a basketball game sooner than swimmers after swimming 100 yards or runners after running a 400-yard dash.[3] One of the reasons for this fact is that basketball is a discontinuous activity with as many as 150 interruptions per game. Swimming and running are continuous activities with much greater intensity but less duration.

A study of movement on defense tends to reflect the strenuousness of various defenses. By means of a pursuit apparatus, Blake[4] found that players in a zone defense traveled less distance than those playing a man-to-man defense. He further found that a 2-1-2 defense was the most economical from the standpoint of distance traveled. Forwards traveled the least distance of all and guards the greatest.

---

[3] Bunn, J. W., "Recovery from Fatigue after Exercise," (Master's thesis, University of Kansas, 1936).

[4] Blake, Raymond, "Distance Traversed by Basketball Players in Different Types of Defense," (Master's thesis, University of Iowa, 1939).

QUESTIONS AND TOPICS FOR DISCUSSION AND REVIEW

1. What main principle is involved in foot work tactics? Give examples.

2. Why is it possible for a basketball player to jump higher by stepping or hopping before the take-off?

3. What factor limits the crouch of a jumper?

4. How can additional height be gained by swinging the arms up forcefully at the take-off?

5. What value accrues from quickly extending the legs downward and swinging the arm downward sharply just before the maximum height of the jump is attained? Illustrate.

6. Why is the effect of spin on a basketball so much more pronounced than the same spin on the baseball?

7. What use is made of spin in basketball?

8. What is the most significant mechanical factor in passing the basketball?

9. How can arch of the ball compensate for inaccuracies in shooting? Illustrate.

10. How is accuracy of direction affected by arch? Why?

11. What effect does distance from the basket have upon a constant error in direction? Illustrate.

12. What is the main limitation to high arch in shooting?

13. What relationship has been found between distance traveled on defense and the kind of defense used?

PROBLEMS

(Answers to problems are given in Appendix D, page 296.)

1. A player is running at the rate of 15 ft/sec. He stops in a distance of 18 inches. How many foot pounds of energy are expended in stopping? The player weighs 160 pounds.

2. When the player in problem (1) stopped, his center of gravity was 3 feet from the forward point of his forward foot and 2 feet from the floor. How much energy must be expended to cause the body to tip forward? Assume that the body is held rigid.

3. A player is able to lower the position of his center of gravity in his body by $2\frac{1}{2}$ inches by quick movements just before the maximum height of his jump is attained. How much higher will he be able to reach by such a maneuver? Show diagrammatically.

4. The direction of a player's jump is at an angle of 10° with the vertical. The player's length from toe to tip of his fingers is 7 feet, 6 inches. How much higher would he be able to reach if his jump had been in a vertical direction? Assume that the force of his jump is the same in each instance.

5. In a hook pass, the radius of rotation of the ball is 1.5 feet. The ball is moving with a velocity of 3 ft/sec. What is the centrifugal force of the ball? Use the minimum weight for the basketball.

6. A shot is made so that the center of the ball and the center of the basket project a line which is at an angle of 45° with the horizontal face of the basket as the ball enters the basket. How much clearance will there be between the ball and the nearest edges of the basket? Use the minimum dimensions for the ball.

7. What is the smallest angle of flight possible to permit the ball to enter without touching the rim?

8. A player's shot deviates 2° from the direct line from the center of the ball to the center of the basket. The player is 25 feet from the basket. Assume that the shot is accurate in all other respects, will it score a goal? Assume also that the center of the ball must fall on or inside the basket to score a goal. If the player was 30 feet away, would the ball score or miss the goal and by how much?

9. What is the least angle of deviation that will just score a goal from 20 feet? 25 feet? 30 feet?

15.

Analysis of
Golf Techniques

The main factor in the golf swing is the transfer of power from the club to the ball. In this respect, batting in baseball and swinging the golf club are similar. In most respects, golf becomes the simpler of the two. The ball, although small, is stationary. The distances to which the golf ball may be hit with the same force are controlled by the pitch of the clubs and the length of the shaft. The pitch of the club head determines the loft of the ball and to that extent the distance. It is a problem of the angle of incidence equaling the angle of reflection and a problem of the flight of a projectile (see page 61). The length of the shaft regulates the linear speed of the club head. A shorter shaft means less force with the same angular speed of swing.

As a result of the above factors, the golf swing can be a controlled one. Regardless of the club, each swing can be with the same force. Each swing can be in the same plane. The problem, then, is to develop a technique so that each golfer can "groove" the "plane" of his swing and can put together a sequence of movements which will produce the same and optimum amount of force each time.

The following application of principles will help each to solve his own problems.

Grip

The overlapping grip which in some form or other is universally used has certain mechanical disadvantages. The stroking movement so far as the hands are concerned is such that the top hand is pushing back while the bottom hand is pushing forward with a fulcrum midway between the center of the hands. The wrist action gives the rotation effect. Thus, the further the hands are spread, within practical limits of course, the greater the power of the stroke. The effective force is increased in proportion to the length of the force arm.

This would indicate that except for those with terrific wrist power the overlapping grip should not be used. This grip incidentally was introduced by a man (Vardon) with very large hands and powerful wrists. Few women have sufficient strength in the wrists. They lose needed power by shortening the force arm when using the overlapping grip. People with small hands should not overlap. Dana[1] studied the effect of the grip on the power of the golf swing. He used 18 subjects and found that 9 of them got more force in their swing by using the "baseball" grip. None of the subjects had had any previous practice in the use of a spread grip for the hands on the golf club. Dana did not measure the relative strength of each individual.

The practice of placing the thumb along the shaft reduces and in some cases eliminates the wrist snap. Power is lost as a result, because the split-second action of the wrist at the moment of contact gives the needed extra force which produces distance. Certainly a person with little strength should not put the thumbs along the shaft of the club.

The hands should be placed so that the fingers are diagonal to the shaft of the club. This position puts the meat part of the hand behind the club. This gives firmness and rigidity to the club at the moment of contact. It prevents recoil so that greater force from the swing is imparted to the ball (Newton's third law—see page 9). The club should also be gripped firmly at the moment of contact for the same reason.

Driving Stroke

Two strokes are involved—the driving stroke and the putting stroke. The drive will be considered first. The movements in the driving

---

[1] Dana, G. E., "An Analysis of Hand-Grip as a Factor Influencing Power of the Golf Swing," (Master's thesis, University of Iowa, 1947).

stroke are principally ones of rotation. The only linear movement is the slight movement of the center of gravity forward during the stroke when the weight is shifted from the rear foot to the front foot. There is rotation about the long axis of the body. The head is held as stationary as possible and the heel of the front foot is held on the ground as long as possible in order to hold this axis in a fixed position.

There is rotation of the club with the shoulder of the front arm as the center of rotation. In order to fix the plane of rotation of the club, the elbow of the rear arm should be kept against the body. This is the most important factor in the control of the club. This position tends to keep the force in one plane and in one direction (see page 67).

Fig. 93. Various stages in the golf swing. The primary essential in controlling the arc of the swing is to use the right elbow as the center of rotation by holding it against the body (in a right-handed stroke).

The front arm should be kept straight. This gives a longer lever. A longer lever gives greater linear velocity of the club head with the same angular velocity. The ball should be met at the bottom of the swing. The club head is moving with the greatest speed in the desired direction of the flight of the ball at this point. To accomplish this, the ball is placed opposite the heel of the front foot when the ball is on level ground. This position is approximately opposite the shoulder of the front arm which is the center of rotation. On a downhill lie, the ball is played a little farther forward to compensate for the slope of the ground. By the same token, the ball is placed opposite the center of the body or even the back heel on an uphill lie (the exact position depends on the slope of the ground).

The sequence of movements is in the same order for both the back swing and the stroke. The body rotation starts first. The club rotation about the front shoulder is next. The wrist snap, at the moment of contact of club and ball so that the arms may be fully extended, is last. The body rotation is slower than the rotation of the arms. If this were not true, the arms would be late in bringing the club to a hitting position when the body movement was finished. The wrist snap is the fastest and comes at the last moment. Figure 93 shows a golfer in the various stages of his stroke.

Figure 94 shows the velocity of two golf strokes at various stages of the swing.

The one factor necessary to produce a rhythmic swing with each movement perfectly timed and in correct sequence is for the golfer not to exceed his optimum speed in swinging the club. The results of the swing will be more effective if the speed is below the optimum rather than if the golfer "presses" (hurries his movements and tries to swing with too great force). However, the tendency is to "press." "Pressing" causes a misdirection of forces with an effective force imparted to the ball of a much lower magnitude than if the swing had been much less forceful.

Pressing, which destroys the rhythm of the sequence of movements, introduces many other disastrous results. The ball may be topped, the club may be grounded, a slice may be developed, a hook may be introduced. Instead of turning to superficial correctives such as changing the stance, the grip, the address, etc., one should rather study the force of his swing. To begin changing factors which are really not causative may in the end add to the problem.

As a guide to the analysis of errors in the timing of the sequence of movements in the swing, the following may be helpful:

1. When the wrist snap comes too late in relation to the rotation of the arms, a slice will occur. The club head lags and is not an extension of the arm at the moment of contact. This causes the ball to receive spin away from the golfer (clockwise for the right-handed golfer). This spin causes the resultant direction of the ball to be at an angle to the right (for a right-handed golfer) of the desired line of flight

(see page 81).   Leaving the plane of the swing and hitting across the ball so as to give the same spin to the ball will produce the same effect.   In this case, the direction of the stroke is at an angle with the desired line of flight.

2. If the body rotation is retarded or the rotation (pivot) is not great enough, a slice will occur.   In this case, the club is caused to hit across the ball because the rotation of the body and the arms is not synchronized.   The clockwise spin for the right-handed golfer is again imparted to the ball.

3. If the wrist snap comes too soon in the sequence of the swing, a hooked ball will occur.   In this case, the club head is in advance of

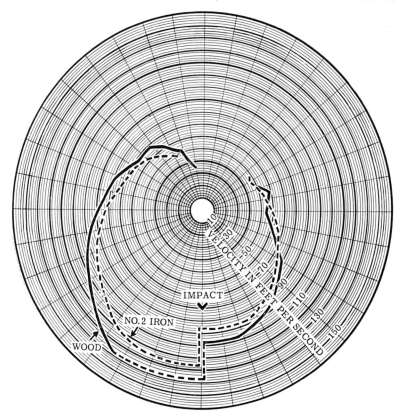

Fig. 94. The effect of the length of the shaft of a golf club is shown in this comparison of the velocity of a No. 2 iron and a wood club as swung by Bobby Jones.   (Courtesy A. G. Spalding & Bros.)

the extended arms.   Counterclockwise spin (for the right-handed golfer) is imparted to the ball.   Its resultant direction will be to the left of the intended line of flight.   Hooking is usually not the result of "pressing" in the total stroke.

4. If the body rotation is too great, a hook is likely to develop.   Too much pivot usually causes counterclockwise spin (for the right hander) to be imparted to the ball.

5. In the case of (2) and (4), if the arms compensate for the lack of body pivot by changing the plane of rotation of the club so that it meets the ball directly, the ball will go straight but not in the direction intended.   The result would be the same as if the ball were addressed incorrectly and a perfect stroke were made.

6. Topping the ball usually occurs from lifting the head.   The golfer is too eager to watch the results of his stroke.   He starts to follow the ball before he hits it and thus fails to hit it squarely.   It may be that he does not have confidence in his stroke and, therefore, desires to follow the ball so that he can find it.   Both the ball and the club head are comparatively small so that a small deviation in position is reflected and magnified in the results of the stroke.   A topped ball is hit into the ground so that much of the force of the swing may be dissipated. It is given top spin and, therefore, may, if not topped too extremely, roll a great distance on a hard smooth surface.

7. Lifting the arms or bending the elbow will also cause the ball to be topped.   The lever is shortened so that the club head will not quite reach the ball for a perfect hit.

8. Hitting behind the ball or under it so that a divot is taken before the ball is struck is usually caused by bending at the waist or knees as the ball is struck.   This, of course, changes the position from the address and has the effect of lengthening the lever.   This error often comes from a feeling (it may be unconscious) that something must be done to lift the ball into the air.   It should be repeated that the club heads are all designed with the angle that will give the proper loft to the ball and distance for that club.

These are a few of the more common errors that beset the golfer.   It can be seen, however, that they occur from an error in the mechanics of the stroke.   Attention should start at this source in analyzing the error.

The stroke should follow through in the plane of the swing after the ball is hit.   The purpose of this is to avoid any possibility of changing the direction of the force of the club (before the ball is hit) as might occur if the plane of swing were changed too soon. The danger is that the plane might be changed before contact with the ball. It is recognized that the club has no effect on the ball after the ball leaves the club.

Another reason for continuing in the plane of the swing after initial contact is because the club is continued in contact with the ball momentarily. This is due to the fact that the ball depresses somewhat on impact. The club, therefore, is able to continue in contact with the ball for a short distance and thus continues to exert force on it. Figure 95 shows the amount of depression of a ball after contact with an iron.

Fig. 95. The effect of contact of the club on a golf ball. Because of the depression made, the golfer must follow through in the plane of the swing. (Courtesy A. G. Spalding & Bros.)

Figure 96 shows the features of the stroke of Bobby Jones. His was one of the most perfect strokes from the standpoint of the mechanical features. Comparative studies[2] of moving pictures of many golfers revealed this fact. The distance between the club head in the various stages of the stroke shows the relative speed of the club head. The greater the distance between successive exposures, the greater the speed of movement. From this, it is readily seen that the greatest speed is at the bottom of the swing.

The absolute accuracy of the velocity at the various stages of the stroke in these figures may be open to question. They are accurate only to the extent that the exposures were taken from a direction at right angles to the plane of the stroke and far enough away to eliminate distortion. A study by Slater-Hammel[3] questions the procedure in the photography which in turn would affect the accuracy of the conclusions which have been drawn. However, the general aspects of the stroke may be observed from Figures 96 and 97.

[2] Rehling, Conrad, "A Stroboscopic Study and Manual on Fundamental Techniques Used in the Golf Drive," (Master's thesis, Springfield College, 1949).

[3] Slater-Hammel, A. T., "Acceleration Characteristics of the Golf Club," *The Physical Educator,* October, 1948.

Fig. 96. A stroboscopic picture showing each stage of an iron stroke by Bobby Jones.   (Courtesy A. G. Spalding & Bros.)

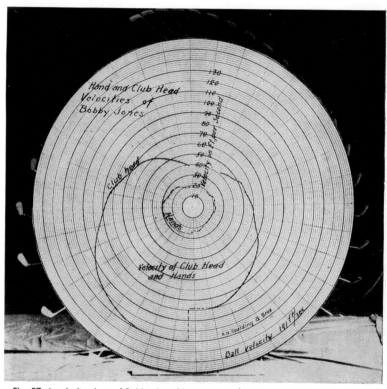

Fig. 97. A velocity chart of Bobby Jones' iron stroke. (Courtesy A. G. Spalding & Bros.)

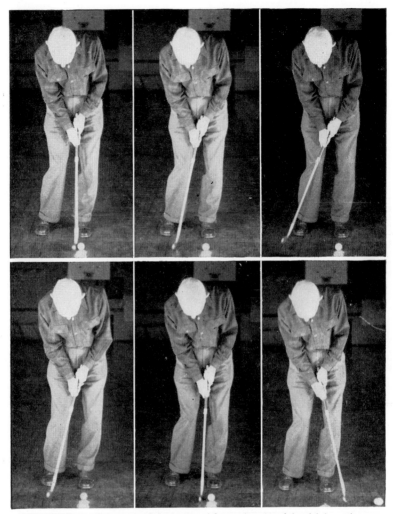

Fig. 98. The various stages of the back and forward stroke of the club in putting.

Putting

Putting consists of an abbreviated stroke in which perfect direction is more important than power. As a consequence, no body rotation is used. The center of gravity is held stationary and over the forward foot. The head is not moved. The elbow of the bottom hand on the club is fixed against the body and is used as the center of rotation for the stroke.   This gives greater control of the stroke.   Only the forearm and wrists are used for developing force.

The back swing is very short—usually not farther than the toe of the rear foot (from 8 to 10 inches).   The speed of the back swing was found to be slower than the forward stroke.   Fako[4] found the time for the back stroke (from a cinematographical analysis of the putting stroke of several prominent golfers) to be .429 seconds and the time for the forward stroke to be .219 seconds (see Figure 98).

The blade of the putter is held and moved at right angles to the intended direction of flight.   The ball is struck at a point just above its center of gravity and just after the club passes the lowest point of the stroke.   The purpose of this is to give forward or topspin to the ball in order to insure a truer roll.   Backspin gives a skidding movement

Fig. 99. The various principles of putting are shown in these drawings.

which causes the ball to react more sensitively to any unevenness in the surface of the putting green.   Whereas the ball with topspin, because of the added forward impetus from the topspin, tends to roll straight over such uneven surfaces.

All of these factors are directed toward perfect control of the direction of movement of the club.   Figures 98 and 99 illustrate the various stages and principles of the putt.

QUESTIONS AND TOPICS FOR DISCUSSION AND REVIEW

1. Why can one make the statement "the main factor in the golf swing is the transfer of power from the club to the ball"?

---

[4] Fako, Paul, "A Mechanical Analysis of the Golf Putt," (Master's Thesis, Springfield College, 1952).

2. If the force and stroke are the same, what controls the distance? Why?

3. What effect does pitch of the club have upon a stroke?

4. What effect does the length of the shaft have upon the stroke?

5. Where is the center of rotation for the club?

6. How is the plane of rotation of the club controlled?

7. Why should the ball be met at the bottom of the swing?

8. What are the possible effects of pressing?

9. What is meant by correcting faults through changing factors which are not causative?   What are the implications?

10. What are causes of a slice?

11. What causes a hook?

12. What causes the ball to be topped?

13. What causes the ball to be grounded?

14. From a mechanical point of view, what are the important factors in the grip?

15. How does putting differ from driving?

16. Why is top spin imparted to the ball?

PROBLEMS

(Answers to problems are given in Appendix D, page 296.)

1. The face of a golf club makes an angle of 30° with the vertical. At what angle will a ball leave the club? If the club makes an angle of 20° at what angle will the ball leave the club?

2. If the club head in problem (1) is traveling at a speed of 130 ft/sec, what distance will the ball go?   How high will it rise?

3. If a club is traveling at the rate of 150 ft/sec, when it meets a golf ball, how fast will the ball leave the club head?   The club head weighs 1 pound.   The ball weighs 1.6 oz.   The coefficient of elasticity of the ball is .85.

4. In a swing the hands of the golfer travel at a linear speed of 30 ft/sec while the club head is traveling 140 ft/sec at the moment of contact with the ball.   What is the relative radius of rotation of the hands to the club head?

5. The radius of rotation of the hands of the golfer in problem (4) is 24 inches.   What is the radius of rotation of the club head?

6. A golf ball is moving forward at a speed of 100 ft/sec and is spinning clockwise at a speed of 35 ft/sec.   Assuming that the force of the spin is directed at right angles to the forward motion, what will be the resultant direction of the ball?   How fast will it travel in that direction?

7. A golf ball weighing 2 ounces is struck by a club moving 150 ft/sec. The ball leaves the club head with a velocity of 238 ft/sec.   What is the effective mass of the club head?   The coefficient of restitution of the ball is .65.

8. A golf ball is dropped on a concrete floor from a height of 200 centimeters.   It rebounds to a height of 84 centimeters.   What is the coefficient of restitution of the ball?

16.

Analysis of
Tennis Techniques

Tennis consists of three factors—service, stroking, and foot work. The foot work is devoted to getting into position to hit the ball. For the most part, both serving and striking the ball are problems of imparting the greatest amount of force to the ball. The principles involved in the swing or in striking are the same as those applicable to batting in baseball. Those involved in serving are the same as the principles for throwing.

Grip

From the standpoint of the factors of force, the grip should be such that there will be a minimum of recoil of the racket at the moment of impact with the ball (Newton's third law—see page 9). In addition, it should permit as much wrist action as possible. To accomplish these points, the meat of the hand should be behind the racket. Shaking hands with the racket when the face is held in a vertical plane will provide the proper grip for the forehand stroke. Figure 100 shows the forehand grip.

For the backhand stroke, a quarter turn of the racket in a clockwise direction (for the right-handed player) will place the meat of the hand behind the racket. Figure 101 shows the backhand grip. Added rigidity for preventing recoil in the back stroke may be obtained by placing the thumb along the handle of the racket. This should be done if the grip of the player is not strong enough to withstand the shock of impact. This technique, however, eliminates the fast wrist

Fig. 100. The grip for the forehand tennis stroke shown from two positions. *1* shows the "meat" of the hand directly behind the racket; *2* shows the position of the fingers to permit free action of the wrist.

action which gives maximum speed to the stroke at the moment of impact. Some players are now employing a two-hand grip in order to impart more force and particularly to provide greater rigidity at the moment of impact. Players with weak grip strength will find this technique beneficial.

The weight of the racket which a player should use is dependent upon the strength of the player. The best advice is to say that each player should use as heavy a racket as he can swing with optimum speed. Force is a factor of mass (weight of the racket divided by

Fig. 101. The grip for the backhand tennis stroke. Note that the hand is rotated so that the "meat" part of the hand is behind the racket to provide rigidity upon impact.

32) and acceleration. Likewise, the choke on the handle is dependent upon the strength of the player. The stronger the player the less the choke. The speed of movement of the face of the racket will be inversely proportional to the amount of choke. To state this relationship in terms of a physical principle, the longer the radius of rotation the greater will be the linear velocity for the same angular velocity (see page 36). Each player, therefore, has a trial and error problem in selecting the proper racket and in determining the choke. However, in keeping with the principles involved, individuals with weak grip and arm strength would choose lighter rackets and use a greater choke. Generally, women need lighter rackets than men.

Striking

The movement in striking and serving is both linear and circular. The linear motion comes from the forward movement of the body. This is the beginning movement in the stroke after position is attained, and it gets the mass of the body into the stroke, thus adding force to the stroke. The effect of this force is readily demonstrated and observed when players are maneuvered out of position and in an attempt to recover find it necessary to step back as they hit the ball. The principle is even more effectively illustrated if the player is running back or reaching out away from the body when he hits the ball. Considerable force is lost and it can be observed clearly. If the greatest force is desired, the rear foot must be in contact with the surface at the moment of impact and the leg should be rigid and extended. This produces the greatest reaction forward (Newton's third law).

The circular movement comes from the rotation of the body about its vertical axis and the rotation of the stroking arm. In order to develop the greatest amount of force the radius of rotation should be as long as possible and the movement should be through as great an arc as possible. The length of the radius has been discussed. In order to swing through a wide arc, the body faces at approximately right angles to the intended direction of the flight of the ball. Since the player faces the net as he awaits the return of the ball by his opponent, he must turn so that he is facing toward the side line as he strokes. To get into position, he usually employs a skip step. The racket must be drawn back as far as possible before the stroke is started in order to increase the arc through which it swings. The wrist is flexed back so that the final movement at impact may be the wrist snap. (Added force is attained by bending a joint—see page 68). The wrist must be rigid and the grip firm at impact to avoid recoil (Newton's third law). The ball should be met as the arm passes the position where it is at right angles to the line of the shoulders. The linear velocity of the racket (assuming that the intended line of flight is parallel to the line of the shoulders) is greatest at this point.

Fig. 102. The collapse of a tennis ball at impact with the racket. This is one reason for a follow through on the stroke. (Courtesy A. G. Spalding & Bros.)

So that force is not lost by stopping or slowing the swing before impact and to avoid muscle injury, the racket should follow through after contact. In view of the fact that the ball collapses as much as one half, the racket is in contact with the ball for a longer period of time than if the ball were more rigid (see Figure 102). This is an added reason for continuing the stroke after the initial impact. The effect of spin which an opponent may impart to the ball is largely offset by meeting the ball with great force. This is due to the flattening of the ball and is one reason for developing great force in the stroke.

The sequence, speed, and direction of all movements, in order to gain the greatest force, must follow the principle discussed on page 67. They must proceed from slow to fast. Each starts at a point where the preceding movement has attained its greatest speed. The direction must be in the direction of the intended flight of the ball. Figure 103 illustrates the stages and principles of the forearm stroke.

Fig. 103. Sequence of movement in the forearm stroke.

Serve

The tennis serve follows the same principles as those employed in the stroke. The movements are similar to those employed in throwing the baseball (see page 142). The sequence of arm movements is identical. Because the ball is hit above the head and because of the line restrictions for the feet, the stride is much shorter than the stride used in throwing the ball. The push off with the swing foot (right foot for right-handed player) is the same as for baseball. The foot remains in contact with the court until after impact to absorb the reaction.

In order to impart the greatest amount of force to the ball, it should be met just in front of the head. The racket will have passed its vertical position at this point. The greatest forward speed is attained at this point. The height of the ball at impact should be such that the arm and racket are fully extended. This produces the longest radius and thus the greatest linear speed. Figure 104 shows the stages of movement in the serve.

Fig. 104. The mechanical principles involved in the tennis serve.

Spin

The presentation up to this point has not involved the factor of imparting spin to the ball. Topspin and sidespin or cut are sometimes desired, since many players use spin as the basis of their play and others often resort to it for strategical purposes.

Since there is a division of force between forward and sideward or downward directions, less forward force is imparted to the ball when spin is used. The resultant direction of the ball is below or to the side of a direction at right angles to the face of the racket (see page 219). The particular effect of cut or sidespin on the ball is that it jumps to the right or left (depending on the direction of the spin) when it rebounds from the court. This makes the return more difficult. Topspin causes the ball to rebound forward more rapidly and with less height. This, likewise, increases the difficulty of return.

To impart topspin to the ball, the racket must be moving up at the moment of contact. Thus the ball should be hit just in front of or above the left shoulder (for a right-handed server). The same movement is necessary when striking the ball on a return hit. The ball is thus not as high or as far in front of the server when hit. The server should also lean back as far as possible. These factors decrease the possible force imparted to the ball because the radius of rotation must be shortened (which means less linear velocity) and the ball is hit before the greatest linear velocity of the racket in the direction of flight is attained.

When a cut is desired, a chopping movement of the arm is used. The principles are the same as in throwing a curve ball. The racket moves across the path of the ball. This move imparts the desired spin to the ball. The radius of rotation of the arm and racket is shortened considerably. The movement is part forward and part sideward or downward. These factors reduce measurably the amount of force imparted to the ball in the direction of flight. Figure 105 shows the direction of movement of the racket in executing a chop stroke.

Fig. 105. The angle of tilt of the tennis racket for making a chop stroke. Back spin or side and back spin will be imparted to the ball.

Direction of Flight of Ball

Because of the limited playing space within which the ball must hit and because the ball must clear the net the angle of the face of the racket with the line of flight of the ball becomes of major importance. In general, the angle of incidence is equal to the angle of reflection (see page 61). In other words, if the ball meets the racket at an angle of 10° with a line perpendicular to the face of the racket, it will leave the racket at this same angle. One must be conscious of this principle and govern his movements accordingly as he attempts to return the ball and to place it at specific spots on the court.

For example, the ball is approaching parallel to a sideline and along a sideline and it is desired to return it in the same but reversed direction. The racket must meet the ball at right angles to the direction of flight of the ball. However, if it is desired to place the same ball at the intersection of the baseline and the opposite sideline, the racket must meet the ball so that the angle of incidence is one half of the angle formed by the line of the approaching ball and the desired line of flight. It is assumed here that the ball is hit from a point directly above the baseline and the sideline. Figure 106 illustrates this situation.

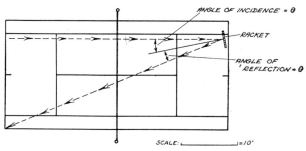

Fig. 106. The relative position of the racket in hitting a ball from the direction shown in order to place it in the opposite corner of the court. The principle of "the angle of incidence equals the angle of reflection" is demonstrated.

One may apply this example to other similar situations on the court. In addition to adjusting the angle of the racket in order to place the ball to right or left and keep it within the playing area, there is the problem of placing the ball at specified distances from the net. Usually the aim is to place the ball as near to the baseline as possible until an advantage is obtained which will permit a change in strategy. This problem involves the force of gravity. Regardless of the force with which the ball is hit, the time of flight before it hits the court is dependent upon the maximum height of the ball above the court during its flight (see page 27). The vertical flight of the ball is at the rate of 32 ft/sec/sec. The net is 36 inches high. Therefore, if a ball were hit from a point 40 feet from the net, it would be necessary for the ball to rise higher than 36 inches if it were to cross the net. If it started at a height of exactly 36 inches and did not rise, it would not clear the net. Thus, if the ball is stroked at a height below the shoulder and the ball is descending, the face of the racket should be tilted slightly up (back of vertical). The ball would thus move slightly up in order to overcome gravity and clear the net. In order to place the ball at the baseline, it should cross the net about $2\frac{1}{2}$ feet above it. Because of this fact the aim should be at the back line and not the net as is often erroneously taught.

These statements can be demonstrated by a mathematical illustration:

$$D = \tfrac{1}{2}at^2 \quad \text{(See page 23.)}$$

Assume that the ball is $2\frac{1}{2}$ feet above the net as it crosses it and that this is the maximum height that it reaches. The time elapsed until the ball hits the court can be found by substituting in the formula. The net is 3 feet high so the ball is $5\frac{1}{2}$ feet above the court.

$$5\tfrac{1}{2} = \frac{32}{2} t^2, \quad t^2 = \frac{5.5 \times 2}{32} = .34, \quad t = .58 \text{ seconds}$$

The distance from the net to the baseline is 39 feet.

$$V = \frac{d}{t} \quad \text{(See page 23.)}$$

Therefore, the ball must be traveling at the rate of 67.24 ft/sec in order to reach the baseline before hitting the court.

$$V = \frac{39}{.58} = 67.24 \text{ ft/sec}$$

This is about the highest speed that the tennis ball reaches by the most powerful players. It is evident, therefore, that for most players, the ball rises higher than $5\frac{1}{2}$ feet as it crosses the net if it is to be hit from baseline to baseline.

The angle of holding the racket in order to clear the net or get the ball to the baseline is dependent upon the distance of the ball from the net, the height of the ball above the court when stroked, the angle of flight of the ball, and whether the ball is ascending or descending. Generally speaking, the edge of the racket is more toward the vertical.

The face of the racket will be tilted up when meeting balls below the shoulder and when the ball is dropping. The face of the racket will be tilted in the opposite direction (down) when the ball is rising, that is, when it bounces from the surface of the court. The exact angle for any situation can be found by assuming specific conditions. The principle that the angle of incidence equals the angle of reflection applies. This has been illustrated on page 247.

Questions and Topics for Discussion and Review

1. How can the grip of the tennis racket affect the amount of recoil when the ball is stroked? What principle is involved?

2. How may the backhand grip be strengthened to reduce recoil?

3. Why is the two-hand grip used?

4. What should be the guide in choosing the weight of a racket?

5. What is the purpose in choking the racket?

6. List all the principles involved in striking the ball. Demonstrate.

7. Illustrate the types of movements employed in striking the ball and the effectiveness of each.

8. Why follow through?

9. Where is the ball hit on the serve to obtain the greatest amount of force?

10. How is the stroke altered to impart spin to the ball? What are the principles involved?

11. Explain and illustrate the statement, "The angle of incidence is equal to the angle of reflection."

12. What determines the height above the court to which the ball must rise after it is struck? Illustrate.

Problems

(Answers to problems are given in Appendix D, page 296.)

1. The ball is approaching an opponent in a line parallel to the side-line and is hit when it is over the intersection of the baseline and sideline. If it is desired to strike the ball so that it will hit the diagonally opposite corner, what angle must the racket make with the base line? The angle of the line of flight of the ball is 25°.

2. If the ball is hit when it is over the center of the baseline, at what angle must the racket be held to make the ball hit the intersection of the baseline and sideline? The ball approaches the striker at an angle of 80° with the baseline.

3. The ball is served so that it makes an angle of 17° with the sideline. If it is returned so that the ball travels parallel to the sideline, what angle will the racket make with the sideline?

4. The ball is hit at the service line (21 feet from the net) just as it leaves the surface of the court. It travels at right angles to the net and is 6 inches

above the net as it crosses the net. This is the maximum height of the ball. How far from the net will the ball hit on the other side of the net? At what velocity will it be traveling?

5. The ball is hit when it is 3 feet above the surface of the court and at a point 3 feet beyond the baseline. It travels at right angles to the net and when it returns to the height at which it was hit, the ball is 10 feet from the opposite baseline. The ball is traveling at a velocity of 50 ft/sec. What is the angle of flight with the horizontal when the ball leaves the racket? How high will the ball rise above the court?

17.

Analysis of Rope Climb and Volleyball

Rope Climb

In the rope climb, Newton's first law and the principles of levers and moment arms are the controlling factors. In order to conserve energy, the action of climbing should be a smooth (uniform) continuous movement. Once the climb has begun, less force will be needed if the body is kept in continuous uniform motion directly toward the top. This is the principle of Newton's first law—a body in motion tends to remain in motion (see page 8).

In order to accomplish smooth, continuous, uniform motion, the principles involving levers are involved. In the first place, there should not be a fully extended reach. The angle of pull of the biceps on the forearm produces the least effective force when the arm is fully extended. The greatest effective force is applied when the direction of force is applied at right angles to the lever (see page 51).

The point at which the greatest effective force is applied is when the upper arm is horizontal—in other words, the biceps are pulling at right angles to the lever, the forearm. This is the point at which the hands should be changed—a new grip or reach taken. Both arms are used to pull when the biceps are not at a right angle to the forearm. In this way, the effective force is kept more nearly constant.

Fig. 107. Sequence of movements in the rope climb, illustrating the mechanical principles involved.

The body should be held so that the center of gravity is directly below the hands—the point of support. In this position, the moment arm is zero and no force is lost in overcoming the effect of a moment arm. The moment of force is equal to the force applied multiplied by the length of the moment arm (the perpendicular distance from the direction of force to the center of gravity of the body in this case— see page 53).

In addition to the above, there may be some slight advantage gained if the legs are flexed as the change in grip takes place. The principle that the momentum of a part is transmitted to the whole is involved. Since, however, the reaction of the leg movement must be absorbed by the arms, the real advantage may be questioned.

A good time for the rope climb of 20 feet from a sitting position is 4.8 seconds. The start must be begun by lifting the heels from the floor first. Figure 107 shows the principles involved in the rope climb.

Volleyball

For practical purposes of analysis there are three fundamental techniques involved in volleyball—the serve, the pass, and the spike.

Serve

Two types of serves are commonly used—the underhand and overhand serve. The underhand serve is usually made with the fist or heel of the hand with a short sharp arm swing. The ball is hit without spin which causes it to zigzag, since spin holds a ball on its course. This type of serve is not considered an offensive serve. Figure 108 shows the underhand serve.

The offensive serve is an overhead serve and is very similar to the tennis serve. The ball can be hit with much more force by the overhead serve than is possible by the underhand method inasmuch as the arm is swung through a greater arc and greater speed of movement can be developed. The ball may be given a cut so that it will curve to the right or the left, or it may be given topspin, which will cause it to drop fast after it crosses the net. For a cut, the fist or heel of the hand is cut across the ball, giving the ball sideward spin in addition to forward force. The resultant of the two causes the ball to curve. The amount of curve depends upon the speed with which the ball spins in relation to the speed of its forward movement. Since the volleyball is very light, it is very sensitive to spin and curves sharply with little effort.

For topspin, which will cause it to drop sharply, the ball is hit while the fist or heel of the hand is moving upward. The ball is above the

Fig. 108. Sequence of movements in the underhand volley ball serve.   (Courtesy Athletic Institute.)

head and the server leans back as far as possible in this case. For a cut serve the ball is forward of the body and not so high as in tennis. The ball is not tossed as high for the cut as it is for the topspin. To obtain the correct height and position of the ball for both types of spin requires considerable practice and is the key to the successful serve. Figure 109 shows the principles involved in the overhead serve.

In order to get the ball over the net, the ball must be hit higher than the net so it will clear it. It must be remembered that the moment the ball leaves the server, the force of gravity begins to affect it. For this reason it is usually better to aim for the back part of the court rather than the top of the net.

The Pass

The pass is of two types—underhand slap or retrieve and the overhead push. In either case the passer should move so that he is close

to the ball and does not have to reach for it.   In this way, he is in a
position to hit it up and can control its direction much more effectively.
The ball should be passed without much spin so that it will not curve
and its flight will be true.   Figure 110 shows the underhand pass.

For the overhead pass the passer should get directly under the ball.
In this way the angle of flight can be judged more accurately.   The
hands are spread apart slightly and the fingers are spread wide.   The
fingers must be rigid at contact in order to prevent recoil and the ap-
pearance of catching the ball.

Fig. 109. Sequence of movements in the overhead serve.   (Courtesy Athletic Institute.)

Fig. 110. Sequence of movements in the underhand pass. (Courtesy Athletic Institute.)

In a pass to the net the ball must be hit high—12 ft or more from the floor. This permits the receiver to get in position under the ball. A set-up pass should be at least 6 feet above the net and 3 feet away from it. This permits the spiker to judge the ball, to get position without fouling, and to reach the highest point of his jump before hitting the ball. Figure 111 shows the overhead pass.

Fig. 111. Sequence of movements in the overhead pass.   (Courtesy Athletic Institute.)

Fig. 112. Sequence of movements in the spike.   (Courtesy Athletic Institute.)

The Spike

The spiker moves forward much as does the high jumper. The movement gives momentum to the body and permits the spiker to stamp the foot sharply to the floor in order to get maximum force for the jump (Newton's third law). But it is essential that the jump be a *high* jump and not a *broad* jump in order to avoid crossing the net line. The spiker must time his jump with the flight of the ball so that he hits the ball when he is at the top of his jump.

The spiker usually attempts to hit the ball with as much force as possible, so he tries to get as much arm swing and force into the ball as does the server. Consequently, he should have his arm drawn back as far as possible before the spiking movement begins. The direction of his force must be at an angle toward the floor in order to keep the ball within bounds. Since the ball is above the net when it is hit and the spike takes place close to the net, no additional elevation is needed to clear the net. Figure 112 shows the spiker in the various stages of his movements.

QUESTIONS AND TOPICS FOR DISCUSSION AND REVIEW

1. List the principles involved in the rope climb.
2. At which point do the arms exert the greatest pull? The least pull?
3. At what point should a new grip be taken?
4. Why should the center of gravity be directly below the grip?
5. List the principles involved in the volleyball serve.
6. Why get under the ball for the overhead pass?
7. Why is the ball hit so high in a pass to the net?
8. Compare movement of spiker to the movement of the high jumper.

Appendix

Appendix

Appendix A

All the formulae presented in the text (Part I) are repeated here as a convenient reference for the reader. If an explanation of the symbols is needed, the reader should refer to Part I. A brief explanation of the trigonometry involved in the formulae follows in Appendix B.

Formulae

1. $D = Vt$

2. V or $V_a = \dfrac{V_0 + V_1}{2}$

3. $V_1 = at$

4. V or $V_a = \dfrac{V_1}{2} = \frac{1}{2}at$

5. $D = \frac{1}{2}at^2$

6. $V_1^2 = 2aD$

7. $R = \dfrac{V^2 \sin 2\theta}{g}$

8. $T_f = \dfrac{2V \sin \theta}{g}$

9. $R + R_2 = \dfrac{V^2 \sin \theta \cos \theta + V \cos \theta \sqrt{V^2 \sin^2 \theta + 2gh}}{g}$

10. $R_1 + R_2 + R_3 = \dfrac{V^2 \sin \theta \cos \theta + V \cos \theta \sqrt{V^2 \sin^2 \theta + G\,(H - c \sin \gamma)}}{g}$
$$+ \sin \alpha + c \cos \gamma$$

11. $D_L = D_r\, xr$

12. $V_L = V_r\, xr$

13. $F = ma$ or $F = m\dfrac{V}{t}$

14. $R^2 = F_1^2 + F_2^2 - 2F_1F_2 \cos \alpha$

15. $F_2^2 = R^2 + F_1^2 - 2RF_1 \cos \theta$

16. $R^2 = F_1^2 + F_2^2$

17. $\cos \theta = \dfrac{F_1}{R}$

18. $R^2 = F_1^2 + F_2^2 - 2F_1F_2 \cos \alpha$

19. $F \times F_a = W \times W_a$

20. $F = \dfrac{WV^2}{gr}$

21. $\tan \theta = \dfrac{V^2}{gr}$

22. $\dfrac{P}{W} = C$

23. $\dfrac{P}{W} = \tan \theta$

24. $e = \dfrac{V_2 - V_1}{U_1 - U_2}$

263

25. $e = \sqrt{\dfrac{h_b}{h_d}}$

26. $V_1 = \dfrac{(m_1 - em_2)U_1 + (1 + e)m_2U_2}{m_1 + m_2}$

27. $R = \dfrac{CpSV^2}{2}$

28. $\dfrac{A^2N^2}{4B_u} > 1$

29. $F = KV^2$

30. $F_a = F_m\left(1 - \dfrac{V_a}{V_m}\right)$

31. $W = Fd$

32. $W = Fd = \frac{1}{2}mV^2$

33. $P = FV$

34. $PE = Wh = mgh$

35. $H = V \sin \theta t - \frac{1}{2}gt^2 + H_1$

36. $S = V \cos \theta t + S_1$

Appendix B

Trigonometric Functions—Tables

Many of the situations in sports activities involve the direction of motion, speed, or force. To analyze many of these situations properly, it is necessary to resolve these factors into their vertical and horizontal components. These procedures involve the use of trigonometric functions. For the convenience of the reader, a brief review of the simple functions of the sine, cosine, tangent, and cotangent are presented herewith. For most situations discussed in the text, only these four functions will be needed. The accompanying tables which give the values of angles from 0° to 90° for the sine, cosine, tangent, and cotangent should also be helpful.

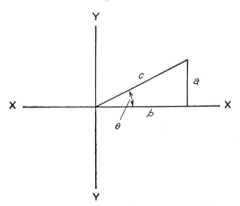

Fig. 113. A right triangle a, b, c laid out in the first quadrant to illustrate the trigonometric functions.

A right triangle may be used to illustrate the trigonometric functions. In Figure 113, this triangle is laid off on an X and Y axis. The hypotenuse of the triangle is c. It is laid off in the direction of a force or movement. The length of c represents the magnitude of the force or the velocity of movement. θ is the angle which this force or movement makes with the X axis.

The force or movement, c, is projected on the X and Y axis by drawing lines perpendicular from the end of c to each of these axes. The length of c when projected on the X axis represents the horizontal component of the force or movement. This component is represented by b. It represents the force or velocity of c in a horizontal direction. The length of c when projected on the Y axis equals the vertical component of the force or movement. This component is represented by a. It represents the force or velocity of c in a vertical direction. If, perchance, a force or velocity c is directed vertically, then c is equal to a and b equals zero. Conversely, if the force or movement c is directed horizontally, then c equals b and a equals zero.

From the above, it becomes obvious that there is a definite relationship between the angle θ which a force or movement makes with the horizontal and the sides of the right triangle represented by a, b, and c. These relationships constitute the basis for the trigonometric functions of the angle. They are indicated by the terms *sin, cos, tangent, and cotangent,* and are represented by the following equations:

$$\sin \text{ of } \theta = \frac{a}{c}$$

$$\cos \text{ of } \theta = \frac{b}{c}$$

$$\text{tangent of } \theta = \frac{a}{b}$$

$$\text{cotangent of } \theta = \frac{b}{a}$$

The sine, cosine, tangent, and cotangent for any angle may be calculated. If a constant magnitude for c is assumed, the value of b may be found by carefully projecting c on the X axis and then measuring the length of the projection. The value of a may be found in a similar manner. When a, b and c are known, the values of sine and so forth are found by substituting in the equations which represent these functions.

For the convenience of the reader these values have been worked out and are shown in the table on page 267—for angles from 0° to 90°. The functions for any other angle may be found by relating the angle to its supplementary angle in the table (see Table VIII).

TABLE VIII

CIRCULAR (TRIGONOMETRIC) FUNCTIONS

Degrees	Sines	Cosines	Tangents	Cotangents	
0°00′	.0000	1.0000	.0000		90°00′
1°00′	.0175	.9998	.0175	57.290	89°00′
2°00′	.0349	.9994	.0349	28.636	88°00′
3°00′	.0523	.9986	.0524	19.081	87°00′
4°00′	.0698	.9976	.0699	14.301	86°00′
5°00′	.0872	.9962	.0875	11.430	85°00′
6°00′	.1045	.9945	.1051	9.5144	84°00′
7°00′	.1219	.9925	.1228	8.1443	83°00′
8°00′	.1392	.9903	.1405	7.1154	82°00′
9°00′	.1564	.9877	.1584	6.3138	81°00′
10°00′	.1736	.9848	.1763	5.6713	80°00′
11°00′	.1908	.9816	.1944	5.1446	79°00′
12°00′	.2079	.9781	.2126	4.7046	78°00′
13°00′	.2250	.9744	.2309	4.3315	77°00′
14°00′	.2419	.9703	.2493	4.0108	76°00′
15°00′	.2588	.9659	.2679	3.7321	75°00′
16°00′	.2756	.9613	.2867	3.4874	74°00′
17°00′	.2924	.9563	.3057	3.2709	73°00′
18°00′	.3090	.9511	.3249	3.0777	72°00′
19°00′	.3256	.9455	.3443	2.9042	71°00′
20°00′	.3420	.9397	.3640	2.7475	70°00′
21°00′	.3584	.9336	.3839	2.6051	69°00′
22°00′	.3746	.9272	.4040	2.4751	68°00′
23°00′	.3907	.9205	.4245	2.3559	67°00′
24°00′	.4067	.9135	.4452	2.2460	66°00′
25°00′	.4226	.9063	.4663	2.1445	65°00′
26°00′	.4384	.8988	.4877	2.0503	64°00′
27°00′	.4540	.8910	.5095	1.9626	63°00′
28°00′	.4695	.8829	.5317	1.8807	62°00′
29°00′	.4848	.8746	.5543	1.8040	61°00′
30°00′	.5000	.8660	.5774	1.7321	60°00′
31°00′	.5150	.8572	.6009	1.6643	59°00′
32°00′	.5299	.8480	.6249	1.6003	58°00′
33°00′	.5446	.8387	.6494	1.5399	57°00′
34°00′	.5592	.8290	.6745	1.4826	56°00′
35°00′	.5736	.8192	.7002	1.4281	55°00′
36°00′	.5878	.8090	.7265	1.3764	54°00′
37°00′	.6018	.7986	.7536	1.3270	53°00′
38°00′	.6157	.7880	.7813	1.2799	52°00′
39°00′	.6293	.7771	.8098	1.2349	51°00′
40°00′	.6428	.7660	.8391	1.1918	50°00′
41°00′	.6561	.7547	.8693	1.1504	49°00′
42°00′	.6691	.7431	.9004	1.1106	48°00′
43°00′	.6820	.7314	.9325	1.0724	47°00′
44°00′	.6947	.7193	.9657	1.0355	46°00′
45°00′	.7071	.7071	1.0000	1.0000	45°00′

| | Cosines | Sines | Cotangents | Tangents | Degrees |

If any two of these terms are known, the other two may be calculated. For example, if a broad jumper takes off at an angle of 26° with the horizontal at a speed of 30 ft/sec., what are his horizontal and vertical speeds at the moment of take-off?

$$\theta = 26°, \qquad c = 30 \text{ ft/sec}$$

The horizontal speed may be found from the equation:

$$\cos \theta = \frac{b}{c}$$

From the table, cos of 26° is found to be .8988.

$$.8988 = \frac{b}{30}$$

$$b = .8988 \times 30 = 26.9640 \text{ ft/sec}$$

The vertical speed may be found from the equation:

$$\sin \theta = \frac{a}{c}$$

From the table, sine of 26° is found to be .4384.

$$.4384 = \frac{a}{30}$$

$$a = .4384 \times 30 = 13.1520 \text{ ft/sec}$$

Square Root—Tables

Many of the problems in the text require the use of squares and square root. For the convenience of the student, tables for the square and square root of numbers are shown in Table IX. The method of extracting the square root of a number is illustrated below for those students who desire to refresh their memories on this procedure.

What is the square root of 56780.631? The square root is found by a method of long division. In the first place, it is known that the square of any single digit number is not greater than two digits. For example, the square of 9, the largest single digit number, is 81. Conversely, then, the square root of a double digit number will be a one digit number. Thus, by inspection of any number, the number of digits in the square root of the number can be determined. In the square root of the number above, there will be three digits to the left of the decimal point and two to the right.

Thus, as a preliminary, this fact is indicated by separating the number into two digit categories each direction from the decimal point, that is, 5/67/80.63/1. The digit 5 is the last category to the left of the decimal point. The square root of this category is determined by inspection or trial and error; in this case, it is 2. The square of two is 4. 4 subtracted from 5 leaves a remainder of 1.

The next category is brought into the dividend to make it 167. Each trial divisor from this point on is found by multiplying the quotient by 20. The trial divisor is then 40. 40 will go into 167 four times. The real divisor then is 44. But $4 \times 44 = 176$, which is greater than the dividend. *Three* therefore is used. $3 \times 43 = 129$. The difference is $167 - 129 = 38$. The new dividend is 3880 and the new trial divisor is $20 \times 23 = 460$. The procedure is continued in the same manner as before. The total computation is shown below:

	238.286
	5/67/80.63/1
2	4
40	167
3	129
460	3880
8	3744
4760	13663
2	9524
47640	413910
8	381184
476560	3272600
6	2759396
	413204

Thus, the square root of 56780.631 is found to be 238.286

The following examples and explanations will be helpful to the student in the use of the square root tables. In order to find the square root of numbers from 1 to 10 one uses the table for numbers from 100 to 1000. If a decimal point is placed between the digits of the numbers in the left hand column, this column will then represent the number. The square root can be read directly from the second column if the decimal point is moved one digit to the left. For example, the square root of 1.4 will be found to be 1.183. The square

Table IX
Square Root Tables

	|	0	1	2	3	4	5	6	7	8	9	|	1	2	3	4	5	6	7	8	9
					100—1000										Proportional Parts						
10		10.00	10.05	10.10	10.15	10.20	10.25	10.30	10.34	10.39	10.44		0	1	1	2	2	3	3	4	4
11		10.49	10.54	10.58	10.63	10.68	10.72	10.77	10.82	10.86	10.91		0	1	1	2	2	3	3	4	4
12		10.95	11.00	11.05	11.09	11.14	11.18	11.22	11.27	11.31	11.36		0	1	1	2	2	3	3	4	4
13		11.40	11.45	11.49	11.53	11.58	11.62	11.66	11.70	11.75	11.79		0	1	1	2	2	3	3	3	4
14		11.83	11.87	11.92	11.96	12.00	12.04	12.08	12.12	12.17	12.21		0	1	1	2	2	2	3	3	4
15		12.25	12.29	12.33	12.37	12.41	12.45	12.49	12.53	12.57	12.61		0	1	1	2	2	2	3	3	4
16		12.65	12.69	12.73	12.77	12.81	12.85	12.88	12.92	12.96	13.00		0	1	1	2	2	2	3	3	4
17		13.04	13.08	13.11	13.15	13.19	13.23	13.27	13.30	13.34	13.38		0	1	1	2	2	2	3	3	3
18		13.42	13.45	13.49	13.53	13.56	13.60	13.64	13.67	13.71	13.75		0	1	1	1	2	2	3	3	3
19		13.78	13.82	13.86	13.89	13.93	13.96	14.00	14.04	14.07	14.11		0	1	1	1	2	2	3	3	3
20		14.14	14.18	14.21	14.25	14.28	14.32	14.35	14.39	14.42	14.46		0	1	1	1	2	2	2	3	3
21		14.49	14.53	14.56	14.59	14.63	14.66	14.70	14.73	14.76	14.80		0	1	1	1	2	2	2	3	3
22		14.83	14.87	14.90	14.93	14.97	15.00	15.03	15.07	15.10	15.13		0	1	1	1	2	2	2	3	3
23		15.17	15.20	15.23	15.26	15.30	15.33	15.36	15.39	15.43	15.46		0	1	1	1	2	2	2	3	3
24		15.49	15.52	15.56	15.59	15.62	15.65	15.68	15.72	15.75	15.78		0	1	1	1	2	2	2	3	3
25		15.81	15.84	15.87	15.91	15.94	15.97	16.00	16.03	16.06	16.09		0	1	1	1	2	2	2	3	3
26		16.12	16.16	16.19	16.22	16.25	16.28	16.31	16.34	16.37	16.40		0	1	1	1	2	2	2	2	3
27		16.43	16.46	16.49	16.52	16.55	16.58	16.61	16.64	16.67	16.70		0	1	1	1	2	2	2	2	3
28		16.73	16.76	16.79	16.82	16.85	16.88	16.91	16.94	16.97	17.00		0	1	1	1	1	2	2	2	3
29		17.03	17.06	17.09	17.12	17.15	17.18	17.20	17.23	17.26	17.29		0	1	1	1	1	2	2	2	3
30		17.32	17.35	17.38	17.41	17.44	17.46	17.49	17.52	17.55	17.58		0	1	1	1	1	2	2	2	3
31		17.61	17.64	17.66	17.69	17.72	17.75	17.78	17.80	17.83	17.86		0	1	1	1	1	2	2	2	3
32		17.89	17.92	17.94	17.97	18.00	18.03	18.06	18.08	18.11	18.14		0	1	1	1	1	2	2	2	2
33		18.17	18.19	18.22	18.25	18.28	18.30	18.33	18.36	18.38	18.41		0	1	1	1	1	2	2	2	2
34		18.44	18.47	18.49	18.52	18.55	18.57	18.60	18.63	18.65	18.68		0	1	1	1	1	2	2	2	2
35		18.71	18.73	18.76	18.79	18.81	18.84	18.87	18.89	18.92	18.95		0	1	1	1	1	2	2	2	2
36		18.97	19.00	19.03	19.05	19.08	19.10	19.13	19.16	19.18	19.21		0	1	1	1	1	2	2	2	2
37		19.24	19.26	19.29	19.31	19.34	19.36	19.39	19.42	19.44	19.47		0	1	1	1	1	2	2	2	2
38		19.49	19.52	19.54	19.57	19.60	19.62	19.65	19.67	19.70	19.72		0	1	1	1	1	2	2	2	2
39		19.75	19.77	19.80	19.82	19.85	19.87	19.90	19.92	19.95	19.97		0	1	1	1	1	2	2	2	2
40		20.00	20.02	20.05	20.07	20.10	20.12	20.15	20.17	20.20	20.22		0	0	1	1	1	1	2	2	2
41		20.25	20.27	20.30	20.32	20.35	20.37	20.40	20.42	20.45	20.47		0	0	1	1	1	1	2	2	2
42		20.49	20.52	20.54	20.57	20.59	20.62	20.64	20.66	20.69	20.71		0	0	1	1	1	1	2	2	2
43		20.74	20.76	20.78	20.81	20.83	20.86	20.88	20.90	20.93	20.95		0	0	1	1	1	1	2	2	2
44		20.98	21.00	21.02	21.05	21.07	21.10	21.12	21.14	21.17	21.19		0	0	1	1	1	1	2	2	2
45		21.21	21.24	21.26	21.28	21.31	21.33	21.35	21.38	21.40	21.42		0	0	1	1	1	1	2	2	2
46		21.45	21.47	21.49	21.52	21.54	21.56	21.59	21.61	21.63	21.66		0	0	1	1	1	1	2	2	2
47		21.68	21.70	21.73	21.75	21.77	21.79	21.82	21.84	21.86	21.89		0	0	1	1	1	1	2	2	2
48		21.91	21.93	21.95	21.98	22.00	22.02	22.05	22.07	22.09	22.11		0	0	1	1	1	1	2	2	2
49		22.14	22.16	22.18	22.20	22.23	22.25	22.27	22.29	22.32	22.34		0	0	1	1	1	1	2	2	2
50		22.36	22.38	22.41	22.43	22.45	22.47	22.49	22.52	22.54	22.56		0	0	1	1	1	1	2	2	2
51		22.58	22.61	22.63	22.65	22.67	22.69	22.72	22.74	22.76	22.78		0	0	1	1	1	1	2	2	2
52		22.80	22.83	22.85	22.87	22.89	22.91	22.93	22.96	22.98	23.00		0	0	1	1	1	1	2	2	2
53		23.02	23.04	23.07	23.09	23.11	23.13	23.15	23.17	23.19	23.22		0	0	1	1	1	1	2	2	2
54		23.24	23.26	23.28	23.30	23.32	23.35	23.37	23.39	23.41	23.43		0	0	1	1	1	1	1	2	2
	|	0	1	2	3	4	5	6	7	8	9	|	1	2	3	4	5	6	7	8	9

Table IX, cont.

Square Root Tables

	0	1	2	3	4	5	6	7	8	9	1	2	3	4	5	6	7	8	9
				100—1000							Proportional Parts								
55	23.45	23.47	23.49	23.52	23.54	23.56	23.58	23.60	23.62	23.64	0	0	1	1	1	1	1	2	2
56	23.66	23.69	23.71	23.73	23.75	23.77	23.79	23.81	23.83	23.85	0	0	1	1	1	1	1	2	2
57	23.87	23.90	23.92	23.94	23.96	23.98	24.00	24.02	24.04	24.06	0	0	1	1	1	1	1	2	2
58	24.08	24.10	24.12	24.15	24.17	24.19	24.21	24.23	24.25	24.27	0	0	1	1	1	1	1	2	2
59	24.29	24.31	24.33	24.35	24.37	24.39	24.41	24.43	24.45	24.47	0	0	1	1	1	1	1	2	2
60	24.49	24.52	24.54	24.56	24.58	24.60	24.62	24.64	24.66	24.68	0	0	1	1	1	1	1	2	2
61	24.70	24.72	24.74	24.76	24.78	24.80	24.82	24.84	24.86	24.88	0	0	1	1	1	1	1	2	2
62	24.90	24.92	24.94	24.96	24.98	25.00	25.02	25.04	25.06	25.08	0	0	1	1	1	1	1	2	2
63	25.10	25.12	25.14	25.16	25.18	25.20	25.22	25.24	25.26	25.28	0	0	1	1	1	1	1	2	2
64	25.30	25.32	25.34	25.36	25.38	25.40	25.42	25.44	25.46	25.48	0	0	1	1	1	1	1	2	2
65	25.50	25.51	25.53	25.55	25.57	25.59	25.61	25.63	25.65	25.67	0	0	1	1	1	1	1	2	2
66	25.69	25.71	25.73	25.75	25.77	25.79	25.81	25.83	25.85	25.87	0	0	1	1	1	1	1	2	2
67	25.88	25.90	25.92	25.94	25.96	25.98	26.00	26.02	26.04	26.06	0	0	1	1	1	1	1	2	2
68	26.08	26.10	26.12	26.13	26.15	26.17	26.19	26.21	26.23	26.25	0	0	1	1	1	1	1	2	2
69	26.27	26.29	26.31	26.32	26.34	26.36	26.38	26.40	26.42	26.44	0	0	1	1	1	1	1	2	2
70	26.46	26.48	26.50	26.51	26.53	26.55	26.57	26.59	26.61	26.63	0	0	1	1	1	1	1	2	2
71	26.65	26.66	26.68	26.70	26.72	26.74	26.76	26.78	26.80	26.81	0	0	1	1	1	1	1	1	2
72	26.83	26.85	26.87	26.89	26.91	26.93	26.94	26.96	26.98	27.00	0	0	1	1	1	1	1	1	2
73	27.02	27.04	27.06	27.07	27.09	27.11	27.13	27.15	27.17	27.18	0	0	1	1	1	1	1	1	2
74	27.20	27.22	27.24	27.26	27.28	27.29	27.31	27.33	27.35	27.37	0	0	1	1	1	1	1	1	2
75	27.39	27.40	27.42	27.44	27.46	27.48	27.50	27.51	27.53	27.55	0	0	1	1	1	1	1	1	2
76	27.57	27.59	27.60	27.62	27.64	27.66	27.68	27.69	27.71	27.73	0	0	1	1	1	1	1	1	2
77	27.75	27.77	27.78	27.80	27.82	27.84	27.86	27.87	27.89	27.91	0	0	1	1	1	1	1	1	2
78	27.93	27.95	27.96	27.98	28.00	28.02	28.04	28.05	28.07	28.09	0	0	1	1	1	1	1	1	2
79	28.11	28.12	28.14	28.16	28.18	28.20	28.21	28.23	28.25	28.27	0	0	1	1	1	1	1	1	2
80	28.28	28.30	28.32	28.34	28.35	28.37	28.39	28.41	28.43	28.44	0	0	1	1	1	1	1	1	2
81	28.46	28.48	28.50	28.51	28.53	28.55	28.57	28.58	28.60	28.62	0	0	1	1	1	1	1	1	2
82	28.64	28.65	28.67	28.69	28.71	28.72	28.74	28.76	28.77	28.79	0	0	1	1	1	1	1	1	2
83	28.81	28.83	28.84	28.86	28.88	28.90	28.91	28.93	28.95	28.97	0	0	1	1	1	1	1	1	2
84	28.98	29.00	29.02	29.03	29.05	29.07	29.09	29.10	29.12	29.14	0	0	1	1	1	1	1	1	2
85	29.15	29.17	29.19	29.21	29.22	29.24	29.26	29.27	29.29	29.31	0	0	1	1	1	1	1	1	2
86	29.33	29.34	29.36	29.38	29.39	29.41	29.43	29.44	29.46	29.48	0	0	1	1	1	1	1	1	2
87	29.50	29.51	29.53	29.55	29.56	29.58	29.60	29.61	29.63	29.65	0	0	1	1	1	1	1	1	2
88	29.66	29.68	29.70	29.72	29.73	29.75	29.77	29.78	29.80	29.82	0	0	1	1	1	1	1	1	2
89	29.83	29.85	29.87	29.88	29.90	29.92	29.93	29.95	29.97	29.98	0	0	1	1	1	1	1	1	2
90	30.00	30.02	30.03	30.05	30.07	30.08	30.10	30.12	30.13	30.15	0	0	0	1	1	1	1	1	1
91	30.17	30.18	30.20	30.22	30.23	30.25	30.27	30.28	30.30	30.32	0	0	0	1	1	1	1	1	1
92	30.33	30.35	30.36	30.38	30.40	30.41	30.43	30.45	30.46	30.48	0	0	0	1	1	1	1	1	1
93	30.50	30.51	30.53	30.55	30.56	30.58	30.59	30.61	30.63	30.64	0	0	0	1	1	1	1	1	1
94	30.66	30.68	30.69	30.71	30.72	30.74	30.76	30.77	30.79	30.81	0	0	0	1	1	1	1	1	1
95	30.82	30.84	30.85	30.87	30.89	30.90	30.92	30.94	30.95	30.97	0	0	0	1	1	1	1	1	1
96	30.98	31.00	31.02	31.03	31.05	31.06	31.08	31.10	31.11	31.13	0	0	0	1	1	1	1	1	1
97	31.14	31.16	31.18	31.19	31.21	31.22	31.24	31.26	31.27	31.29	0	0	0	1	1	1	1	1	1
98	31.30	31.32	31.34	31.35	31.37	31.38	31.40	31.42	31.43	31.45	0	0	0	1	1	1	1	1	1
99	31.46	31.48	31.50	31.51	31.53	31.54	31.56	31.58	31.59	31.61	0	0	0	1	1	1	1	1	1
	0	1	2	3	4	5	6	7	8	9	1	2	3	4	5	6	7	8	9

Table IX, cont.
Square Root Tables

	0	1	2	3	4	5	6	7	8	9	1	2	3	4	5	6	7	8	9
	1000—10000										**Proportional Parts**								
10	31.62	31.78	31.94	32.09	32.25	32.40	32.56	32.71	32.86	33.02	2	3	5	6	8	9	11	12	14
11	33.17	33.32	33.47	33.62	33.76	33.91	34.06	34.21	34.35	34.50	1	3	4	6	7	9	10	12	13
12	34.64	34.79	34.93	35.07	35.21	35.36	35.50	35.64	35.78	35.92	1	3	4	6	7	8	10	11	13
13	36.06	36.19	36.33	36.47	36.61	36.74	36.88	37.01	37.15	37.28	1	3	4	5	7	8	10	11	12
14	37.42	37.55	37.68	37.82	37.95	38.08	38.21	38.34	38.47	38.60	1	3	4	5	7	8	9	11	12
15	38.73	38.86	38.99	39.12	39.24	39.37	39.50	39.62	39.75	39.87	1	3	4	5	6	8	9	10	11
16	40.00	40.12	40.25	40.37	40.50	40.62	40.74	40.87	40.99	41.11	1	2	4	5	6	7	9	10	11
17	41.23	41.35	41.47	41.59	41.71	41.83	41.95	42.07	42.19	42.31	1	2	4	5	6	7	8	10	11
18	42.43	42.54	42.66	42.78	42.90	43.01	43.13	43.24	43.36	43.47	1	2	3	5	6	7	8	9	10
19	43.59	43.70	43.82	43.93	44.05	44.16	44.27	44.38	44.50	44.61	1	2	3	5	6	7	8	9	10
20	44.72	44.83	44.94	45.06	45.17	45.28	45.39	45.50	45.61	45.72	1	2	3	4	6	7	8	9	10
21	45.83	45.93	46.04	46.15	46.26	46.37	46.48	46.58	46.69	46.80	1	2	3	4	5	6	8	9	10
22	46.90	47.01	47.12	47.22	47.33	47.43	47.54	47.64	47.75	47.85	1	2	3	4	5	6	7	8	9
23	47.96	48.06	48.17	48.27	48.37	48.48	48.58	48.68	48.79	48.89	1	2	3	4	5	6	7	8	9
24	48.99	49.09	49.19	49.30	49.40	49.50	49.60	49.70	49.80	49.90	1	2	3	4	5	6	7	8	9
25	50.00	50.10	50.20	50.30	50.40	50.50	50.60	50.70	50.79	50.89	1	2	3	4	5	6	7	8	9
26	50.99	51.09	51.19	51.28	51.38	51.48	51.58	51.67	51.77	51.87	1	2	3	4	5	6	7	8	9
27	51.96	52.06	52.15	52.25	52.35	52.44	52.54	52.63	52.73	52.82	1	2	3	4	5	6	7	8	9
28	52.92	53.01	53.10	53.20	53.29	53.39	53.48	53.57	53.67	53.76	1	2	3	4	5	6	7	7	8
29	53.85	53.94	54.04	54.13	54.22	54.31	54.41	54.50	54.59	54.68	1	2	3	4	5	6	6	7	8
30	54.77	54.86	54.95	55.05	55.14	55.23	55.32	55.41	55.50	55.59	1	2	3	4	5	5	6	7	8
31	55.68	55.77	55.86	55.95	56.04	56.12	56.21	56.30	56.39	56.48	1	2	3	4	4	5	6	7	8
32	56.57	56.66	56.75	56.83	56.92	57.01	57.10	57.18	57.27	57.36	1	2	3	4	4	5	6	7	8
33	57.45	57.53	57.62	57.71	57.79	57.88	57.97	58.05	58.14	58.22	1	2	3	3	4	5	6	7	8
34	58.31	58.40	58.48	58.57	58.65	58.74	58.82	58.91	58.99	59.08	1	2	3	3	4	5	6	7	8
35	59.16	59.25	59.33	59.41	59.50	59.58	59.67	59.75	59.83	59.92	1	2	3	3	4	5	6	7	8
36	60.00	60.08	60.17	60.25	60.33	60.42	60.50	60.58	60.66	60.75	1	2	2	3	4	5	6	7	7
37	60.83	60.91	60.99	61.07	61.16	61.24	61.32	61.40	61.48	61.56	1	2	2	3	4	5	6	7	7
38	61.64	61.73	61.81	61.89	61.97	62.05	62.13	62.21	62.29	62.37	1	2	2	3	4	5	6	6	7
39	62.45	62.53	62.61	62.69	62.77	62.85	62.93	63.01	63.09	63.17	1	2	2	3	4	5	6	6	7
40	63.25	63.32	63.40	63.48	63.56	63.64	63.72	63.80	63.87	63.95	1	2	2	3	4	5	5	6	7
41	64.03	64.11	64.19	64.27	64.34	64.42	64.50	64.58	64.65	64.73	1	2	2	3	4	5	5	6	7
42	64.81	64.88	64.96	65.04	65.12	65.19	65.27	65.35	65.42	65.50	1	2	2	3	4	5	5	6	7
43	65.57	65.65	65.73	65.80	65.88	65.95	66.03	66.11	66.18	66.26	1	2	2	3	4	5	5	6	7
44	66.33	66.41	66.48	66.56	66.63	66.71	66.78	66.86	66.93	67.01	1	1	2	3	4	4	5	6	7
45	67.08	67.16	67.23	67.31	67.38	67.45	67.53	67.60	67.68	67.75	1	1	2	3	4	4	5	6	7
46	67.82	67.90	67.97	68.04	68.12	68.19	68.26	68.34	68.41	68.48	1	1	2	3	4	4	5	6	7
47	68.56	68.63	68.70	68.77	68.85	68.92	68.99	69.07	69.14	69.21	1	1	2	3	4	4	5	6	7
48	69.28	69.35	69.43	69.50	69.57	69.64	69.71	69.79	69.86	69.93	1	1	2	3	4	4	5	5	6
49	70.00	70.07	70.14	70.21	70.29	70.36	70.43	70.50	70.57	70.64	1	1	2	3	4	4	5	5	6
50	70.71	70.78	70.85	70.92	70.99	71.06	71.13	71.20	71.27	71.34	1	1	2	3	4	4	5	6	6
51	71.41	71.48	71.55	71.62	71.69	71.76	71.83	71.90	71.97	72.04	1	1	2	3	3	4	5	6	6
52	72.11	72.18	72.25	72.32	72.39	72.46	72.53	72.59	72.66	72.73	1	1	2	3	3	4	5	5	6
53	72.80	72.87	72.94	73.01	73.08	73.14	73.21	73.28	73.35	73.42	1	1	2	3	3	4	5	5	6
54	73.48	73.55	73.62	73.69	73.76	73.82	73.89	73.96	74.03	74.09	1	1	2	3	3	4	5	5	6
	0	1	2	3	4	5	6	7	8	9	1	2	3	4	5	6	7	8	9

TABLE IX, CONT.
SQUARE ROOT TABLES

	0	1	2	3	4	5	6	7	8	9	1	2	3	4	5	6	7	8	9
					1000—10000									Proportional Parts					
55	74.16	74.23	74.30	74.36	74.43	74.50	74.57	74.63	74.70	74.77	1	1	2	3	3	4	5	5	6
56	74.83	74.90	74.97	75.03	75.10	75.17	75.23	75.30	75.37	75.43	1	1	2	3	3	4	5	5	6
57	75.50	75.56	75.63	75.70	75.76	75.83	75.89	75.96	76.03	76.09	1	1	2	3	3	4	5	5	6
58	76.16	76.22	76.29	76.35	76.42	76.49	76.55	76.62	76.68	76.75	1	1	2	3	3	4	5	5	6
59	76.81	76.88	76.94	77.01	77.07	77.14	77.20	77.27	77.33	77.40	1	1	2	3	3	4	5	5	6
60	77.46	77.52	77.59	77.65	77.72	77.78	77.85	77.91	77.97	78.04	1	1	2	3	3	4	4	5	6
61	78.10	78.17	78.23	78.29	78.36	78.42	78.49	78.55	78.61	78.68	1	1	2	3	3	4	4	5	6
62	78.74	78.80	78.87	78.93	78.99	79.06	79.12	79.18	79.25	79.31	1	1	2	3	3	4	4	5	6
63	79.37	79.44	79.50	79.56	79.62	79.69	79.75	79.81	79.87	79.94	1	1	2	2	3	4	4	5	6
64	80.00	80.06	80.12	80.19	80.25	80.31	80.37	80.44	80.50	80.56	1	1	2	2	3	4	4	5	6
65	80.62	80.68	80.75	80.81	80.87	80.93	80.99	81.06	81.12	81.18	1	1	2	2	3	4	4	5	6
66	81.24	81.30	81.36	81.42	81.49	81.55	81.61	81.67	81.73	81.79	1	1	2	2	3	4	4	5	6
67	81.85	81.91	81.98	82.04	82.10	82.16	82.22	82.28	82.34	82.40	1	1	2	2	3	4	4	5	5
68	82.46	82.52	82.58	82.64	82.70	82.76	82.83	82.89	82.95	83.01	1	1	2	2	3	4	4	5	5
69	83.07	83.13	83.19	83.25	83.31	83.37	83.43	83.49	83.55	83.61	1	1	2	2	3	4	4	5	5
70	83.67	83.73	83.79	83.85	83.90	83.96	84.02	84.08	84.14	84.20	1	1	2	2	3	4	4	5	5
71	84.26	84.32	84.38	84.44	84.50	84.56	84.62	84.68	84.73	84.79	1	1	2	2	3	4	4	5	5
72	84.85	84.91	84.97	85.03	85.09	85.15	85.21	85.26	85.32	85.38	1	1	2	2	3	4	4	5	5
73	85.44	85.50	85.56	85.62	85.67	85.73	85.79	85.85	85.91	85.97	1	1	2	2	3	3	4	5	5
74	86.02	86.08	86.14	86.20	86.26	86.31	86.37	86.43	86.49	86.54	1	1	2	2	3	3	4	5	5
75	86.60	86.66	86.72	86.78	86.83	86.89	86.95	87.01	87.06	87.12	1	1	2	3	3	4		5	5
76	87.18	87.24	87.29	87.35	87.41	87.46	87.52	87.58	87.64	87.69	1	1	2	2	3	4	4	5	5
77	87.75	87.81	87.86	87.92	87.98	88.03	88.09	88.15	88.20	88.26	1	1	2	2	3	3	4	5	5
78	88.32	88.37	88.43	88.49	88.54	88.60	88.66	88.71	88.77	88.83	1	1	2	2	3	3	4	5	5
79	88.88	88.94	88.99	89.05	89.11	89.16	89.22	89.27	89.33	89.39	1	1	2	2	3	3	4	4	5
80	89.44	89.50	89.55	89.61	89.67	89.72	89.78	89.83	89.89	89.94	1	1	2	2	3	3	4	4	5
81	90.00	90.06	90.11	90.17	90.22	90.28	90.33	90.39	90.44	90.50	1	1	2	2	3	3	4	4	5
82	90.55	90.61	90.66	90.72	90.77	90.83	90.88	90.94	90.99	91.05	1	1	2	2	3	3	4	4	5
83	91.10	91.16	91.21	91.27	91.32	91.38	91.43	91.49	91.54	91.60	1	1	2	2	3	3	4	4	5
84	91.65	91.71	91.76	91.82	91.87	91.92	91.98	92.03	92.09	92.14	1	1	2	2	3	3	4	4	5
85	92.20	92.25	92.30	92.36	92.41	92.47	92.52	92.57	92.63	92.68	1	1	2	2	3	3	4	4	5
86	92.74	92.79	92.84	92.90	92.95	93.01	93.06	93.11	93.17	93.22	1	1	2	2	3	3	4	4	5
87	93.27	93.33	93.38	93.43	93.49	93.54	93.59	93.65	93.70	93.75	1	1	2	2	3	3	4	4	5
88	93.81	93.86	93.91	93.97	94.02	94.07	94.13	94.18	94.23	94.29	1	1	2	2	3	3	4	4	5
89	94.34	94.39	94.45	94.50	94.55	94.60	94.66	94.71	94.76	94.82	1	1	2	2	3	3	4	4	5
90	94.87	94.92	94.97	95.03	95.08	95.13	95.18	95.24	95.29	95.34	1	1	2	2	3	3	4	4	5
91	95.39	95.45	95.50	95.55	95.60	95.66	95.71	95.76	95.81	95.86	1	1	2	2	3	3	4	4	5
92	95.92	95.97	96.02	96.07	96.12	96.18	96.23	96.28	96.33	96.38	1	1	2	2	3	3	4	4	5
93	96.44	96.49	96.54	96.59	96.64	96.70	96.75	96.80	96.85	96.90	1	1	2	2	3	3	4	4	5
94	96.95	97.01	97.06	97.11	97.16	97.21	97.26	97.31	97.37	97.42	1	1	2	2	3	3	4	4	5
95	97.47	97.52	97.57	97.62	97.67	97.72	97.78	97.83	97.88	97.93	1	1	2	2	3	3	4	4	5
96	97.98	98.03	98.08	98.13	98.18	98.23	98.29	98.34	98.39	98.44	1	1	2	2	3	3	4	4	5
97	98.49	98.54	98.59	98.64	98.69	98.74	98.79	98.84	98.89	98.94	1	1	2	2	3	3	4	4	5
98	98.99	99.05	99.10	99.15	99.20	99.25	99.30	99.35	99.40	99.45	1	1	2	2	3	3	4	4	5
99	99.50	99.55	99.60	99.65	99.70	99.75	99.80	99.85	99.90	99.95	1	1	2	2	3	3	4	4	5
	0	1	2	3	4	5	6	7	8	9	1	2	3	4	5	6	7	8	9

root of 4.9 is 2.214.   Now, if the square root of 4.98 is desired one must
turn to the column headed by 8 and move the decimal to the left, one
digit.   The square root is thus 2.232.

To find the square root of a number from 10 to 100 one must use the
tables headed 1000 to 10,000.   The numbers in the left hand column
are the numbers for which the square roots may be found in the column
headed by 0.   The decimal point in this latter column must be moved
one place to the left.   For example, the square root of 10 is 3.162; of
49, it is 7.000.   The square root of 81.7 is found by turning to the
column headed by 7 and moving the decimal point one digit to the
left.   Thus, the square root of 81.7 is found to be 9.039.

The square root of 81.75 is found by adding the number in column 5
which is headed by "proportional parts" to 9.039.   The square root
then is $9.039 + .005 = 9.044$.

For all other square roots from 1000 up to 10,000, the tables are
read directly.   For example, the square root of 517 is found to be
22.74.   517.6 would be $22.74 + .01 = 22.75$.   The square root of
7842 is found to be 88.55.

For the square roots above 10,000 one uses the table from 100 to
1000 for all numbers with an odd number of digits for the whole
number and the table from 1000 to 10,000 for all numbers with an even
number of digits for the whole numbers.   The results should be
multiplied by 10 or some power of 10 as is indicated.   For example:

$$\text{the square root of } 21{,}670 = 14.72 \times 10 = 147.2.$$
$$\text{the square root of } 216700 = 46.56 \times 10 = 465.6$$
$$\text{the square root of } 2166700 = 14.72 \times 100 = 1472$$

Appendix C

Principles of Cinematographic Analysis

Motion pictures have been used for years to study athletic performance. They have proved to be a tremendous boon to a scientific analysis of the techniques employed by athletes in all phases of sports, as well as an effective means of demonstrating the mechanical principles involved in athletic competition.

The direction of movement, related body movements, sequence of movements, speed, force, distance, angles, conditions of equilibrium, and so forth, may be determined directly or indirectly by means of the analysis of motion pictures. However, in order to obtain accurate results from a cinematographic analysis of an activity, certain basic principles must be followed. Dr. Thomas K. Cureton, Jr., has made a notable contribution to procedures in athletic research through cinematography. He has not only outlined the methods and principles necessary for cinematographic analysis but he has applied these principles to several well chosen activities. His contribution is so valuable that much of his material is reproduced here for the convenience of the student who may be interested in research in this field.

Excerpts from "Elementary Principles and Techniques of Cinematographic Analysis as Aids in Athletic Research"*

By Thomas Kirk Cureton, Jr.

Elementary Techniques

Equipment.—It is not the purpose of this article to treat equipment but it seems necessary to mention a few minimum essentials. Any ordinary 16 mm. camera may be used for work on films. . . . It is

---

* Reprinted from *The Research Quarterly* of The American Association for Health, Physical Education, and Recreation, May, 1939.

very advantageous to have a variable speed camera with ordinary and
telephoto lens. A tripoid is important and preferably one which
locks. An editing outfit will be found essential. The Filmo Enlarger . . . is very useful for a 16 mm. projector. . . . Pictures
$2\frac{1}{4}''$ x $3\frac{1}{4}''$ may be made directly from the 16 mm. film with the enlarger.

There is great advantage in a 35 mm. camera of the "Eyemo" type
because the negative film may be printed directly to make pictures of
the same size for reproduction. These are large enough to be useful,
but they may be enlarged to make better reproductions than the 16
mm. enlargements. . . .

One of the real difficulties is burning the film when used in high
wattage projectors. While the 250- or 400-watt projector may be
used, the writer found a Model No. E 67 Keystone Projector serves for
class experimentation. This model is equipped with a hand crank,
variable speed control, low wattage lamp, and has the film track sepa-
rated from the lamp almost 2 inches. This absolutely prevents burning the film. Overheating the film will cause it to shrivel and
shrink. . . .

The technique of taking pictures is not elaborated. . . . Even if
one does not take pictures, there are numerous sports films which may
be purchased or rented. . . .

APPLICATION OF CINEMATOGRAPHIC ANALYSIS

Many varied applications of the elementary analytical techniques
are possible. When applied to swimming, running, jumping, throwing, pitching, batting, kicking, vaulting, gymnastics, and, in fact, to any
of the high speed or precision activities, the resulting film, serving as
the source of measured data, becomes invaluable. Measurements have
been applied to the javelin in flight with an average of 3.3 per cent
experimental error. Measurements on the human body in action have
been made with a routine experimental error less than one per cent,
including activities such as giant swings and up-starts in the gymnasium, somersault dives and the flutter kick in swimming, the high
jump and broad jump in track, as well as many other athletic skills.
The number of applications are limitless.

Measuring Angles.—Angular measurement has the great advantage
of requiring no multiplier or correction factor to obtain true size dimensions, except as there may be aspects of perspective, field, lens, or

photographic errors involved. The angles are scaled directly with a protractor. The film is placed in the projector and projected on a flat vertical surface with the lens directed horizontally and perpendicular to the screen, or surface.* The angles are scaled directly with a protractor. In Illustration I a shot putter is shown projecting the shot at an angle of 40 degrees.

The angular measurement may be effectively used to measure body lean in running, angular relations of the limbs and trunk, the angle of take-off in the broad jump, high jump, or pole vault, the range of ankle action in the flutter kick photographed under water, the angular relation of the head with the trunk in walking posture, and many other similar relations. In swimming the angular separation of the legs in the frog kick, the planing angle of the body, the angle of lean at the moment of taking-off for a dive from the springboard, are all easily measured, as are the angulations between body segments in various

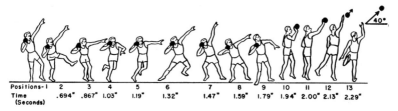

Illus. I. Angle of projection of shot.

diving postures. This is the most feasible method of studying the range of movement of parts of the body in all types of dynamic exercises.

In the case of solid objects of symmetrical shape, like the shot, the center of the object is estimated and one of the angle lines is drawn through this. In some instances of work with the human body, it is important to be able to estimate the center of gravity closely. In joint action, the apex of the angle of movement may be taken as the point at which the sides of the angle join.

Thus it was determined that the angle of take-off of the shot in the case of good shot putters is 40-42 degrees at the hand, and 45 degrees contact with the ground when maximum distance is obtained. Johnny

* Cardboard may be used to preserve the tracing of the projected image. This is not very convenient for mailing as it will not roll. Special paper, tracing cloth, or roll map cloth may be used.

Weismuller was shown to have a range of ankle action of nearly 90 degrees at a time when some teachers were insisting upon a straight rigid ankle.

Measuring Linear Distances.—Projected images on the screen are usually not true life size. The size of the image varies directly as the distance from the lens to the screen. The further the projection lens away, the larger is the image, and vice versa. If, however, some dimension is known which appears in the picture, corrections may easily be made. These corrections are known as *reduction factors* or *multipliers.* For instance, Weismuller's true height from top of head to tip of the toe in the swimming position is 74″. When measured on the screen with a given location of the projector and screen, the same distance measured 41.2 centimeters. Each centimeter on the screen is, therefore, equivalent to

$$\frac{74 \text{ in.}}{41.2 \text{ cm.}} = 1.797 \text{ inches} = \text{Multiplier}$$

Every measurement on the screen must be multiplied by this factor to bring the measurements up to true size. Weismuller's kick measured at the narrower beat 8.2 cm. or 3.2 inches. Its real width is $8.2 \times 1.797 = 14.7$ inches.

It is always important to measure some object or dimension in the field being photographed. Neglect to do this will spoil the possibility of determining the true size of various measurements taken from the screen. To preserve these a written memorandum is needed. It may be helpful to include a numbered card in the visual field and use this number as a key for further reference. Trigonometric methods may be used to determine the distance or size of objects far away when no direct measurement of an object in the field is possible. It is usually helpful to try to locate a horizontal line in the field, such as, the top of a level fence, or horizontal roof line on a house.

Such measurements of length are usually quite accurate if the pictures are clearly defined. The usual technique is to measure a vertical and horizontal dimension on some object in the field being photographed. Careful record and description should be made of these measurements, using numbered cards in the picture and a diary record to avoid confusion later.

Very minor errors may occur in such linear measurements. A

straight line may not photograph as such because of buckling of the film in the projector, or of similar buckling of the negative in the plate holder of a camera.

Measurements of Speed and Force.—Among the more important types of measurements are those of speed, and indirect measurement of force by its calculation from physical formulas.

Measurement of velocity is based upon the relation:

$$\text{Velocity} = \frac{\text{Distance}}{\text{Time}} = \text{Speed}$$

It is thus necessary to measure the distance moved by the body, or body part or object being studied, and to count the number of *frames* or *clicks* in the projector mechanism dur-

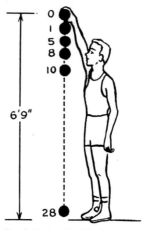

ing the action. For instance, in our laboratory Bell & Howard projector, there are three clicks to each frame of the film. It becomes less confusing to work in terms of clicks rather than total frames.

In order to time the film the usual procedure is to photograph a falling object in the same field as the action being timed (Ilustration II).

However, for routine work this may be done once with the camera spring tightly wound. If the camera is rewound after each shot, it is not necessary to photograph a falling object each time.

The calculation involves the law of falling bodies:

Illus. II. Timing the film by photographing a falling object.

$S = \frac{1}{2}gt^2$ wherein, $S =$ distance in feet

$g = 32.2$ feet/sec.^{2}
(acceleration due to gravity)

$t =$ time in seconds.

Photograph a heavy white ball released from a measured height and its fall downward to strike a smooth hard surface on the ground. In the example,

$$S = 6.75 \text{ feet (actually measured)}$$
$$6.75 = \tfrac{1}{2}gt^2$$

$$t^2 = \frac{6.75}{16.1} = .419 \text{ seconds.}$$

$$t = \sqrt{.419} = .65 \text{ seconds.}$$

(Stop watch time, average of six trials .662 seconds)

The number of shutter clicks from start to finish were counted to be 28. Therefore, the time per click equals $\dfrac{.65}{28} = .023$ sec.

Each counted frame should be multiplied by .023 to convert clicks to seconds of time.

The accuracy of this procedure may be checked by photographing the fall of the weights on an Atwood machine, or an apparatus which traces vibrations of an electrical timing fork on a smoked glass surface. Since the time of each vibration is known from the rating of the fork, the vibrations may be counted and the total time compared with the photographic result. Another approximate check is to time with a stop watch the falling object. The latter is only a rough check but agreement can be shown to better than 1/10th of a second over an average of a series of trials when the person serving as timer also drops the ball, thus eliminating the reaction time error at the start.

An application may be given to determining the velocity with which a baseball leaves a pitcher's hand. A very fast speed camera was used. A 69-inch drop of an iron ball corresponded to 235 clicks. The time per click was computed to be .00255 seconds, corresponding to 130.7 frames per second exposure.

The ball was measured for velocity in a 4.00 ft. distance just after leaving the hand. Twenty clicks were counted corresponding to the time. Dividing the distance by the time gives an average velocity of 80.0 ft./sec., or 26.6 yards/sec., or 54.5 miles/hour for the speed.

Many other interesting applications are possible. The take-off velocity in jumping and running reflects the effectiveness of the release and application of power. The parabolic flight of any jumper, diver, or thrown object follows the mechanical laws of projection.

$$S_1 = V_1 t_1 \cos \sigma_1 \text{ wherein}$$

$S_1 =$ Distance in feet.

$t_1 =$ Time in seconds.

$V_1 =$ Projection velocity.

$\sigma_1 =$ Angle of projection.

In the above formula the assumption is that the object returns to the same elevation from which it started. With a shot leaving the hand about seven feet from the ground, a correction must be applied from the further point in the trajectory which is level with the hand to the ground, horizontally applied.

In Illustration III there is an actual reproduction of a shot put.

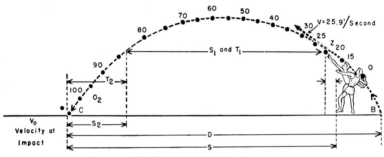

Illus III. Analysis of shot put.

The shot follows a parabolic course of flight and covers distance S. If the shot had departed from point B and landed at point C, the above given formula would apply. In reality, the shot left the hand at point Z, 7.3 feet above the ground. The modified formula which provides the necessary corrections is as follows:

$S_1 = V_1 \cos \sigma_1 t_1$

$S_2 = V_0 \cos \sigma_2 t_2$

$L =$ Correction to toe board.

$S = S_2 + S_1 + L$

V_1 (velocity of shot leaving the hand)

σ_1 (angle at which shot left the hand)

t_1 (time of flight in upper parabola Z to R)

t_2 (time of shot in falling from R to C)

V_0 (velocity of shot in striking the ground)

σ_2 (angle of contact with ground)

In the above problem the computed distance was 37.53 feet and the actually measured distance from the toe board was 37.5 feet.

Force may be computed but not measured directly. Three basic physical formulas are involved:

$$\text{Power} = \frac{\text{work}}{\text{time}} = \frac{\text{Force} \times \text{Distance}}{\text{time}}$$

$$= \frac{F \times S}{t} = FV$$

Work or Kinetic Energy = Force × Distance

$$FD = \tfrac{1}{2}MV^2$$

Memery and Cornell applied photographic data to these formulas, and derived important principles for the shot-put technique. They found that the force and power with which athletes can extend the arm against the weight and inertia resistance of the shot definitely increase in proportion to the extent with which the body is brought into play. Power was computed to equal 108.77 ft. lbs./sec. in the put from a standing position without shift or leg swing. This increased to 159.99 ft. lbs./sec. with the addition of the supplementary body movements. Photographic measurements have enabled the collection of basic data which have permitted building prediction equations for shot putting, which when applied to any selected individual make coaching diagnosis of great value.

Knight and Hepp made a similar analysis of the track racing start . . . . By combining photographic analysis with electrical timing of the start, basic data were collected that has permitted the close prediction of the short sprint time. They used the physical equation of Newton (2nd law of motion):

$$F = Ma \text{ or } F = \frac{W}{g}a \qquad\qquad F = \text{force in lbs.}$$
$$W = \text{body weight in lbs.}$$
$$a = \text{acceleration.}$$

Photographic measurement of the acceleration factor, and simple measurement of the $\dfrac{W}{g}$ factor enabled the computation of propelling force in the running. The time in the short sprint can be closely predicted from the force and angle of the body lean. . . .

Further Typical Examples of Analytical Cinematographical-Mechanical Studies

Harris made an interesting analysis of the gymnastic up-start. Subjects of excellent, medium, and poor ability were photographed in the gymnasium while executing the up-start under prescribed conditions.

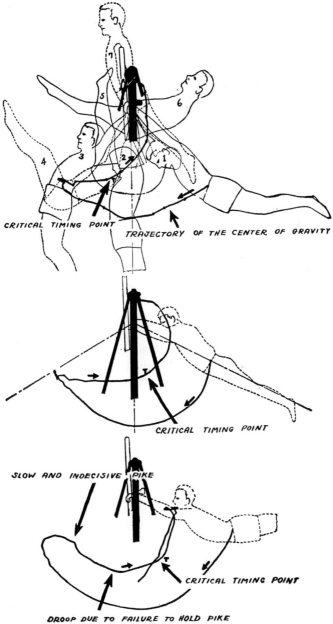

CRITICAL TIMING POINT

TRAJECTORY OF THE CENTER OF GRAVITY

CRITICAL TIMING POINT

SLOW AND INDECISIVE PIKE

CRITICAL TIMING POINT

DROOP DUE TO FAILURE TO HOLD PIKE

Illus. IV. Analysis of the hip-start.

A diary was kept of each act photographed. In Illustration IV three examples are shown for comparison with each other.

In the top example subject Welser executes an up-start with good form. The tracing of the center of gravity may be related to the body position at any stage of the act. It may be noticed that after the legs were piked and the body was in its backswing that the forceful straightening of the body was timed so that it occurred just before the center of gravity came beneath the horizontal bar (T). In this case the force was sufficient and the timing proper to raise the center of gravity from (T) to (B) and finally to (R), the body making a three-quarter revolution around the bar during this act. In the middle illustration another subject almost fails because of delaying the straightening-thrust too long. It may be observed that the body has actually passed beneath the bar before the center of gravity starts its major rise upward. In the lower illustration, the subject failed. The reasons for failure may be seen to be portrayed in the trajectory of the center of gravity. At the time of piking the legs (position P), the movement lacks definiteness and, failing to hold the legs in the pike position, they drooped downward causing a marked lowering of the center of gravity to (L). The straightening-thrust was also delayed much too long (T), so that although the movement lifted the center of gravity fairly high, it was not high enough, nor was it possible to pull the body in over the bar by arm strength. The subject, therefore, fell downward to (B). Data collected from these films have made the basis of some important principles of teaching the up-start.

Lanoue made an unusual study of diving, using films taken by the writer at the Olympic Games, Los Angeles, 1932. Illustration V shows Richard Degener executing a gainer $1\frac{1}{2}$ somersault. The camera was placed opposite a point about three feet in front of the end of the board and sighted at an elevation about five feet above the board. The camera was locked on a tripod so as to take in the field without shifting the position of the camera.

By studying the Olympic Divers of 1932 Lanoue was able to come to the following conclusions:

Average Hurdle Height (distance above board)...... 29 inches
Average Hurdle Length............................ 33.2 inches
Average Height of Dives (c. of g. above board)...... 76.6 inches
Average Dive Length (from end of board to vertical at
   point of entry)............................... 80.5 inches
Average Take-off Angle (from horizontal).......... 74 degrees
Average Angle of Entry (from horizontal).......... 80 degrees

Lanoue demonstrated that he could predict the height or distance of a dive from measurements made from the film just as the diver left the board.   These studies contributed interesting facts about timing of dives.   The photographs permitted an analysis of the principles governing rotation and twisting in dives.

Popular reproductions may be made directly from the 35 mm. film by printing the negative film.   Examples of this application are available in the Chicago Park District study of Al Greene, and in the diving illustrations used in the new Red Cross text on "Swimming and Diving."

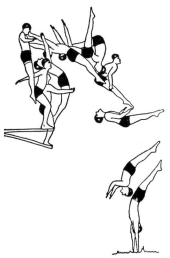

DEGREE OF DIFFICULTY

		Standing		Running	
		1M	3M	1M	3M
Layout	A				2.5
Pike	B			2.4	2.3
Tuck	C		2.1	2.2	2.2

Illus. V. Analysis of diving.   *Common faults:* (1) Going out too far, (2) Too early an opening (3) Going into pike early, (4) Loose pike, (5) Poor entry, (6) Bringing arms down at start *Essentials:* (1) Arms stretching back on takeoff, (2) Head and arms held back while legs are brought up, (3) Arms at sides in pike, (4) Open just past first somersault, (5) Knees and ankles locked.   *Coaching suggestions:* (1) Dive starts same as a dutchman, though the back push is emphasized more, (2) Head thrown back throughout dive, (3) Hands placed on outside middle of thighs with fingers under, (4) Arm swing or thrust equally good on opening, (5) Pike gainer necessary preliminary, (6) Arms back and head forward on entry.

Analysis of the Giant Swing (Forward)

A final application may be made to the analysis of the giant swing. The subject used weighed 160 pounds, was 5' 9" tall, and from hand grasp on the bar to the toes measured 79".   Illustration VI shows a tracing made of a slow motion film of the act.   A falling ball dropped 79" required 280 clicks in the projector, or one click was equivalent to .00232 seconds.

TABLE I

DATA ON GIANT SWING

Positions in Giant Swing	Description of Positions in Giant	Distance c. of g. to Bar (ft.)	Traveled by c. of g. from Position Numbered to Next	Time (sec.)	V (ft./sec.)	F_c (lbs.)
16	Top (start)	3.49	5.80	.629	9.22	121.2
14	Top right	4.15	5.69	.644	8.84	93.2
12	Right	4.00	5.75	.329	17.5	379.7
10	Lower right	4.15	6.56	.255	25.7	789.3
8	Bottom	4.51	6.46	.313	21.3	498.9
6	Lower left	4.46	6.10	.369	16.5	302.7
4	Left	3.33	5.44	.376	14.4	308.8
2	Upper left	2.72	5.18	.378	13.7	341.3

The centrifugal force due to the rotational velocity was computed from the formula:

$$F_c = \frac{W}{g} \frac{V^2}{r} \quad \text{wherein}$$

W = Weight of subject in lbs.

g = 32.2 ft./sec.^{2}

V^2 = velocity (ft./sec.)^2

r = Distance in feet from c. of g. to bar.

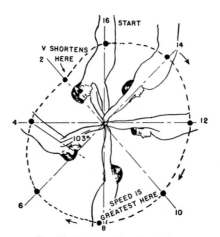

Illus. VI. Analysis of the giant swing.

By stop watch the average time required for the top half of the rotation was .95 seconds, the lower half .60 seconds. From the moving picture film the four quadrants required: top (.629), right (.329), bottom (.313), left (.376). The stop watch total time is 1.55 seconds compared to 1.647 seconds from the film. This gives a rough check on the reasonableness of the results.

From the above it may be observed that the greatest speed of rotation is obtained in the position 10 toward the bottom. The critical phase is at position 2 where the body rocks up and over on the shoulder joint. This has the effect of moving the c. of g. toward the bar, decreasing r, this, in turn, increasing the velocity of rotation, thus aiding the body to assume the starting position again. It may be noticed that in position 10 there is developed 789.3 lbs. of centrifugal force, or tendency to pull away from the bar. It shows why the hands must be strong to do this event. Part of the body weight must be added to the centrifugal force equivalent to the component acting at position 10. This is sufficient to illustrate the possibility of studying events of this type in detail.

Avoiding Errors of Measurement

Everyone has seen examples of photographic distortion, such as persons with feet larger than the body, buildings with unnaturally curved edges or narrowing sharply toward the top, owing to the fact that the camera was pointed upward, thus causing a perspective error. In a famous argument between two German authorities, Dr. Erich Kling called attention to several fallacies upon which the conclusions of Dr. Waitzer were based, owing to photographic errors in the film data on track running. Neblette gives a fine summary of such photographic errors. A few of the more common ones will be briefly mentioned together with a few suggestions for elimination or correction.

Perspective Errors.—The cause of the perspective error is fundamentally that of some part of the object being photographed being closer to the lens than some other part in the same visual field. The part relatively close appears large compared to the part farther away. This is a common illusion which everyone has probably noticed, for instance, when looking down a railroad track. The rails appear to come together in the distance. The size of the image is related to the distance of projection, and the size of the picture on the film is related to the distance at which it was taken by the following law:

$$\frac{\text{Distance of Object to Lens}}{\text{Size of Object}} = \frac{\text{Distance of Image to Lens}}{\text{Size of Image on Film Plate}}$$

The errors of measurement are almost negligible in routine work on stable objects. This may be indicated in the following table which resulted from a check made on the accuracy with which body measurements could be reproduced by moving picture photography.

Perspective errors are greatly magnified when the camera is very close to the object. A possible means of minimizing this error is to use a telephoto lens and place the camera farther away. In photographing runners, for instance, Fenn used this method and had the runners run behind a white lattice work, the dimensions of which were carefully determined, and by locating the camera some distance away and using a telephoto lens for clarity, good pictures were obtained with a minimum of perspective error. The pictures were taken in a narrow zone directly in front of the lens with the runners running perpendicularly across the line of sight of the camera.

Illustration VII shows this relation. The objects a, b, and c are not at equal distance from the camera lens. Measurements on *a* will not be comparable with those on *b*. These differences are minimized in the arrangement shown in a', b', and c'.

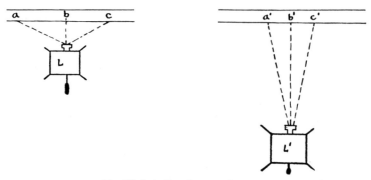

Illus. VII. Reduction of perspective error.

It may be noted in Illustration VII that the distance aL is greater than the distance bL. When the camera is moved back, the difference in the lengths $a'L'$ and $b'L'$ is very slight. Hence, the perspective error is reduced. The fundamental rule is that the object to be photographed should be directly in front of the lens and aligned in a plane perpendicularly to the lens, either horizontally or vertically. Pictures taken from underwater on an upward slanting angle will be distorted.

The parts nearer the camera will appear to be nearer and deeper in the water than the parts further away. Such errors may be noted in some of the underwater photography of swimmers. Most films of diving taken by spectators are useless for analytical purposes because the camera is very seldom aligned perpendicularly to the line of parabolic flight of the dive.

Lens Aberrations.—The causes of slight errors due to irregularities in the shape or quality of the lens or to the regulation of the light pencils passing through the lens include the following:

a) Astigmatic Distortion—Due to uneven curvature of the lens which results in irregularities of refraction of the light rays.

b) Chromatic Aberration—Due to the dispersing properties of glass and affected by quality of glass; this is illustrated by the spectrum phenomena. The primary cause is the passage of the rays through the peripheral edges of the lens, these acting as prisms in distorting and dispersing the light rays.

c) Spherical Aberration—Due to unequal refraction of the light rays, particularly noticeable when the rays pass through the peripheral borders of the lens. Corrected by using a smaller diaphragm opening and better light for the pictures.

While the above types of errors are of consequence in the selection of lenses, and in the study of the physical phenomena of refraction, they represent minor problems which in all but a very few instances may be neglected.

Slight errors due to minor irregularities in the perfection of the lens are ignored in this article. Since most of the modern equipment is good, errors of astigmatic distortion, chromatic aberration, and spherical aberration are so negligible that they may usually be ignored in routine work.

However, when objects are photographed through glass plate, or with camera above water and the object beneath, the possibility of error is great. This may be exemplified in pictures taken from underwater vats in pools or at Silver Springs, Florida. Not only are the perspective errors great, due to the nearness of the swimmers to the lens, but turning the camera away from a perpendicular shot through the glass vat causes distortion.

Water Refraction.—The fact should be recognized that objects photographed under water will appear closer to the surface than they really are when they are viewed from above the surface. The light rays are bent toward the normal when passing into a more dense medium, and they are bent away from the normal when passing from a more dense to a less dense medium (III, VIII). Light rays coming from an object under water are bent. The observer views the object as if the ray or line of sight were a straight line. In fact, the real object is lower than the apparent object.

The marked activity in underwater photography of swimming and lifesaving at this time suggests care in photographing and interpreting pictures which are supposed to be scientific exhibits. Photographs taken of breast strokers from the side often show one leg lower than the other. This is particularly true when the camera is close to the subject. Correction involves getting the camera directly above the subject or in line with the direction of body motion.

A photograph of Tsuruta, champion Japanese breast stroker, taken from above water and from one side of the pool, shows a distinct scissor-kick action in violation of the rules. This photograph could not be legitimately used to prove the point because of both perspective and refraction errors.

Linear Distortion.—The causes of linear distortion wherein straight lines are not reproduced as such are: curvature of the film or plate field, referring to the focal points of oblique and axial pencils forming on a curve rather than on a flat plane within the camera. This error may be caused by buckling of the film or plate within the camera or projector. In some of the cheaper projectors the film is not held flat within the film track and this causes distortion of the projected image. This may be checked by photographs of strings suspending weights, in other words, photographing a gravity line.

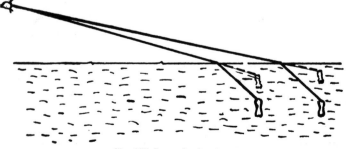

Illus. VIII. Error of refraction.

Errors of Scaling.—Students will vary considerably in their ability to scale pictures accurately. Practice is necessary to get accurate results. Sharp outlines in the negative or projected image are very helpful. The basic problem is securing well-timed and sharp-edged images in the photography. Only experience in camera operation can produce this. Skill and suitable conditions are essential.

Enlargements.—Good enlargements may be made from 16 mm. film by means of the enlarging attachment made to fit any Filmo projector. This device consists of a tapered box at the small end of which a special fixed-focus enlarging lens is mounted. The regular projection lens is removed and the enlarger is slipped on to the projector in such a way that the enlarging lens replaces the regular lens. A bayonet-like shaft on the enlarger comes into firm contact with the projector aperture plate and automatically focuses the enlarging lens. A set screw locks the entire unit firmly into place.

A film pack adapter, supplied with the enlarger, is loaded with a pack and slipped into place at the large end of the tapered box. The hinged cover at the top of the box is then raised so that the film may be viewed as it is projected upon the white surface of the film pack adapter slide.

When a scene from which an enlargement is desired appears upon the screen, the projector clutch is disengaged, the enlarger shutter closed, the pack adapter slide removed, and the picture is projected just as one would project a single frame upon a screen. Then the enlarger shutter is pressed, giving an instantaneous exposure and producing a properly-timed negative from any correctly exposed frame of negative or positive film.

In this way serial reproduction may be made of selected frames in the film. It may be desired to reproduce every tenth frame in even increments of time advancement, or to reproduce the frame corresponding to every half second, or to select key positions in the form.

Location of the Center of Gravity.—Since in all of the physical equations the body may be treated as a mass concentrated at a single point called the Center of Gravity, research workers should know how to locate this point. It moves within a limited range with the movements of the limbs and the bending of the trunk. . . . The center of gravity postural apparatus has helped determine some of the changes.

In the vertical standing position the center of gravity is located approximately in the center of the waist on a level with the umbilicus. It lies within what is called the "belt line." However, lifting the arms overhead raises the center of gravity about two centimeters. A lift of the leg forward as in track running moves the center of gravity forward and upward. Fenn has shown that its range of movement may be as great as 11 cm. Good work in analyzing films requires ability to estimate changes in the center of gravity quite closely. While the center of gravity may be computed for any body segment in any position, this is tedious and time-consuming work and usually not worth while.

TABLE II

PHOTOGRAPHIC AND MEASUREMENT ERROR

Item Measured	Multi- plier	Projected Image Measure- ment (cm)	Corrected to Life Size (cm)	Actual Measure- ment of Subject	Deviation (cm)	Per Cent Error
Height..........	14.78	11.7	173.00	173.0	0	0
Shoulder Width...	14.78	2.9	42.86	43.0	.14	.33
Head Width......	14.78	.9	13.30	12.1	1.20	9.94
Hip Width.......	14.78	1.8	26.60	26.3	.30	1.14

$$\text{Standard Error} = \sqrt{\frac{\Sigma d^2}{N}} = .624 \text{ cm.}$$

Such measurements of length or width are usually quite accurate if the pictures are clearly defined and the film is projected and traced with reasonable care. If the projector is a very cheap one, the film may buckle and a straight line may not photograph as such. If the work is to be precise, it will pay to check this type of error. A tight gravity line may be photographed as a test. . . .

CONCLUSION

Analytical work on films promises to contribute much to technical knowledge of athletic action. Intensive work of this type is just now beginning to be reported at an accelerated rate. The facts derived by the painfully slow process will accumulate to make possible much more scientific views of the principles employed in athletic performances. Such knowledge should contribute greatly to the improved manuals of pedagogy.

Appendix D

Answers to Problems

Chapter 2

1. Runner with center of gravity 6 in. back
3. Center of gravity of 150 lb man three-quarters as high as 200 lb man
4. 3 ft   5. $\frac{1}{2}$ ft up
6. Higher—$1\frac{1}{2}$ in.
7. Yes, 18 in. $\times$ 24 in. Two answers—6:9, 6:12; 2.90 in.-lb, 5.80 in.-lb per pound of wt.
8. The first is three-quarters more stable

Chapter 3

1. a .3584; .5878; .7447; .7071; .9336
   b .8660; .6691; .0523; .7071; .500
   c .2493; .7813; 3.2219; 1.000; 4.0108
   d 3.2709; 1.1106; .1944; 1.000; .3057
2. 31 ft/sec
3. 23.62 ft/sec, 27.17 ft/sec, 1.48 sec
4. 5.59 ft   6. 32 ft/sec, 1 sec
5. 18°, 1.56 ft   7. 45.25 ft/sec, 40 ft/sec
8. 1.414 sec, 56.56 ft
9. 5.13 ft/sec, 9.64 ft/sec; 3.11 ft, 2.06 ft
10. 5.18 ft   11. 25.26 ft/sec, 22.75 ft/sec
12. 27.19 ft/sec, 12.68 ft/sec, 2.51 ft
13. 9.828 ft/sec, 28.7 ft/sec, 1.51 ft
14. 9.41 ft/sec, 19°   15. 21°, 10.75 ft/sec, 1.81 ft
16. 31.04 ft/sec
17. 23.62 ft/sec, 27.17 ft/sec, 8.72 ft
18. .64 ft   20. $16\frac{1}{2}$°
19. 270.62 ft, 3.125 sec   21. 663.00 ft
22. 27.65 ft, 27.62 ft, 27.51 ft, 27.62 ft
23. None   24. .1296 ft

25. .16 ft　　　　　　　　　　**27.** 47.7 ft, 45.92 ft, 47.13 ft

26. 47.65 ft, 7.2 ft, 14.2 ft　　　**28.** 13.29 ft, 44.21 ft/sec, 1.53 sec

29. 2 ft 8 in.; 13.07 ft/sec; 7.545 ft/sec; 15.09 ft/sec; 3.85 ft

30. 70°—2 ft 8 in.; 13.07 ft/sec; 4.73 ft/sec; 13.9 ft/sec; 2.43 ft
　　　57°—2 ft 8 in.; 13.07 ft/sec; 8.49 ft/sec; 15.56 ft/sec; 4.33 ft
　　　55°—2 ft 8 in.; 13.07 ft/sec; 9.14 ft/sec; 16 ft/sec; 4.67 ft

31. 2.5 rev/sec, or 15.7 radians/sec

32. 2 rev/sec at 12 in.
　　　$\frac{2}{3}$ rev/sec at 3 ft
　　　12.56 ft/sec at 12 in.
　　　12.56 ft/sec at 3 ft

Chapter 4

1. 260 lb, 2600 lb　　　　　**3.** 82.45 lb

2. 66.7 lb, 133.4 ft/sec^2　　**4.** 31.45

5. Yes, 30° with line of scrimmage toward opposite goal

6. Would gain 15° with line of scrimmage

7. 69.44 lb; 282.84 lb; 330.56 lb; 117.16 lb

8. 146.25 lb, 237.25 lb　　　**10.** 751 lb

9. 34.64 lb　　　　　　　　　**11.** .6 lb

12. Above his center of gravity—greater moment arm

13. 3.5 ft radius, 577.5 ft-lb; 3 ft radius, 495 ft-lb

14. 300 lb; 660 lb; 330 lb

15. 480 ft-lb, 210 ft-lb, the $3\frac{1}{2}$ in. position

16. 38°, 144.53 lb

17. 70 in.-lb; 121.24 in.-lb; 140 in.-lb; 121.24 in.-lb; 70 in.-lb; 0 in.-lb

18. 3 ft from center of gravity to foot, 64°

19. Second shoe, .8 and 1.48　　**24.** 67.9 ft/sec

20. 180 lb; 5 lb/sq in.　　　　　**25.** .65

21. 438.75 lb　　　　　　　　　**26.** 4.36 oz

22. 75.88 ft/sec　　　　　　　　**27.** Farther by ratio of 1 to $1\frac{1}{2}$

23. Foul　　　　　　　　　　　**28.** The 180-lb man, 120 lb

29. 9.5 lb wall, 30.5 lb ground; 14.64 lb wall, 25.36 lb ground

30. Second pair, .67, .75　　　　**31.** 127.50 lb; 37°

Chapter 6

1. 722.5 ft-lb　　　　　　　　**3.** 168 ft-lb; 260 lb

2. 15.49 ft/sec; 722.5

4. 31.3 ft; 78.4 ft/sec; 196 ft-lb; 29.4 lb

5. 32 ft/sec; 2560 ft-lb

6. Plan A, 94.12 ft-lb

7. 2250 ft-lb

8. 3125, 781.25

9. 39.2 lb

Chapter 7

1. 85.5 ft-lb

2. 241.5 ft-lb

3. 37.91 ft-lb; 4°

4. 37.91 ft-lb hindrance

5. 99.47 lb

6. 3062.5 ft-lb, 24 ft

7. .177 sec

8. .312 sec

Chapter 8

1. 4.22 ft/sec

3. 520.7 lb

4. Height will vary with the sine of the angle

5. 19.6 ft/sec; 7.72 ft; 1.11 sec

6. 3.01 ft, 16.04 ft/sec, 4.02 ft

7. 12.54 ft, 9.6 ft

8. 159.25 ft

9. 23.95 ft; 2.19 ft

10. Four times greater when shot held at shoulder

11. 74.75 ft/sec; 25.23 ft farther for longer hammer

12. 1.5 in.

13. .06 in.

Chapter 9

1. 11°

2. 11°, same, 11°

3. 27.9 ft; 16.16 ft; 28°; 17°

4. 163.93 lb; 81.96 lb; 40.98 lb

5. $67\frac{1}{2}$°

6. 76.33 ft/sec

7. 178.43 ft

8. 40°

9. Right handed batter, .15564 sec

10. 141.67 lb

11. 16.66 ft; 30 ft

Chapter 10

1. 40.6 ft; 3.18 sec, 74.55 ft/sec

2. 2.55 sec; 81.55 ft/sec; first kick in air; 6.3 sec longer

3. Yes, before he catches ball

4. second 97.54 $\frac{a}{g}$

5. 1715 lb

6. Problem 5, 800 lb

7. 11.16 ft/sec

8. 14.14 ft/sec, the latter

Chapter 11

1. 23.4

2. Kick at angle of 26°; 89/64 more

3. 31.40 ft-lb
4. Swimmer, problem 3, .9 ft-lb
5. 360 in.-lb of work per arm: 30 ft-lb, total 60 ft-lb, 5 ft/sec

Chapter 12

1. 9 ft/sec, 1.27 ft
2. 5.83 ft
3. 164.16 ft-lb
4. 7.75 ft
5. 4.8 rev/sec

Chapter 13

1. 160 lb
2. Fall back, 39+°
3. 768 lb
4. 700 lb, gymnast in problem 3
5. Yes, 1½; 2.4975
6. 1.8 more force with turning lever 20 in. long
7. 1.6 ft

Chapter 14

1. 562.5 ft-lb
2. 256 ft-lb
3. 2½ in.
4. .29 ft
5. 13
6. 1.66 in.
7. 28°
8. Miss by 1.5 in.; miss by 3.57 in.
9. 2°; 1° 44'; 1° 27'

Chapter 15

1. 60°, 70°
2. 457 ft; 404 ft
3. 255 ft/sec
4. Club 4.6 greater, 140 to 30
5. 9.2 ft
6. 19° to right of original direction, 105.95 ft/sec
7. 1.04
8. .42

Chapter 16

1. 12.5°
2. 1½°; with the base line
3. 81.5°
4. 21 ft; 83 ft/sec
5. 28°; 11.6 ft

Index

Index